PLANNING INDUSTRIAL STRUCTURES

The quality of the materials used in the manufacture of
this book is governed by continued postwar shortages.

Planning Industrial Structures

By CLARENCE W. DUNHAM

*Associate Professor of Civil Engineering, Yale University; Consulting Structural
Engineer for the New York Office of the Anaconda Copper Mining Co. Formerly
Assistant Chief Draftsman, Bethlehem Steel Co.; Assistant Engineer, The Port
of New York Authority; Chief Structural Designer, Phelps Dodge Corp.
Member, American Society of Civil Engineers, American Institute
of Consulting Engineers, American Concrete Institute, Con-
necticut Society of Civil Engineers, American Society for
Engineering Education*

FIRST EDITION

NEW YORK   TORONTO   LONDON

McGRAW-HILL BOOK COMPANY, INC.

1948

PLANNING INDUSTRIAL STRUCTURES

He who is privileged to plan important structures
has an excellent opportunity for creative
thinking, and he carries a great responsibility

PREFACE

The importance of engineering planning is being recognized more and more. If the basic concept and the general plan of a project are not practicable and thoroughly sound, the excellence with which the details are worked out will not remedy these fundamental defects.

The planning of structures is such a vast subject that it cannot be treated completely in one volume of reasonable size. For this reason, the author has restricted his discussion to the planning of industrial structures. Since, however, an amazing variety of construction is encountered in the building of industrial plants and the works incidental thereto, the author has been obliged to select only certain typical structures and some specialized ones to illustrate specific principles and arrangements, hoping that a reader who studies these will develop the ability to plan others also.

In engineering practice, structures are planned in considerable detail before the sizes of members are computed. This is one of the truths that the author wishes to emphasize. When an engineer knows what he wants his structure to be, it is not usually difficult for him to make the necessary computations to dimension all its parts. Seldom does he select a series of specific members, calculate their sizes, and then fit them into a structure somewhat as a child makes his toy house out of the blocks on hand.

The first step in the planning of a structure involves the determination of such basic things as the kind and magnitude of the service that the structure is to perform; its general size and shape; its location with respect to topography, neighboring structures, and other important features; and the material of which it is to be made. The next stage of the planning is the further development of this general plan. This includes the creation of the framing scheme, the determination of basic dimensions, the choice of the types of members, the adoption of the principal architectural features, and the arrangement of the parts to make a whole structure that will accommodate the equipment and the activities that it is to house or to support.

As defined by Hardy Cross, the words *planning* and *designing* denote these two stages in the development of a structure. However, the author has used these words synonymously in many cases when referring to this general creative planning and development work which is the subject of this book.

For practical purposes, the general planning and designing of a structure constitute a progressive whole. The decisions affecting the former may be made by the chief engineer and by those who authorize the building of the structure, giving consideration, however, to the recommendations of the other engineers and of the architects. The decisions affecting the design are generally made by a group of men composed of the engineers, operators, architects, and others who are concerned directly with the proper arrangement and performance of the structure and who have the responsibility of seeing that the structure serves its purpose well. The planning and designing are parts of the work that require creative engineering and good judgment of a high quality.

An expert planner and designer of structures is generally a man who has had considerable experience in engineering. He has acquired such good engineering judgment and structural sense that he usually knows whether or not his plans are practicable; only occasionally will he need to make approximate calculations to see whether or not a proposed member will be of the right type and of proper general proportions for the particular service that it is to perform. He knows that after the plans are well developed and after they seem to be the most suitable that can be devised for the purpose, the calculation of the sizes of the members, the arrangement of connections, and the establishment of all minor dimensions—the detailed designing—can be done by himself or by others without the likelihood that these computations will reveal any weaknesses that will necessitate serious changes of the general plans.

The designer of structures should have a thorough knowledge of fabrication and construction procedures, of the peculiar features and the proper use of materials, and of the theory of structural action. He should know what is practicable and what is not; what is safe and what is dangerous; what is economical and what is wasteful. Such knowledge is of great value.

The author's first objective in writing this book is to assist the reader in the acquisition of this practical knowledge that is so essential for the planning of structures. Many of the principles of planning that are discussed with special reference to industrial buildings are applicable also to the planning of many other structures. The author's second objective is to show the reader the influence of the characteristics of a building material upon the designing of a structure to be made of that material and to show him various illustrations of typical members, arrangements of members, and details of connections that will assist the reader in the wise planning of structures of his own. The author's third objective is to help the reader to increase his knowledge of structural action and to develop the ability to visualize his structures as complete, almost living entities so that he can *see* in his mind how they will resist the applied forces and how they will deform under the action of the applied loads.

Many are the varieties of construction that are used by different engineers and for different purposes. Not all can be pictured in detail in a limited space; nevertheless the author has included a great many illustrations that demonstrate how structural parts may be fitted together. He illustrates some of the planning of structures to secure proper lighting and ventilation; he emphasizes the effect that soil conditions may have upon the planning of structures; he illustrates the principles that are applicable to the bracing of buildings; he shows considerable typical construction of floors, walls, and roofs; he gives many illustrations of structures made of structural steel, reinforced concrete, and wood; and he discusses some of the problems of foundations for structures and machines. A study of both the text and the illustrations should help the reader to create structures of his own that are practicable, strong, and durable.

A principle of military operations is supposed to have been stated somewhat as follows: "A poor plan that is carried out energetically and promptly is better than a more perfect plan that is executed weakly and too late." To a certain extent this may apply to the planning of structures; however, the work of the engineer is not soon lost in the confusion of events. His ideas are transformed into physical realities that stand and look him in the face; by the success of their performance and by the quality of the service they render he is judged. It behooves him, therefore, to give to his planning the time and the thought necessary for success so that he, the owners, and the users of the structures can be proud of them.

The author has had many years of happy and beneficial association with Hardy Cross, Wilbur Jurden, O. H. Ammann, Allston Dana, Ralph Smillie, and many others. Scarcely can he help incorporating some of their ideas into his own. Wherever he has done so he would make grateful acknowledgment to them all. He is especially grateful to Hardy Cross for the benefit of his point of view on the deformations of structures and on many other important matters in structural engineering and planning. W. A. Cuenot, who read the manuscript and made helpful suggestions, Frank Rubino, who assisted with the preparation of the drawings in Chapters 6, 7, and 8, and D. M. Feinman, who did most of the typing, have rendered considerable service. The author wishes also to express his thanks to those individuals, companies, and corporations who have contributed material and illustrations used in this book.

NEW HAVEN, CONN.   CLARENCE W. DUNHAM
    January, 1948

CONTENTS

Chapter 1

GENERAL PLANNING OF STRUCTURES

1·1 Introduction. Good thinking and planning in advance of action may pay splendid dividends; the lack of them may cause regrets and needless expense. This truism certainly applies to industrial design and construction. Once a structure is completed, it is usually difficult and costly to remodel it.

The designer of industrial buildings should always remember that, in new construction particularly, the structure is to be built to house specific equipment, materials, and people; it is to become part of an operating unit; it is to be built only once but used for an indefinitely long time. Hence, within reasonable limits, consideration for any difficulties in the solution of structural problems should be secondary to the provision of the best plan for mechanical layout and operation, and for the wise use of space. Provision can best be made in advance for the hundred and one things that facilitate efficient and satisfactory operation: light, ventilation, utilities, materials-handling equipment, elevators, offices, sanitary facilities, accessibility, heating, drainage, pits and other underground accessories, clearances, acoustics, lightning and fire protection, installation and repair of equipment, and future expansion.

Cheapness of construction alone is not an adequate measure of good design; neither is wastefulness to be commended. Satisfaction with the safety of a structure, with its utility, its appearance, its maintenance, and with the operating conditions within it—these things will be remembered long after the contract price has been forgotten.

Sometimes a structure is to be built for miscellaneous manufacturing, the owner expecting the occupancy to vary in personnel and equipment. Such cases are generally the exception. However, no building should be planned with such restricted space that the equipment and layout cannot be modified at all. In spite of his best efforts, no one can foresee all the changes and improvements of equipment and processes that may occur through the years; in the future, the owner may wish to incorporate some of them into his plant. Generally it is better to furnish

1

adequate vertical and horizontal clearances in the original design, and even provision for expansion, than it is to worry about how to secure them later on.

The planning of an important industrial structure is a thing of great importance. It is worthy of the talents of the best men within or available to a company or corporation. Shortsighted indeed is he who thinks that all men are equal in creative ability because their physical beings are not too dissimilar. Not only should important planning be entrusted to capable men, but these men should be compensated according to their value. The best results in planning are generally obtained when engineers, operators, and architects all cooperate, each realizing that one individual can seldom have the knowledge and ability that enable him alone to find the best solution for each of the many problems to be settled. A wise engineer will be open-minded, will listen to suggestions made by others, will weigh various ideas, and will do his utmost to see that the main purpose of the plant—efficient operation—is not hampered by structural considerations. On the other hand, these considerations may sometimes be sufficiently important to carry great weight in the planning of the general layout of the equipment and the building.

Too frequently revisions of designs are made necessary during construction because of hasty or inadequate planning. Such revisions are extremely annoying to all concerned. The owner generally pays heavily for them because the extra work is not included in the original contract. Nevertheless, such troubles should be faced and corrected promptly; one should not insist upon going ahead with the building of structures that are known, in the early stages, to be unsatisfactory. On the other hand, the reasons for making such changes should be really important, and the results ultimately economical and desirable. Revisions should not be just the product of differences of opinions and personalities.

The planner and the designer of industrial structures will have many and widely differing problems to solve. He should give careful attention to what has been done in the past, yet he should look constantly for new and better ways of doing things. Many features of construction used in the past are based upon various practical as well as theoretical considerations of which any one individual may not be fully aware. On the other hand, developments in materials, processes, and technical knowledge are progressing apace, and they will almost certainly continue to do so. It will tax almost anyone's abilities to the limit if he is to keep up with all these developments, even those in his own general line or specialty. The fact that something is new does not automatically make it the best solution for any particular problem. The designer should look for and adopt that which is good, safe, and advantageous—whether it is old, new, or a combination of both.   A valuable maxim to follow might be phrased as follows: "Keep that which experience has proved to be good; adopt radical innovations only when absolutely satisfied that they are better; study each problem carefully; and have the courage to do whatever is best."

Planning should be regarded as an art rather than a science.   So different are the conditions affecting each major problem, and so varied are the objectives to be attained, that one can seldom find a previously completed plan that can be copied in his case, and far less often can he find the answer already determined and described in a book.   Nevertheless, by practice and study combined, one may develop facility in creative planning so that he may start with a wish or idea, plus the physical conditions that nature and man-made works have provided at a given site, and then create a feasible, economical, and satisfactory plan that will attain his objective.   This creative planning, if done expertly, is engineering of a high order.

The principles to be applied and the general methods of attack used in the planning of the structures illustrated in this volume are intended to introduce the reader to the broad subject of the planning of structures, to acquaint him with some of the tools of his trade so that, by practicing with them himself, he will acquire facility in their use.   Just as a young carpenter may learn his trade in the building of small houses, then apply his skill to the creation of far greater structures, so the young engineer may learn how to plan some specific structures, then increase and apply his knowledge in other fields.   Above all, he should first learn the importance of thought and careful planning of a structure *before* attempting the detailed calculation of the sizes of the members composing it.

An engineer is automatically engaged in the field of economics. However, it seems that all too often those who plan and design structures think so much about the economies of construction costs that they give too little consideration to the matter of service to be rendered by the structure, and to the user's feeling of satisfaction with the result.   This is especially so in the field of industrial construction.   It is well to save where saving is wise, to be generous where generosity is equally wise.

The planning of structures requires engineering knowledge, skill, and good judgment.   How are these attributes to be acquired? Although they come imperfectly from the reading of books, the author hopes to start the reader thinking about them.   A good theoretical background and sufficient application of it in practical engineering enable one to acquire a sense of the appropriateness of members for various uses. Within reasonable limits, an experienced man may guess the sizes of the parts required, and he automatically does so in his planning so that he is confident that his plans are practicable even before the calculations are made. He will develop the habit of thinking about what structural service is required, how a structure and its parts will deform, and how members will act and interact. He will also develop the ability to select the proper materials for the required service. In fact, he should become able to create, efficiently and wisely, a structure for the use of man.

In a single book one cannot illustrate all existing or possible construction. One can, however, show types, their basic features and advantages, details of good and unwise construction, and materials that may be used. The author's chief purposes are to do these and to show the kind of thinking that goes into the proper planning of structures. He hopes to introduce the reader to what Hardy Cross calls "structural carpentry"—how parts of structures can and should fit together, whether made of steel, wood, or concrete. He does not intend to discriminate against various types of construction, kinds of materials, or ideas of people, but to bring to the reader's attention some of the things that should be considered when structures are planned. He wishes also to show the reader that there is much to be thought about. By necessity, the details will vary with the different problems met in practice.

The illustrations taken from the author's personal experiences are given only to emphasize their reality and because they are cases for which he knows the background. It is not necessarily important to know *what* was done in any given case, but it is very instructive to know *why* those particular things were done instead of others.

1·2 Planning vs. Detailed Designing and Calculation. When a concern decides to build a plant, or a new structure within an existing plant, and when its capacity and the nature of its product are determined, the general scale of the resultant cost is more or less determined also. When the layout of the equipment and facilities, and the general type of construction, are approved, the range of the cost is still more restricted. Thereafter, variations in the designs can produce only a limited effect upon this expenditure. For a given, desired production for a plant, the planning period is the time during which economies can be made, both in operating costs and in construction. All too often this period is restricted because of the desire to get things under way once the project is approved. Let us put this idea in another way. Whether there are a few columns more or less, whether the beams are

6 or 8 ft. on centers, even whether the allowable unit stresses in the materials are a given figure or 10 per cent higher—these things have a minor effect upon the total cost of the project compared to the basic planning. If the plan is poor, the details of the members cannot alter that fact.

In most new industrial projects, the structures are, or should be, studied simultaneously with the mechanical layout and operating procedures. The general types of construction, the materials to be used, and often the general framing schemes are determined largely before much, if any, computation of the sizes of the members is done. As stated previously, this planning requires engineering knowledge and ability of a high order. The detailed structural design is nevertheless important, but deciding upon the general scheme and engineering features is likely to be more so. In other words, making a member economical yet strong enough to serve its purpose is one thing; deciding what kind of member to use, where to put it, and why to use it at all are other but very important things.

Figure 1·1 is a general study of the layout of a portion of a large extrusion mill. The space for equipment, the size and direction of the crane runways, and the general manufacturing procedures largely determine the type of construction, the spacing of columns, and the general shape of the building. After the general plan has been prepared, after the basic features of the structure are known to be practicable, and after the proposed building has been found to be satisfactory for its purpose, then the detail designing is undertaken.

Consider again the matter of the allowable unit stress to be used in the proportioning of the members in such a structure as that of Fig. 1·1. Many purlins, roof trusses, crane girders, and other members have their critical sections computed upon the basis of the specified permissible unit stress in the steel. Yet many also are the members and detail parts of members that will be proportioned upon the basis of practicable, minimum sizes. Great, too, is the cost of roof and wall coverings, windows, floors, foundations, mechanical and electrical equipment, utilities, and land. When one thinks in these terms, he will realize that a change in the specifications to increase the allowable unit stress in the steel 20 per cent from 20,000 to 24,000 psi results in a surprisingly small relative saving in the cost of the building, whereas this change affects greatly its reserve strength and safety. Not only is the seeming decrease in the weight of steel required applicable merely to a portion of the steelwork, it probably will have little effect upon the cost of fabrication and erection as a whole.

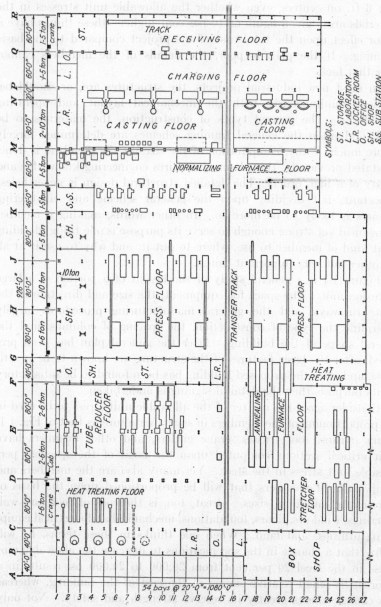

FIG. 1·1. General layout of a large extrusion plant.

The decision upon how conservative one should be in the determination of the permissible unit stresses to be used in the computation of the sizes of members may be controlled by building codes.   If not regulated by them, he should think about how well he knows the magnitudes of the loads that may be applied to his structure, about what the impact effects may be, about the relative magnitudes of dead loads and live loads, and about how stiff the structure or member ought to be. It is obvious that he should be conservative when great uncertainties exist regarding the loads and impacts; when the dead loads are definite and relatively large, he has less of the unknown to worry about.   As for the advisable degree of stiffness, he may have little experience upon which to base his judgment.   For example, a 51-ft. crane girder was designed to support one side of the runway for a high-speed bridge crane.   The girder was designed for the loads usually assumed for that particular make, span, and capacity of crane.   The maximum unit stress appeared to be the limit permitted by the specifications.   The drawing was traced and ready for the shop.   The engineer in charge inquired about the probable deflection; when estimated, this appeared to exceed $1\frac{1}{4}$ in.   Would or would not this sagging of one side of the runway be objectionable?   For a slow crane it might be acceptable, but the engineer decided that it should not be accepted for high-speed service.   Therefore, the girder was made deeper and was designed upon the basis of 12,000 psi maximum tension, and for a deflection of less than half that of the original design.   Was this a correct action?   At least, the extra cost was relatively small, and the performance of the girder proved to be entirely satisfactory.   If the other girder had been used and if its deflection gave the operators the feeling of insecurity, they would not thank the designers.

In another case, a large concrete gallery for conveyors was built in a tunnel under 50 ft. of earth.   The engineer ordered the allowable computed stress in the reinforcement to be increased to 25,000 psi because there was practically no way of increasing the load on the structure, and the original dead load was reasonably determinable.   The structure has been supporting the load safely.

Figure 1·2 shows graphically an imaginary quantitative relationship between the allowable working stress in structural steel, for instance, and the probable life of the building as a usable structure.   Much sound judgment is needed in determining the proper position to take between reduced cost and much lower reserve strength on the one hand, and additional cost and unreasonable length of life of the structure on the other.

Almost any structure is considered to be safe until it falls down. After its failure, the economies of the original design are no longer considered to be wise or even important. The structure failed, and it is

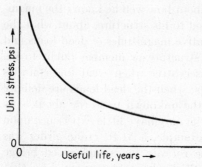

useless! Nevertheless, many structures are replaced because of obsolescence rather than because of structural weakness; hence too great conservatism may be wasteful.

Fig. 1·2. Fictitious curve to indicate general character of relationship between magnitude of allowable unit stress and probable life of the structure.

As an example of some of these principles applied to the planning of a building, assume that a manufacturer wishes to construct a small machine shop with a floor area 80 by 160 ft. Should its cross section look like one of the sketches in Fig. 1·3? A few of the good and bad points about each of these arrangements are the following, referring to the sketches:

(a) A clear width across the entire building avoids intermediate obstructions within the floor area; the crane may serve all pieces of the equipment; the roof trusses and crane bridge are long and relatively heavy; daylight and ventilation come from the windows in the walls only.

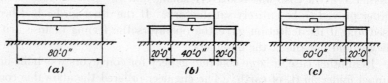

Fig. 1·3. Some simple cross sections for a building.

(b) Here the central aisle is narrow, and there are two 20-ft. side aisles; the crane bridge and roof trusses are light; the columns are small but numerous; handling materials in the side aisles may be slow and expensive unless extra cranes are installed; light and ventilation may be uniform because of the openings in the outer walls and the central section; and the clearance in the side aisles is small.

(c) This is a compromise between (a) and (b). It lacks a large part of the advantages of each; and it has part of the disadvantages of both.

The usefulness of these three layouts may differ greatly; the cost of the structures, little. Consider the following few points:

1. The roof areas are practically the same, yet (a) has less eave construction, flashing, and drains than the others.

2. The wall areas of (b) and (c) are less than in (a) at the ends only.   Hence, if the cost of the walls and windows is proportional to the total of their areas, the plan in Sketch (a) will be slightly more expensive.   However, the details of the walls in (a) will probably be more simple, and the heavy beams holding the upper portions of the side walls of the other schemes will be costly.

3. The floors of all three arrangements are nearly the same; however, those of (b) and (c) may not be so fully usable as in (a).

4. The foundations of (a) may be larger but less costly than those of the others because of the smaller number needed in (a).

5. If bridge cranes, gib cranes, or trolley beams are needed in the side aisles of Sketches (b) and (c), the cost of this equipment and its supports will undoubtedly exceed any saving in the cost of the longer crane bridge and roof trusses in (a).

A few considerations like these show that variations in the structural layout for any given material and building may have minor effects upon the cost of the building but may affect the economy of operations greatly.

A few strong, simple members are likely to be more economical than many small ones which serve the same purpose but which must be at least of a minimum size in any case.   Offsets, corners, and generally fussy construction usually increase the cost of a structure.   It often happens that extra members have to be added to support machinery, pipes, platforms, stairs, and walkways, but it is best to locate these things in advance if possible, then to plan the basic framework to accommodate them as simply as possible.

Furthermore, the cost of a structure is not likely to be completely proportional to its floor area.   For example, if the width of the building of Fig. 1·3(a) is decreased to 75 ft. to save a little expense, one can see easily why the expenditure will not be changed by the same ratio because much of the structure remains the same; yet the reduction of width may result in congestion of equipment, cramped working spaces, unsatisfactory passageways, and general dissatisfaction with the accommodations.   To repeat, the usefulness of a structure is of prime importance.

The modern tendency—and it is a wise one—is to plan industrial structures in such a way as to secure the most open, unobstructed floor space that conditions make it reasonable to obtain without excessive cost.   Such accessories as sanitary facilities, locker rooms, and control rooms may be placed in basements, on mezzanine floors, or even in small extensions adjoining the main structure.   This gives the operators the maximum opportunity to attain whatever layout of equipment future experience may indicate to be desirable.

1·3 Appearance. Industrial structures need not be displeasing in their appearance; neither should they be unduly costly because of an attempt to beautify them. With due consideration to general shapes, proportions, arrangements of windows, materials, color, and the grouping of structures, the resultant effect can generally be pleasing without much increase in cost over that of the cheapest things that will enclose

Fig. 1·4. This modern structure of the Progressive Welder Co., Detroit, Michigan, is simple yet neat and attractive in appearance. It really costs little more to make it so when it is planned properly. (*Design and construction by the Austin Co.*)

the equipment. It generally is a real advantage if an architect studies these matters during the time that the general planning is going on. If he makes perspective drawings of the proposed buildings, they will help everyone concerned to visualize the finished product.

When a new plant is being studied, the basic architectural type of the construction, the common basic features, and the material to be used should be chosen so that all the buildings can be made in accord with the same motif. When a new structure is being built among or alongside existing ones, it should be made to harmonize with its surroundings, not to clash with them. Obviously, a plant should not be a collection of many styles of construction.

Industrial construction is functional and should be so frankly, but without being ugly. It should be simple and neat. An attempt to camouflage its purpose or to make it appear what it is not is likely to yield disappointing results.   This matter of architectural appearance is one of those intangible but nevertheless important problems to be considered.   The various photographs in this book illustrate some of the different types of buildings and the various details of architectural treatment.

1·4 **Relation of Materials to Types and Details of Construction.** The materials of which a structure is to be built should

Fig. 1·5.   A multistory building that utilizes glass blocks as part of the curtain walls.   Notice the landscaping.   This is the plant of the Miles Laboratories, Elkhart, Indiana.   (*Courtesy of Owens-Illinois; photograph by Hedrich-Blessing Studio.*)

be decided upon during the early part of the general planning period, with the choice based upon such matters as cost, availability, type of structure, permanence, climate, speed of construction, fire hazards, appearance, and foundation conditions.   This is of great importance because steel, concrete, wood, and even bricks have their own peculiar characteristics, and there are forms of construction for which each is particularly suitable and advantageous.   Steel is a strong material, well adapted to slender members, long spans, large story heights, and both heavy and light construction; it comes to the field in prefabricated members that can be erected quickly.   Concrete is generally poured in place at the site in a plastic state, requiring timber or other forms to support it temporarily and give to it the requisite shapes; it is especially suitable for low, heavy, short-span, fireproof buildings, but it is expensive when large, heavy members are to be constructed high in the air. For foundations, floors, and massive parts it is exceedingly advantageous. Wood is suitable for small, low, light, short-span, temporary or even fairly permanent structures, which are usually built of relatively short, standard, commercial sizes of lumber that can be fabricated readily and quickly in the field. Bricks and masonry blocks are especially useful for walls and partitions. Sometimes it may be worth while to employ them as bearing walls in low structures, but this use should be studied carefully if there is any likelihood of large lateral forces, earthquakes, explosions, or foundation settlements.

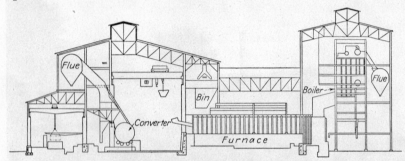

Fig. 1·6. Cross section through the Smelter of the Morenci Reduction Works of the Phelps Dodge Corp. at Morenci, Arizona. In such a specialized plant as this, the building is designed almost completely in accordance with the requirements of the equipment and of structural strength. Neatness and proportion should not, however, be overlooked.

Construction in each of the commonly used materials has its own technique of workmanship, its own economic factors, and even its own general style or type of framing. A designer is not wise if he plans a framework, then looks around to see from what he can make it. If a building has been planned properly as a steel structure, there will be many difficulties when one tries to make the same members out of concrete or timber. When concrete or wood must be used for a structure, the limits of practicable spans and loads may react upon the mechanical layout. For this reason, it is best to face the issue of limitations of the material in the first place and to plan accordingly, rather than to revise the layouts later. These various limitations and many details of practical construction will be discussed more fully in subsequent chapters.

1·5 General Factors Affecting Type of Construction. The greatest influences upon the general shape and type of construction to be used are probably the nature of the operations to be carried on and the equipment required to perform them. Some others are mentioned here, but they will be discussed more fully elsewhere. They are the following:

1. Property cost, or available land, may determine whether a building should be an extensive single-story one or whether the layout should be based upon a multistory structure covering less area.

2. The character of the foundation material may influence the type of structure to be used, especially if the soil is weak.

Fig. 1·7. An architectural drawing of the attractive modern plant of the Continental Can Co., Utica, New York. Such drawings as these are very useful when planning such important structures because they enable one to visualize clearly the architectural features of the structures. Walter Kidde Constructors were the engineers and builders.

3. Available materials may compel the designer to plan a structure so that those on hand can be used.

4. Local building codes, fire-protection requirements, and safety regulations may restrict the freedom of choice of types and materials to a certain extent.

5. Equipment may be too heavy and large to be supported economically on the floors of the upper stories of a multistory building; preferably it should have heavy foundations resting directly upon the ground.

6. Any ordinary building must have a foundation and a roof. For any total floor area required, a two-story building will probably cover only a little over one-half this area of ground. The economies in the foundation and the roof should be compared to the cost of an intermediate floor and other extras; and the effect upon the layout and operation of equipment should be studied.

7. Lighting, ventilation, utilities, and even roof drainage may affect many details of a design; they may have some influence upon the basic type that is most suitable.

8. Climate, heating, and air conditioning may have a great effect upon the general shape of a structure and the choice of materials to be used, as well as

upon many of the construction details. Since a large part of the losses of heat are through the roof, a compact, multistory structure may be worthy of consideration.

Such problems as these deserve careful study. By wise planning, those who create the plans, and those who convert them from ideas to realities, can produce a plant of which they will all be justly proud.

Chapter 2

EXPLORATION OF THE SITE

2·1 Important Effects of Foundation Conditions upon Type of Construction. One of the first things to be done in planning industrial construction is the investigation of subsurface conditions at the site. If possible, preliminary work of this nature should be done prior to purchase of the property, and the conditions should be ascertained sufficiently to make sure that the site is satisfactory. All too frequently land is purchased with only a superficial inspection of the surface; thereafter the engineers have to meet the situation as best they can. In one case in the author's personal experience, preliminary explorations revealed that foundation construction at the tentatively chosen site would cost over $100,000 more than if reasonably good ground could be located. In spite of the fact that the layout work was well under way, a better site was found, and the plans were revised to suit the new conditions.

The owner who fails to investigate soil conditions in advance is likely to become a thoroughly angry possessor of unsatisfactory structures, or to be minus some of his cash reserves owing to unanticipated costs made necessary by unforeseen foundation troubles. He would scoff at one who blindly entered a business venture. Why should he start a building program upon a literally unknown foundation?

Foundation conditions are likely to affect the choice of materials and the type of structure for any given case. If the soil is soft and weak in bearing power, it may be wise to use low, light structures covering large areas. For example, one company planned to build a narrow, tall structure to house a bucket elevator 90 ft. high. If located where operating conditions made it desirable to place it, this building would have rested upon a deep layer of spongy soil in a subterranean ravine. Rather than take risks or spend considerable money for deep foundations, pumps were substituted for the elevator, thus permitting the use of a low, light building that could be supported by the soil alone. If differential settlements of a structure are likely to occur unless unduly expensive foundations are used, it may be best to adopt steel-frame or

15

timber construction that is sufficiently flexible to accommodate itself to minor unequal settlements without serious harm. Brick and concrete walls are likely to crack under such conditions; even when reinforced strongly, the latter generally cannot bridge over long distances. If masonry walls are desirable for other reasons, it may be possible to design them with enough stress-relieving joints to avoid unsightly cracking in spite of the settlements. As a matter of fact, brick walls may crack somewhat through the jointing without having it become noticeable, but the permissible movement is slight. However, this is one of their advantages in comparison to rigid, poured-concrete walls.

The use of continuous beams, girders, and trusses may increase the spans that will be satisfactory economically. When foundation conditions are bad, one should seriously question dependence upon such continuous structures; hence these conditions are likely to affect the very starting point of the planning of the structural framework.

Whether to design a structure of such type, materials, and details that differential settlements will be accepted knowingly, or whether to spend considerable money to make the foundations such that harmful settlements will not occur is a very important question. It is one that should not be answered hastily; inexperienced persons should not answer it at all. Figure 2·1 shows a warehouse founded upon an earth fill about 30 ft. deep—generally a dangerous procedure. In this case, however, it proved to be satisfactory and economical owing to the special gravelly material, excellent compaction, and the fact that the walls and floor were made monolithic and somewhat like a shallow, inverted boat. Under other conditions, such a seemingly radical design might be extremely unwise.

When poor foundation conditions must be met, it is sometimes economical to use multistory structures or buildings with long spans in order to minimize the number of individual foundations. This may occur when piles or caissons are to be used through soft strata to rock or strong materials at lower levels. These conditions are likely to affect the desired type of structure, and even the mechanical layout.

It is better to plan with all possible information available than it is to compel the designers of a structure to meet the situation regardless of cost just because the general plans have progressed too far to be changed.

2·2 Value of Free Information on Soil Conditions. Data on soil conditions given by old residents and neighbors should seldom be trusted unless checked by other evidence. Regardless of good intentions, such "trusted" data caused one of the most unfortunate plant relocation problems in the author's experience. Even borings made upon adjacent property may be unreliable in many districts where neighboring conditions may vary about as widely as the dispositions of human beings. All free evidence in the case is welcome, but one should check it and be sure that it is trustworthy.

This applies particularly in the glacial territory shown in Fig. 2·2, in rough country where erosion may have cut subsurface ravines or created

FIG. 2·1. The change house at the extreme right and the warehouse in the center of this view of the Morenci Reduction Works are founded upon approximately 30 ft. of compacted sand and gravel fill, using mat foundations. The machine shop at the left is partially on unexcavated ground; the remainder of the structure is on concrete piers and footings built before placing from 1 to 10 ft. of fill. (*Courtesy of Phelps Dodge Corp.*)

localized deposits of soft materials, in dolomite or other soluble rock that may contain caverns or hollow seams, and near water fronts where beach erosion or forgotten man-made works may cause surprises. In plains territory like the Middle West and where thick sedimentary deposits are known to cover large areas, as in Chicago, data from surrounding areas may be very useful.

2·3 Definitions. The *foundation* of a structure may be defined as the soil that supports it, or the word may refer to the part of the structure that transmits the weight of the entire edifice to the soil. Although this double usage may seem to be confusing, the sense of the text will generally clarify what is intended.

Superstructure generally means the main frame, shell, or body of a

structure above the ground, constituting the portions that house the
equipment and operations for which the building is erected.

Substructure usually means the walls, footings, piles, and other
portions of a structure that transmit the loads from the superstructure

Fig. 2·2.   Sketch map showing centers of radiation and area covered in North
America during the Pleistocene ice age.   (*After Chamberlin and Salisbury.   From
Legget, "Geology and Engineering."*)

to the soil.   This is the same as the second meaning of the word
foundation.

Ground water denotes the water saturating the soil rather permanently.   Its source is generally rainfall that penetrates down from the
surface somewhere.   The top of the ground water is called the *water
table* or *ground-water table.*   The ground water may be moving slowly

downgrade through the soil—sometimes appearing as springs—or it may be stagnant, forming marshy places when the water table is at or near the surface.

2·4 Methods of Making Shallow Soil Explorations. If a capable foundation engineer or geologist inspects the site of a plant, he may be able to judge the situation so well that only a few detailed investigations need be made to give him a good idea of what lies below

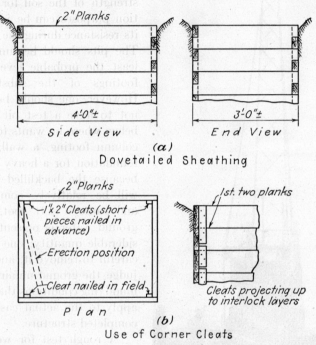

Side View   End View
(a)
Dovetailed Sheathing

Plan
(b)
Use of Corner Cleats

Fig. 2·3. Sheathing for test pits.

the surface. Even he should get something to substantiate his conclusions.

Various means of making preliminary investigations of soil conditions will be discussed in some detail.

One of the simplest ways to learn what is below the surface of the ground is to dig a hole and find out. Such holes—called "test pits"— show the depth of the top soil, thicknesses of strata, and the real nature, fineness, compactness, and moisture condition of the soil. They are especially suitable for shallow explorations; if over 20 to 25 ft. deep, they become relatively expensive. They require no special equipment

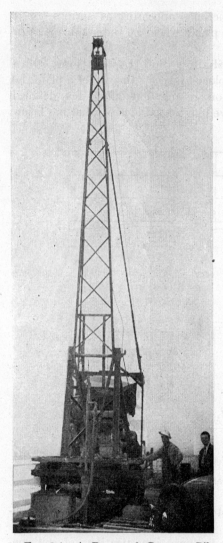

Fig. 2·4. A Raymond Concrete Pile Co.'s Gow-type wash-boring drill rig. Such equipment as this is exceedingly useful. (*Courtesy of Dames & Moore, Foundation Engineers, San Francisco and Los Angeles, California.*)

aside from picks, shovels, and manpower. If they are less than about 2 ft. wide by 4 ft. long in cross section, a man has difficulty working in them; if they must be lined with shoring as in Fig. 2·3, they should be larger. The strength of the soil for foundation purposes can be judged by its resistance during the digging. The pits should be sunk to at least the probable level of the footings of the substructure. However, one should be careful not to have a test pit dug far below where he wants to place a column footing, a wall, or the foundation for a heavy machine because the backfilled material will be relatively compressible and cause a soft spot. When ground water is present in considerable quantity, one must be careful to remove it, and not to judge the ground unfairly under muddying conditions that do not apply to the actual case of the completed structure.

A rough test for weak soils may be made by applying one's weight squarely on the heel of one shoe. The pressure thus produced by a man weighing 160 lb. is about 3,000 lb. per sq. ft. If a pronounced impression, say ⅛ in., is made in the soil, then the soil is poor indeed.

Driving a steel sounding rod into the ground may give useful data regarding the location of rock and gravel when overlain by shallow strata of mud, clay, or topsoil. However, information secured by this means should be viewed with great skepticism because boulders are not bedrock, and thin sand or gravel strata may have less desirable materials under them.

Auger borings are made by a large bit on the end of a rod or pipe having a handle, by means of which a hole may be bored in the earth. Such equipment is generally better than a sounding rod, but its utility is limited.   In clay, it clogs up; in sand, the hole may fill in before samples of underlying materials can be secured; and to penetrate gravelly deposits is difficult.

2·5 Borings for Making Deep Soil Explorations. When the soil is soft or medium clay, test pits may be of little real value because there is danger that materials underlying the substructure may be plastic, may flow slowly under pressure, and may cause excessive settlement due to consolidation.   It is necessary to explore these deeper strata.   Various types of borings and soil tests have been developed for such purposes.

Figures 2·4 and 2·5 show the general nature of the equipment used by contractors in making *wash borings*. A steel pipe casing is driven into the ground.   A smaller pipe inside it is operated like a churn drill, follows it down, and delivers a stream of water through the nozzle at its lower end, washing out the dirt inside the casing.   The water and dirt flow up through the annular space, sometimes being caught in a tub at the top.   As the boring is sunk deeper, additional sections of pipe are coupled on.   By closely watching the effluent, an experienced operator can judge with reasonable accuracy when the boring passes from one stratum to a different one; by observing the ease and rate of penetration, he can *estimate* the relative bearing qualities of the various materials.

Wash borings are generally very easy to make in clays, silts, loams, sands, and small gravel.   They are satisfactory when one wishes to know only the depth to rock or certain strata, or the kind of materials in and the thicknesses of those strata.   They give little reliable evidence regarding the compactness, consistency, strength, and water content of those strata because the recovered materials are entirely disturbed, the fine particles are separated from the coarser ones, and even the latter are considerably mixed.   However, these borings do show the general constituents of the various layers.

When wash borings are used to locate rock, there is great difficulty in distinguishing between it and boulders because the boring equipment cannot penetrate or dislodge large stones.   The presence of gravel near the bottom of a boring should warn the operator that boulders are

likely to be encountered. Even though additional borings are made
near the first one that was thought to have hit boulders and even though
considerable irregularity in elevation is detected by them, the operator
still may not know whether he has encountered boulders or irregular
bedrock.

To clarify such a situation, the water pipe of a wash boring may be
withdrawn and a *core boring* made below the casing. The cutting of

FIG. 2·5. A close-up of drilling procedure of a Gow-type wash-boring rig. Taking
a sample of the discharge to see general type of material encountered. (*Courtesy of
Dames & Moore, Foundation Engineers, San Francisco and Los Angeles, California.*)

the rock may be done by rough diamonds, hardened shot, or steel teeth.
In any case, the inner pipe or drill is rotated rapidly until it grinds its
way down into the rock, leaving a core of the latter inside the pipe.
When this core is broken off and drawn up to the surface, it shows the
nature and stratification of the rock. However, to tell whether one
has encountered bedrock or boulders, it is generally advisable to penetrate the rock 5 or 10 ft.

The data obtained from borings are generally recorded in graphic form, called "logs," or soil profiles.   Figure 2·6 shows the data obtained from a boring made in Los Angeles, California.

2·6 Soil Samples.   Undisturbed soil samples should be taken from the various strata underlying the site of an important building unless the substructure is to be carried to rock or to very good gravel or hardpan overlying the same.   This applies especially to silts and plastic clays.   Even though a stratum may be thick, it is advisable to obtain samples at frequent intervals in order to determine its uniformity. The casing of a wash boring can be cleaned out by flushing it with water after the drilling has been stopped; the water pipe may be re-

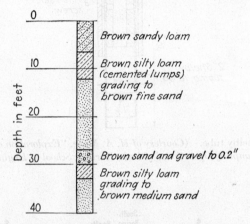

Fig. 2·6.   Log of boring 10 as reported by Dames & Moore, Los Angeles, California. (For location, see Fig. 2·11.)

moved, and then a sample of the soil below the casing may be taken in its natural state.

The equipment for taking undisturbed samples may be of various types, one of which is shown in Fig. 2·7.   Essentially, it consists of a cylindrical casing attached to a long driving rod or pipe.   Inside the shell is a thin metal tube into which the soil is forced by the driving. The shell can be opened up to permit the removal of the sample without taking it out of the tubular container.   Of course, undisturbed samples are not really undisturbed; the term is relative only.   However, they do give a good idea of the properties of the soil in its natural condition. Any samples that are taken carelessly or with poor equipment not only will be unsatisfactory but they may be deceptive.

The tube and its sample of soil should be removed from the sampler, then sealed immediately with paraffin to keep it from drying out.   After

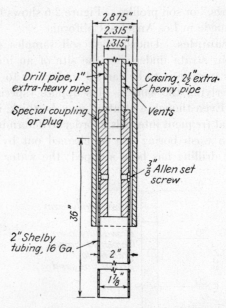

FIG. 2·7.   A Shelby tube.   (*Courtesy of H. A. Mohr, "Exploration of Soil Conditions and Sampling Operations," 3d ed., Harvard School of Engineering.*)

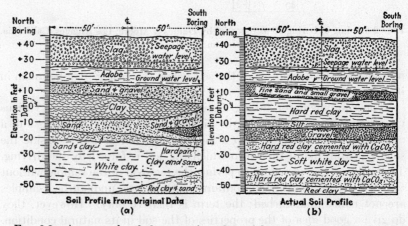

FIG. 2·8.   An example of the necessity of careful work when taking borings. Based upon the original borings, the soil profile at the left was prepared.   Later, after four new borings had been made, the profile at the right was drawn.   Comparison of the two profiles shows how misleading inadequate data may be.   (*Courtesy of Engineering News-Record.*)

labeling and boxing, the samples should be sent to a good soil-mechanics laboratory for testing. Generally, tests should be made to determine the moisture content, shearing strength, compressibility, consolidation, and permeability so that an estimate of the safe bearing value and the probable settlement of the soil can be made. Although these tests may not give absolute and minute knowledge of the behavior of the soil under load, they do give the capable, experienced engineer a real basis for his judgment in the planning of a foundation.

It is very instructive to have soil profiles drawn from the data found in the borings. Figure 2·8(a) shows the conditions interpreted from some early borings made at the site chosen for a 567-ft. reinforced-concrete stack. Notice that the strata of clay appear to be tapered, indicating probable uneven settlement and tilting of the structure toward the side where these layers are thickest. The condition did not seem to be reasonable. Therefore, additional borings were made and soil samples were taken. The results of the borings are shown in Fig. 2·8(b), indicating that the original borings were improperly made or that the data were incorrectly reported.

2·7 Subsurface Conditions to Be Considered with Great Care. There are certain conditions that are especially bad for foundations. The owner and his engineers should recognize them and should seek the assistance of experts when dangers exist. Some suggestions are the following:

1. Make sure that soft strata do not underlie seemingly good surface materials. Clay, silt, or possibly quicksand (very fine, saturated sand) may exist there.

2. Old foundations, submerged cribbing, and similar hidden obstructions may cause serious trouble with some types of foundation.

3. Unequal settlements are likely to be caused by a plastic stratum whose thickness varies, as in Fig. 2·8(a); by a layer of soft silt or clay extending under part of a building whereas sand is below the remainder (the silt may consolidate more than the sand); by lenticular deposits of clay, silt, sand, and gravel scattered under the site, the compressible ones causing soft spots. On the other hand, moderate uniform settlement due to deep layers may not be harmful in itself.

4. When large, heavy buildings are to have their substructures carried down to rock or gravel, the contours or elevations of the hidden supporting stratum should be ascertained so that the parts of the substructure can be designed properly. If the building is supposed to rest upon rock near the surface, one should look for filled-in ravines. Perhaps these are full of boulders; they may be the course of underground streams that would cause serious troubles in the conduct of work—with resultant extra costs.

5. When a building is to have a basement, pits, or stepped floors, one should make sure that he will not have to blast out hard rock when he intended to excavate sand. Another source of difficulty is a high water table, causing expensive construction and requiring a waterproofed substructure. Remedying a wet, leaky basement after its completion is usually a costly job.

6. When piles are to be used to support a structure, the water table is important because timber piles should not extend above it. Field data on groundwater conditions should be secured over a long period to see if there is any seasonal variation in the water table. Is there any likelihood that adjacent excavations, sewers, wells, or other things may lower it in the future? Furthermore, information should be secured to determine the required lengths and the best types of pile to be used.

7. If ground water under pressure is encountered, it may cause upheaval of the bottom of an excavation.

2·8 Load Tests of Soils. Actual tests of the load-bearing capacity of soils in place may be advisable. When settlements, especially uneven and unpredictable ones, are likely to prove disastrous to a structure, such tests are advisable before the foundation is designed.

The basic purpose of these tests is to load the soil gradually, measure the corresponding settlements over a period of at least several hours, and continue to increase the loading until a distinguishable breakdown of the resistance of the soil occurs, or until the load safely carried is considerably above that desired. In granular soils, the settlements usually occur quickly, then stop; in plastic ones, they increase slowly as the soil flows out from under the load, or as the water is squeezed out of it.

A few points to watch or provide for in making load-bearing tests are the following:

1. Apply the tests at the proposed elevation of the bottoms of the footings, digging a large test pit if necessary.

2. A loaded area of 1 sq. ft. is often used, but tests made upon areas of 2 sq. ft., or even larger, are likely to yield more reliable results.

3. In plastic soils especially, embed the lower end of the loading mast in the soil at least a little way in order to simulate the relative dimensions of the proposed size of footings and their depth, otherwise the squeezing out of the soil under a load will occur at far lower pressures than it will under the confining effect of surrounding materials.

4. Give the various increments of loading sufficient time to act, in order to make sure that settlements have practically ceased, before applying more load.

5. When the critical load is determined, find the allowable unit pressure by dividing the test result by the desired safety factor—perhaps from 1.5 to 2.5, depending upon the nature of the individual case and the importance of the structure. For plastic soils, the critical load may vary considerably. It is sometimes

defined as the one at which the total settlement reaches 1 in. Local building codes may specify its magnitude.

6. Remember that the results of a load test on a relatively small area cannot be applied directly to a large area, especially in plastic soils, because the pressure-distributing effect of the soil dissipates rapidly the pressure from the former whereas it cannot do so in the case of the latter.

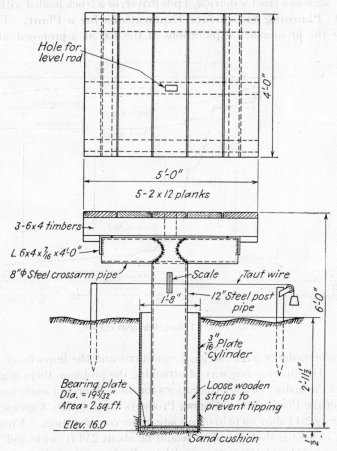

FIG. 2·9. A platform for making a load test of soil.

7. Regardless of scale readings or other means used to measure settlements, take very careful level readings with some reliable point or bench mark as a datum in order to check the results obtained otherwise.

The equipment used in making load-bearing tests of the soil under a 567-ft. reinforced-concrete stack at Douglas, Arizona, is shown in Fig. 2·9. The soil profile at the site is given in Fig. 2·8(b). Figure 2·10 shows the time-settlement curve for one of these load tests.

A method that may be used for quick load tests of soil and piles, in lieu of such rather costly loading platforms as that shown in Fig. 2·9, is the application of loads by means of hydraulic jacks. The jacks may be directly upon the bearing plate or pile, whereas their upward reaction may be delivered to a grillage of some sort upon which rests some heavy object, such as a tractor derrick, a pile driver, or a truck loaded with sand.

2·9 Planning Subsurface Explorations for a Plant. The extent of the preliminary explorations of the soil at a proposed site will

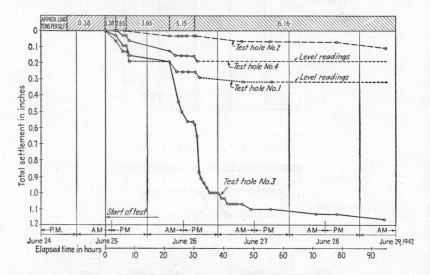

FIG. 2·10. Time-settlement curves.

vary in accordance with the local conditions and the importance of the plant. To illustrate one way of attacking the problem, there is given a little of the history of the explorations for the California Condenser Tube Plant of the Phelps Dodge Copper Products Corp. in Los Angeles.

Figure 2·11 shows a plan of one site under consideration. A tentative layout indicated that the plant would be about 250 ft. wide and 750 ft. long, with 75- and 100-ft. crane aisles. Borings 1 to 8, inclusive, were made to give a general idea of conditions—especially to see if there were any strata of soft clay or silt. They covered the area in general so that, if desirable, the plant could be located along either Garfield Ave. or the Pacific Electric tracks. It was finally placed as shown in outline on the map. Then, since the heaviest parts of the structure were near the ends, borings 9 and 10 were subsequently made to secure more information at the final situation. Figure 2·6 shows the findings from boring 10.

Briefly, a few scattered borings should be made first, followed by additional ones when the final location is selected.   At least one of the preliminary borings should penetrate to a depth of 50 to 100 ft., perhaps more, to explore the deep strata unless hardpan, rock, or similar materials are encountered at higher elevations.   In the case of a plant in Nebraska, which was to have circular, reinforced-concrete pits 70 ft. deep, scattered borings were made; then, when the buildings were located tentatively, additional borings were made at the positions of the

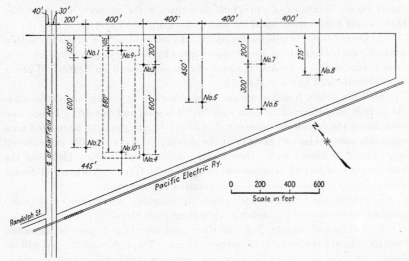

FIG. 2·11.   Plan of preliminary borings at site of California Condenser Tube Plant, Phelps Dodge Copper Products Corp., Los Angeles, California.

pits to make sure that the caissons would not encounter boulders or bedrock.

The number of borings to be made to secure adequate data for final construction at any given site will depend upon many things.   If preliminary borings show uniformity of soil conditions over the site, few, if any, additional borings need be made.   This was the case at the site pictured in Fig. 2·11.   If the ground is found to vary considerably at different places, the final site should be investigated more thoroughly; if the structures are to be heavy and important, more careful explorations are generally justified.

The following suggestions are for consideration when a contract for the making of borings is being prepared:

1. Negotiate only with reputable companies doing such work.
2. Locate the approximate positions of the desired borings, give their num-

ber, and indicate the intended depths. Give the contractor some leeway as to location so that he may not be hindered by unexpected conditions.

3. Specify the type of boring desired, and whether or not undisturbed soil samples are to be taken. For important work, samples should be secured from at least one boring, taking a sample from each stratum, or not over about 10 ft. c.c. in thick strata.

4. A unit-price contract will enable the owner to order additional borings (the same for soil sampling) if the logs of the borings show the materials to be variable and of poor quality. He can also explore carefully the conditions at the finally chosen locations of important structures if the property is acceptable. Have a unit price agreed upon for such extra work.

5. Do not take borings too far apart. In one contract on which the author worked, two borings about 150 ft. apart in rocky territory spanned a subterranean ravine carrying an underground stream and caused an "extra" of about $80,000 to be paid to the contractor.

6. When heavy foundations are to go to rock, core borings should be made about 10 ft. into the rock to make sure that it is solid and suitable. In one case with which the author was connected, a heavy building was to be erected on a mountain side. The two borings at the downhill corners actually encountered large pieces of buried rock, whereas subsequent operations revealed that the lower portion of the site was covered with about 50 ft. of rock scrap and debris. This condition caused considerable redesign of the structure.

7. Specify core borings at least $1\frac{1}{2}$ in. in diameter. Smaller ones may be unsatisfactory because of the difficulty of getting good cores.

8. Specify soil samples not less than approximately $2\frac{1}{2}$ in. in diameter. Smaller ones are not suitable for proper testing. The nature of the soil will influence the type of tests to be made; e.g., shearing, moisture content, compressibility, and consolidation tests are important for clay and silt.

9. Have soil samples tested by a reliable laboratory or engineer.

10. Specify time limits for starting and completing the work.

11. Have the contractor furnish a report showing the exact locations of the borings, also the log of each one. Preferably have him turn in daily reports showing the progress made and the results found. If one of the engineer's own men can be on hand to watch the work, or if he can be sent to the site once or twice a day, decisions affecting further work may be made more quickly when conditions are encountered that make them necessary.

12. Be sure that the exploratory work is done carefully and that the results are clearly presented, because legal difficulties may result if the information is indefinite or confusing.

13. When issuing boring data for use by contractors in bidding on construction work, be sure to give the logs of the borings as reported by the company that made them. State that their interpretation, the soil profiles, and the contract drawings are based thereon and are believed to be reasonably correct but that they are not guaranteed. However, be sure to give the contractors all the data available and make no attempt to minimize the difficulties to be expected.

2·10 Use of Subsurface Information in Designing Foundations. That foundations should be designed after adequate soil data are secured and that they should be adapted to the particular conditions of the structures and the site, is axiomatic. As stated previously, data from soil explorations may show the engineers enough so that the general type of foundation and the basic character of the structures can be determined. However, the details of the foundations cannot be

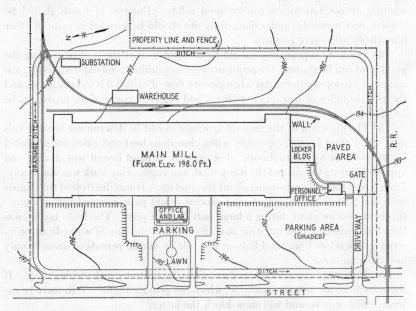

FIG. 2·12. Plan of site, including buildings, transportation, grading, parking, drainage, and fencing.

worked out until after the structures are designed and the positions and magnitudes of the loads on each part are ascertained. For these reasons further discussion of actual types and planning of substructures will be postponed until after the superstructures and the planning of them have been considered. Chapters 13 and 14 contain data on the planning of foundations themselves.

2·11 Miscellaneous Features to Investigate. There are many other features to be investigated before one purchases land. A few of them are such matters as these:

1. The area should be adequate. Perhaps a preliminary layout of a plant will be necessary to determine this. If the land is not extensive enough and if the shape of the property does not permit a satisfactory layout, no one will be

pleased with it.   Future expansion, parking areas, space for railroad sidings, and storage areas should be considered in this connection.

2. Zoning regulations and local building codes may affect what one is allowed to build upon a given site.

3. Floods and high tides may be a hazard.   The records of state and local authorities, as well as the physical evidence of past damage in the vicinity, should be investigated.   Such conditions may determine the detailed locations for various structures upon the property, the elevations at which floors must be set, and whether or not basements can be used safely.   Dangers of floods should be studied very seriously, and a dangerous site should be avoided in spite of other temptingly attractive features.

4. The local topography should be mapped so that the cost of grading the plant yard can be studied, the problem of surface drainage solved tentatively, the adequacy of slopes determined when gravity flow of material is to be utilized, and the practicability of intraplant railroad and highway connections proved to be satisfactory.

5. The direction of the prevailing winds should be determined because this may affect plant layout, especially when obnoxious heat and gases are produced by the plant or by its neighbors.   For example, a plant layout was studied and approved during the rush of the war period, and engineering work was under way. Then one of the engineers asked about this matter.   It was discovered that fumes from one part of the manufacturing process would pass over and through practically the entire plant during a large part of each year.   The basic layout was therefore revised.   This question may also arise in the case of water-front properties where odors from mud flats at low tide or during periods of drought may become a nuisance.

6. It should be possible to secure access to a site by rail and highway.   If these facilities are not yet available, who must provide them?   Will there be extensive fills or cuts, and will snow block the latter?

7. The title to property should be clear, and any restrictions stated in the deed should be ascertained.

8. If easements have been granted in the past, will these bind the purchaser of the property?   Furthermore, if easements and rights of way across neighboring properties are needed, agreements should be made in advance to guarantee that they can be obtained.

9. It is important to make sure that electric power, water, gas, sewers, and other necessary utilities are or can be made available.   If they must be brought to the site, who pays for the work?   Is suitable water for plant operations available?   Can wastes be disposed of?

10. To be investigated, too, are taxes, assessments, fire and police protection, and the probable development of adjacent properties.

Chapter 3

DAYLIGHTING INDUSTRIAL PLANTS

3·1 Introduction. Common sense and experience indicate that industrial operations can generally be carried on most efficiently and comfortably when adequate illumination is provided—when seeing is easy. Since daylight is repeatedly present, since man's eyes have been developed through the ages to utilize it in seeing, and since it is free for the taking, it is economical and wise to use it for illumination in industrial plants whenever practicable.

Of course there are special instances where complete dependence upon artificial lighting is desirable, or even necessary. However, the complete "blacking out" of industrial plants should be questioned before it is adopted for permanent construction and operation. Such drastic action may be advantageous in case of war, but the resultant cost of power for lighting may prove to be burdensome during times of peace. If mankind's thinking and planning are to be concentrated perpetually upon warfare, then we must drastically change our ideas about many things, including our mode of living.

The purpose of this chapter is to show how industrial buildings can be planned to secure the most satisfactory results from the use of daylight. This should be one of the starting points in the design of a structure, its shape and details.

3·2 General Principles. The unit measure of illumination is called a *foot-candle*, which is the intensity of light upon a surface one foot square and located one foot from a standard candle. Hence, the distribution of illumination over any area is measured by the foot-candles of illumination at all points of that area. Obviously these intensities may vary at different locations.

Since a given light source illuminates its surroundings in all directions around it, all points equidistant from that source have the same intensity of illumination, and they lie in the surface of an imaginary sphere with that source as its center. Therefore, for any given case, the intensity of illumination varies inversely as the surface of this imaginary sphere, or as $1/r^2$, where r is the distance from the source to the point in question.

Everyone in the Temperate Zone of the Northern Hemisphere knows that the intensity of daylight varies from dawn to dusk; that it varies also with the seasons from winter to summer, and with weather conditions from cloudy to clear, somewhat as indicated in Fig. 3·1. On a clear day in summer, the sunlight may have an intensity of 9,000 to 10,000 ft.-candles; when a large cumulus cloud passes over the sun, the intensity may drop to 3,000 or 4,000 ft.-candles. However, the human

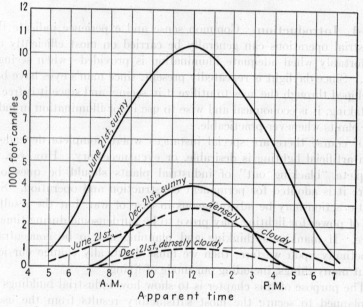

FIG. 3·1. Approximate intensity of total daylight; latitude 42° N.

eye can adjust itself quickly to these seemingly violent changes. On the other hand, large variations in light of low intensity are likely to be much more troublesome and to interfere with visibility. In planning for the use of daylight, one must face this situation and make the windows of a structure of such size and place them in such positions as to take the greatest possible advantage of the light within the range of practicable construction and costs, providing auxiliary artificial lighting to supplement it when necessary.

Naturally, the best plans will be ineffective if the windows become and remain dirty. Designers sometimes blame the operators for this condition, whereas the real cause of poor maintenance may be in the design itself. If a structure is so made that it is difficult or dangerous for a man to clean the windows, he will seldom do it except under compulsion—and no one should blame him. Furthermore, dirt may collect on the inside of the glass more than on the outside. There are plants in which even a nimble monkey would have difficulty in negotiating the spaces amidst the steelwork high above cranes, machines, furnaces, and what not. Provisions for easy access to windows should be made in the original plans.

The intensity of illumination required for proper general visibility depends upon many things. Table 3·1 gives some general data as a guide. The optimum to be attained is uniform distribution of light; intensity enough to avoid eyestrain; elimination of excessive highlights and shadows, yet with sufficient contrast between the background and the objects to be seen; and proper control to avoid dimness at one time or place and glare at another. Patches of sunlight moving across the floor may so brighten certain spots that the human eye cannot adjust itself rapidly enough to look at one object in the sunlight and then immediately thereafter at another in relative darkness. Avoidance of this contrast is one of the advantages to be secured by the use of light from the north. Localized artificial lighting of high intensity may be needed for special work requiring great accuracy of vision. This matter will be discussed in the next chapter.

In order to design the fenestration (window arrangement) of a structure, one should determine the minimum intensity of light that will be satisfactory for the performance of good work. This may vary in different departments or portions of the floor area. Then the designer should endeavor to provide enough windows to secure these results. Sometimes it may be possible to plan the original layout so as to use space along the walls near the side windows for equipment whose operation requires the best visibility. At any rate, one should start with a desired goal, then try to reach it, rather than to "stick some windows around" and then let the operators do the best they can under the conditions.

Table 3·1 Approximate Foot-candles Needed for Adequate Visibility

	Foot-candles
Rough work, furnace rooms, locker rooms, warehouses, and places requiring only a little visibility	5
General manufacturing of large objects, and offices requiring moderate visibility	10
General work, and offices requiring fairly good visibility	15
Processes, drafting rooms, and work requiring really good visibility	20
Special fine work of manufacturing and inspection, fine drafting, and things requiring excellent visibility	20–50 or more

Table 3·2   Foot-candles of Illumination from Vertical Windows at the Working Plane

Feet back from window	Window heights										
	5'2"	6'10"	8'6"	10'3"	11'11"	13'7"	15'4"	17'0"	18'9"	22'2"	25'7"
5	25.0	29.75	34.75	38.5	41.75	44.25	46.5	48.4	50.0	52.7	55.0
10	13.1	16.35	20.0	24.25	28.0	31.9	35.0	37.5	40.0	43.5	46.5
15	7.5	9.75	12.25	15.5	19.0	21.75	24.25	27.0	29.75	34.25	38.0
20	4.8	6.2	8.0	10.25	13.4	16.0	18.0	20.9	23.0	27.5	31.5
25	3.3	4.25	5.5	7.25	9.6	11.5	13.75	16.0	18.05	22.1	25.75
30	2.35	3.15	4.1	5.5	7.25	8.75	10.5	12.35	14.35	18.15	21.25
35	1.75	2.38	3.15	4.2	5.5	6.75	8.1	9.75	11.5	14.7	17.5
40	1.36	1.83	2.43	3.25	4.4	5.5	6.5	7.8	9.2	12.05	14.5
50	0.85	1.15	1.58	2.1	2.8	3.4	4.2	5.0	6.0	8.0	10.1
60	0.6	0.79	1.06	1.41	1.88	2.3	2.9	3.4	4.05	5.55	7.15
70	0.43	0.57	0.75	1.0	1.35	1.7	2.08	2.5	2.95	3.95	5.05
80	0.32	0.43	0.56	0.75	1.02	1.28	1.55	1.88	2.2	3.05	4.0
90	0.24	0.34	0.45	0.59	0.79	0.98	1.2	1.45	1.75	2.43	3.1
100	0.2	0.27	0.36	0.47	0.65	0.77	0.95	1.15	1.38	1.9	2.5
110	0.16	0.22	0.3	0.4	0.56	0.65	0.79	0.95	1.15	1.6	2.1
120	0.14	0.19	0.25	0.35	0.49	0.52	0.69	0.75	0.9	1.3	1.7
130	0.12	0.16	0.23	0.32	0.44	0.5	0.62	0.7	0.8	1.1	1.41
140	0.1	0.14	0.2	0.29	0.4	0.48	0.57	0.65	0.75	0.95	1.2

Courtesy of Detroit Steel Products Co.

Table 3·3 Foot-candles of Illumination from Vertical Windows above the Working Plane

Feet back from window	Sill 15' above working plane (Window heights)					Sill 25' above working plane (Window heights)					Sill 35' above working plane (Window heights)					Sill 45' above working plane (Window heights)				
	3'6"	5'2"	6'10"	8'6"	10'3"	3'6"	5'2"	6'10"	8'6"	10'3"	3'6"	5'2"	6'10"	8'6"	10'3"	3'6"	5'2"	6'10"	8'6"	10'3"
5	3.0	4.0	5.1	6.0	6.65	1.15	1.5	1.8	2.1	2.5	0.6	0.85	1.1	1.35	1.6	0.43	0.85	1.4	1.95	2.9
10	5.8	7.4	9.8	11.2	12.0	2.2	3.0	3.55	4.3	4.7	1.25	1.85	2.25	2.85	3.6	1.2	1.7	2.4	3.25	4.15
15	6.6	8.0	10.6	12.8	13.8	2.95	4.4	5.15	6.5	7.1	1.9	2.7	3.3	4.3	5.2	1.7	2.45	3.3	4.05	5.1
20	6.0	7.65	9.8	12.05	13.6	3.5	5.1	6.25	7.75	8.95	2.38	3.3	4.0	5.4	6.6	2.25	3.2	4.0	4.75	5.75
25	5.1	6.8	8.5	10.6	12.2	3.8	5.2	6.6	8.3	9.75	2.73	3.6	4.5	5.9	7.25	2.65	3.8	4.55	5.35	6.25
30	4.3	5.8	7.45	9.2	10.65	3.6	5.0	6.5	8.35	10.00	2.85	3.7	4.6	6.0	7.5	2.85	4.15	4.9	5.75	6.55
35	3.6	4.8	6.35	7.8	9.05	3.4	4.6	6.15	7.75	9.15	2.7	3.55	4.5	5.9	7.45	2.75	3.95	4.85	5.65	6.4
40	3.05	4.0	5.4	6.6	7.8	3.1	4.15	5.5	6.95	8.1	2.45	3.35	4.3	5.75	7.1	2.55	3.65	4.6	5.45	6.15
45	2.5	3.4	4.45	5.5	6.55	2.8	3.7	4.9	6.2	7.25	2.25	3.05	4.0	5.3	6.8	2.35	3.45	4.35	5.2	5.85
50	2.05	2.8	3.7	4.65	5.5	2.55	3.25	4.35	5.5	6.5	2.08	2.8	3.65	4.9	6.4	2.15	3.15	4.0	4.9	5.5
55	1.65	2.4	3.0	3.85	4.75	2.25	2.9	3.85	4.9	5.8	1.9	2.55	3.3	4.45	5.85	2.0	2.85	3.7	4.5	5.25
60	1.25	2.0	2.5	3.25	4.0	2.0	2.55	3.4	4.35	5.15	1.73	2.3	3.0	4.05	5.4	1.85	2.6	3.45	4.15	4.9
65	1.1	1.65	2.1	2.75	3.4	1.75	2.3	3.05	3.85	4.55	1.55	2.1	2.7	3.7	4.8	1.65	2.35	3.15	3.9	4.6
70	0.9	1.4	1.8	2.4	2.95	1.5	2.05	2.7	3.35	4.0	1.4	1.9	2.4	3.35	4.25	1.5	2.15	2.9	3.6	4.3
75	0.75	1.15	1.5	2.05	2.5	1.35	1.85	2.4	3.0	3.5	1.25	1.75	2.18	3.0	3.85	1.35	1.95	2.65	3.35	4.05
80	0.6	1.0	1.3	1.8	2.2	1.2	1.6	2.15	2.65	3.1	1.15	1.58	2.0	2.7	3.45	1.2	1.8	2.4	3.1	3.8
85	0.5	0.85	1.15	1.55	1.9	1.05	1.45	1.9	2.35	2.75	1.06	1.43	1.83	2.4	3.1	1.12	1.65	2.23	2.85	3.55
90	0.45	0.75	1.0	1.35	1.75	0.9	1.25	1.65	2.05	2.45	1.0	1.3	1.68	2.2	2.75	1.03	1.5	2.08	2.65	3.3
95	0.43	0.6	0.9	1.2	1.55	0.8	1.1	1.45	1.8	2.2	0.93	1.2	1.53	2.0	2.5	0.95	1.38	1.95	2.45	3.05
100	0.4	0.55	0.8	1.08	1.4	0.65	0.9	1.2	1.5	1.95	0.9	1.13	1.4	1.83	2.33	0.88	1.25	1.85	2.3	2.85
105	0.35	0.5	0.7	0.9	1.25	0.5	0.75	1.0	1.35	1.75	0.81	1.05	1.3	1.68	2.1	0.80	1.18	1.7	2.15	2.65
110	0.3	0.45	0.61	0.8	1.1	0.37	0.6	0.85	1.02	1.55	0.76	1.0	1.24	1.55	1.98	0.75	1.03	1.58	2.05	2.48
115	0.28	0.39	0.54	0.7	0.98	0.32	0.54	0.73	0.89	1.35	0.73	0.96	1.18	1.45	1.85	0.70	0.97	1.45	1.94	2.3
120	0.25	0.36	0.48	0.63	0.87	0.27	0.46	0.63	0.76	1.2	0.69	0.92	1.14	1.38	1.73	0.67	0.92	1.4	1.83	2.15
125	0.23	0.32	0.43	0.55	0.78	0.25	0.39	0.55	0.71	1.1	0.67	0.88	1.09	1.30	1.60	0.64	0.89	1.3	1.73	2.08
130	0.21	0.29	0.39	0.5	0.7	0.24	0.35	0.47	0.67	0.98	0.64	0.85	1.05	1.25	1.52	0.60	0.87	1.18	1.61	1.93
135	0.2	0.27	0.35	0.45	0.63	0.21	0.30	0.41	0.58	0.86	0.62	0.82	1.02	1.20	1.43	0.59	0.82	1.10	1.53	1.84
140	0.19	0.25	0.32	0.41	0.58	0.19	0.27	0.37	0.51	0.76	0.60	0.8	1.0	1.19	1.36	0.57	0.79	1.05	1.45	1.75

All values figured for an overcast sky, 6 months' collection of dirt.
All glass 20' high.
3'6"—2 panes high.   6'10"—4 panes high.
5'2"—3 panes high.   8'6"—5 panes high.   10'3"—6 panes high.
Courtesy of Detroit Steel Products Co.

Table 3-4 Foot-candles of Illumination from 30° Sloping Windows above the Working Plane

Feet from plane of window	Sill 15' above working plane				Sill 25' above working plane				Sill 35' above working plane				Sill 45' above working plane			
	Window heights				Window heights				Window heights				Window heights			
	3'0"	6'0"	9'0"	12'0"	3'0"	6'0"	9'0"	12'0"	3'0"	6'0"	9'0"	12'0"	3'0"	6'0"	9'0"	12'0"
5	1.6	2.6	3.3	3.9	0.6	1.0	1.5	2.1	0.5	0.8	1.1	1.5	0.2	0.4	0.6	0.8
10	4.8	8.3	10.6	16.9	1.6	2.3	3.5	4.6	0.9	1.5	2.2	2.9	0.5	0.8	1.3	1.8
15	7.0	13.8	18.4	21.3	2.5	4.1	6.3	7.4	1.3	2.3	3.4	4.5	0.8	1.6	2.3	2.9
20	4.9	10.1	16.3	19.3	3.3	6.2	8.9	10.1	1.7	3.1	4.6	6.0	1.2	2.4	3.3	4.3
25	3.5	6.8	11.9	16.2	3.9	7.1	9.6	11.6	2.0	3.8	5.7	7.5	1.6	3.1	4.5	5.8
30	2.5	4.9	8.5	12.8	3.5	6.8	9.5	11.9	2.4	4.6	6.7	8.9	2.0	3.9	5.8	7.4
40	1.3	3.0	5.1	7.8	2.6	5.4	8.1	11.1	2.9	5.6	8.1	10.6	2.5	4.7	7.1	9.1
50	0.8	1.9	3.6	5.3	1.9	4.0	6.3	8.6	2.3	4.6	6.9	9.1	2.3	4.5	6.9	8.9
60	0.5	1.4	2.5	3.8	1.4	3.0	4.5	6.4	1.7	3.6	5.5	7.5	1.9	3.9	6.0	8.0
70	0.4	1.0	1.7	2.7	1.0	2.1	3.2	4.7	1.3	2.6	4.3	6.1	1.6	3.2	5.0	6.7
80	0.33	0.7	1.2	1.9	0.7	1.4	2.2	3.3	0.9	2.0	3.2	4.8	1.3	2.6	4.0	5.5
90	0.28	0.5	0.9	1.4	0.5	1.0	1.6	2.3	0.7	1.5	2.4	3.5	1.0	2.0	3.1	4.4
100	0.23	0.37	0.6	1.0	0.37	0.7	1.2	1.6	0.5	1.1	1.9	2.6	0.8	1.6	2.5	3.5
110	0.2	0.28	0.5	0.7	0.28	0.6	0.9	1.3	0.4	0.9	1.4	2.0	0.6	1.3	2.1	2.9
120	0.18	0.25	0.4	0.5	0.23	0.5	0.7	1.0	0.4	0.7	1.1	1.6	0.5	1.1	1.8	2.4

All values figured for an overcast sky, 6 months' collection of dirt.
Courtesy of Detroit Steel Products Co.

The following general data are taken largely from information issued by the Detroit Steel Products Co.:

1. For windows of height h in one side wall only, the limit of the useful working space is about 2 to 3 h back from the windows; beyond that, the intensity is generally less than 10 ft.-candles. When windows are on both sides and the building is only 50 to 60 ft. wide, the useful space may be about three times the sum of the window heights.

2. The maximum intensity of illumination on the working plane should not be greater than about three times the minimum, the latter being generally at least 10 ft.-candles. Greater variations, unless very widely separated and with a gradual change of intensity, are likely to be unsatisfactory. A uniformly distributed, moderate intensity of light is likely to be better than bright spots scattered in relatively dim areas.

3. The area of the windows should be at least 30 per cent of the floor area if 10 ft.-candles are to be available on cloudy days and with 6 months' dirt on the windows.

4. The upper part of a side window is the most effective in lighting the central portion of a building.

5. Increasing the size of side windows affects the minimum intensity more than in direct proportion to the change in size, whereas it has less effect upon the maximum intensity.

6. Sloping windows (when clean) let in more direct sunlight than do vertical ones. However, experience seems to show that they collect more dirt and are more difficult to clean than the latter.

7. In general, vertical windows "6 months dirty" lose about 50 per cent of their efficiency, whereas those on a 30° slope with the vertical lose about 75 per cent, and those on a 60° slope (skylights) may lose 83 per cent. Perhaps 75 per cent of the dirt will be on the inside, probably because wind and rain partly clean the outside.

8. The direction of the daylight and the shadows cast by it should be considered when the layout and detail locations of equipment are planned so that men will not cast shadows on their own work.

If the interior finish of a manufacturing plant is of a pleasing color, this may add considerably to the comfort of the workers; it may also improve their efficiency. In some cases, properly contrasting colors may aid them in seeing. Color may also be used to warn them about parts that are sources of danger.

3·3 Intensity Curves. Experiments have been made to determine the variation in intensity of the light coming in through vertical windows in the walls of buildings. Tables 3·2 to 3·4 are based upon data issued by the Detroit Steel Products Co., the manufacturers of Fenestra windows. The values are for windows "6 months dirty" and for cloudy days. Although these figures should not be accepted as exact values, they are useful in judging different designs. Table 3·2 can be used for lower tier windows in side walls; Table 3·3, for higher rows and monitor windows. Both tables show the variation in intensity with distance from the windows. The working plane is assumed to be 3 ft. above the floor.

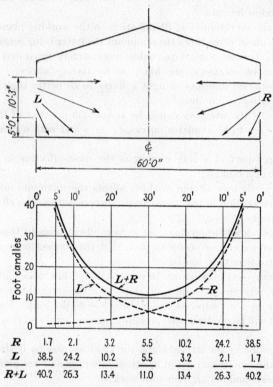

R	1.7	2.1	3.2	5.5	10.2	24.2	38.5
L	38.5	24.2	10.2	5.5	3.2	2.1	1.7
R+L	40.2	26.3	13.4	11.0	13.4	26.3	40.2

FIG. 3·2. Intensity curve for continuous side windows.

In estimating the intensity of daylight at various points in a building, curves may be plotted for the effect of each window as though it were the only one, then a summation curve may be plotted by adding the ordinates of all curves at each particular point. It is necessary to consider the light from both sides and both ends of a building unless partitions cut off the light from some of them or unless they are too far away.

Figure 3·2 shows the intensity curves for continuous windows 10 ft. 3 in. high along both sides of a long, single-story building 60 ft.

wide. In plotting the curves, the ordinates are taken from Table 3·2, neglecting the second decimal place as inconsequential. Differences in the levels of the working plane—whether floor, benches, or machines— have little effect except perhaps near the windows. The rapid decrease of intensity from the windows to the center of the building is shown clearly by the $L + R$ curve. If the windows occupied only 70 per cent of the length of the bays (center to center of columns), the intensity of the light might be assumed as 70 per cent of that shown for the curves in Fig. 3·2. Of course this does not apply to benches close to the wall spaces between windows. Naturally, columns, beams, bracing, crane girders, and other obstructions may cut off some of the daylight, but their effect in reducing the computed intensity of illumination cannot be ascertained easily. Allowance for such things is largely a matter of practical judgment after a study of each particular situation. These interferences should be minimized in the planning of a structure.

In using the data in Table 3·2, variations of the height of sill from 3 to 6 ft. above the floor may be neglected. However, this distance should be borne in mind when workbenches along the wall are considered. For heights of sills differing from those shown in Table 3·3, values may be interpolated from the data given.

An examination of Table 3·3 shows that zero illumination from any high window is assumed to be directly under it. This assumes no useful reflection of light from opposite walls, structural parts, equipment, and the underside of the roof. This is proper for most factory buildings except for multistory structures, offices, and similar places where the walls are light in color and can be (and are) kept clean. To estimate the illumination due to 30° sloping windows, use Table 3·4. It is similar to Table 3·3 except that the point of zero intensity is to be offset to the intersection of the plane of the window and the working plane. The window heights are also different.

3·4 Monitors. Since side windows are not of much value in lighting the interior of large buildings, something should be done to improve the situation. One remedy is the use of a monitor, as shown in Figs. 3·3 and 3·4. The roof may be flat or sloping. The area of glass in a monitor plus that in the side windows should be about 30 per cent of the floor area. Figure 3·3(a) shows the intensity curves for a building 100 ft. wide with a 40-ft. monitor. Narrow monitors like that of Fig. 3·3(b) are not efficient. Most of the light is wasted in illuminating the roof framing, and only the portion represented by the angle α reaches the working plane. Monitors should be from 40 to 50 per cent of the width of a structure or the aisle under that portion of the building.

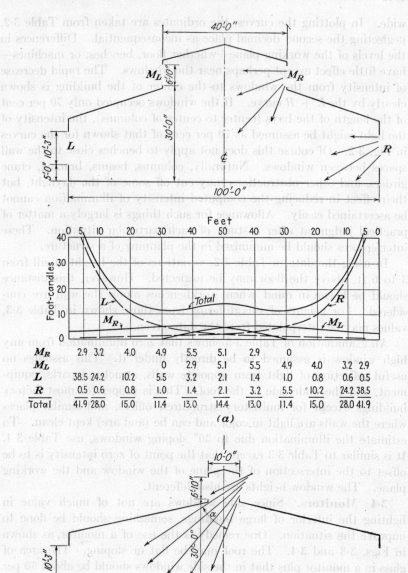

M_R	2.9	3.2	4.0	4.9	5.5	5.1	2.9	0			
M_L				0	2.9	5.5	5.5	4.9	4.0	3.2	2.9
L	38.5	24.2	10.2	5.5	3.2	2.1	1.4	1.0	0.6	0.6	0.5
R	0.5	0.6	0.8	1.0	1.4	2.1	3.2	5.5	10.2	24.2	38.5
Total	41.9	28.0	15.0	11.4	13.0	14.4	13.0	11.4	15.0	28.0	41.9

(a)

(b)

FIG. 3·3.   Intensity curve for continuous side windows and monitor.

(a) View looking lengthwise of one of the side aisles. Notice the arrangement of the corrugated siding and windows.

(b) View along the central aisle, showing the monitor and its windows. The light is coming in primarily from the right.

FIG. 3·4. The machine shop at the Morenci Reduction Works of the Phelps Dodge Corp. at Morenci, Arizona.

In this case the monitor almost triples the intensity of illumination at the center of the building, and it greatly evens out the lighting of the whole middle half. It should be noticed that the values used for M_R and M_L are interpolated from Table 3·3, being the averages of the tabulated figures for 25 and 35 ft. above the floor.

When a large building is composed of two or more portions with single long monitors over each section, somewhat as shown in Fig. 3·5,

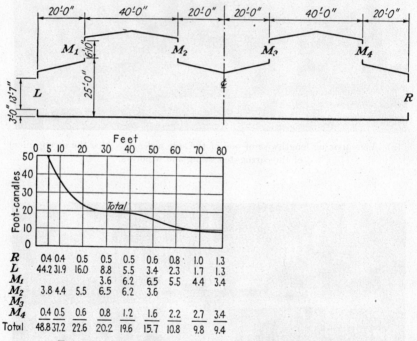

		0	5	10	20	30	40	50	60	70	80
R		0.4	0.4	0.5	0.5	0.5	0.6	0.8	1.0	1.3	
L		44.2	31.9	16.0	8.8	5.5	3.4	2.3	1.7	1.3	
M_1				3.6	6.2	6.5	5.5	4.4	3.4		
M_2		3.8	4.4	5.5	6.5	6.2	3.6				
M_3											
M_4		0.4	0.5	0.6	0.8	1.2	1.6	2.2	2.7	3.4	
Total		48.8	37.2	22.6	20.2	19.6	15.7	10.8	9.8	9.4	

FIG. 3·5.   Intensity curve for two widely separated monitors.

it is obvious that the central portion will be poorly lighted. A more efficient arrangement should be used.

High monitor windows are very effective; small, low ones may not be worth their cost. However, they should not be so high that the appearance of a building is unsatisfactory; neither should the sum of the heights of both windows exceed one-half to one-third of the width of the monitor. Increasing the height of monitor windows improves the minimum illumination faster than it does the maximum.

3·5 **High-low-bay and Saw-tooth Roofs.** When a building is too wide for a single monitor or when better illumination is necessary, a series of monitors can be used, running lengthwise or crosswise of the building. This arrangement is sometimes called "high-low-bay" construction. One possible section for a very large building is shown in Fig. 3·6, where the total intensity curve is also given. When the high bays run crosswise of a building, the lighting from the side windows should be combined with that from the monitors, the latter coming at

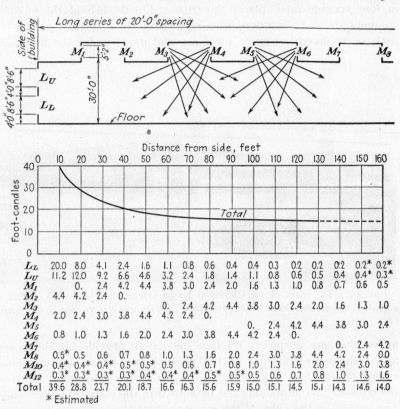

	10	20	30	40	50	60	70	80	90	100	110	120	130	140	150	160
L_L	20.0	8.0	4.1	2.4	1.6	1.1	0.8	0.6	0.4	0.4	0.3	0.2	0.2	0.2	0.2*	0.2*
L_U	11.2	12.0	9.2	6.6	4.6	3.2	2.4	1.8	1.4	1.1	0.8	0.6	0.5	0.4	0.4*	0.3*
M_1		0.	2.4	4.2	4.4	3.8	3.0	2.4	2.0	1.6	1.3	1.0	0.8	0.7	0.6	0.5
M_2	4.4	4.2	2.4	0.												
M_3						0.	2.4	4.2	4.4	3.8	3.0	2.4	2.0	1.6	1.3	1.0
M_4	2.0	2.4	3.0	3.8	4.4	4.2	2.4	0.								
M_5										0.	2.4	4.2	4.4	3.8	3.0	2.4
M_6	0.8	1.0	1.3	1.6	2.0	2.4	3.0	3.8	4.4	4.2	2.4	0.				
M_7														0.	2.4	4.2
M_8	0.5*	0.5	0.6	0.7	0.8	1.0	1.3	1.6	2.0	2.4	3.0	3.8	4.4	4.2	2.4	0.0
M_{10}	0.4*	0.4*	0.4*	0.5*	0.5*	0.5	0.6	0.7	0.8	1.0	1.3	1.6	2.0	2.4	3.0	3.8
M_{12}	0.3*	0.3*	0.3*	0.3*	0.4*	0.4*	0.4*	0.5*	0.5*	0.5	0.6	0.7	0.8	1.0	1.3	1.6
Total	39.6	28.8	23.7	20.1	18.7	16.6	16.3	15.6	15.9	15.0	15.1	14.5	15.1	14.3	14.6	14.0

* Estimated

Fig. 3·6.   Intensity curve for high-low-bay construction.

right angles to the former. In Fig. 3·6 the end windows are assumed to be too far away to affect the results appreciably. The right-hand portion of the curve is dotted to show that the effects of windows to the right of M_{12} (80 ft. to the right of M_8) are not included. The windows marked L_U are taken as though 15 ft. above the floor.

This general type of construction is very simple and advantageous. When the trusses are parallel to the high bays, they may be placed within the high portions so that the purlins for the high roofs rest upon their top chords whereas those for the low portions are supported on the bottom chords. This type of framing is economical, permits the over-all height of a structure to be at a minimum, and eliminates the effect of a maze of trussing as one looks down the building. However, it permits little future modification, may cause cross trusses (jack trusses) to be depressed if any of the interior columns must be omitted or long spacing used, places the trusses directly behind the monitor windows so as to interfere somewhat with their effectiveness, gives little or no overhead space for pipes and ducts under the low roofs

Fig. 3·7. The plant of the Cleveland Diesel Co. at Cleveland, Ohio. This is a modern design with continuous windows. (*Design and construction by the Austin Co.*)

unless they are purposely set high enough to provide for them, and may reduce the efficiency of the ventilation. These monitors must extend the full length of the trusses—clear to the side walls—to cover the trusses. Windows may not be needed in the ends above the walls. The sashes in the sides of the monitors near their outer ends are not needed particularly because the wall windows are so effective in this region.

When the trusses are placed under the level of the low roofs, there is more flexibility of arrangement, and the monitors may run parallel to or across the trusses, the ends may be set back from the outside walls, or these monitors may be boxlike units set at intervals on the roof. Some of these arrangements are pictured in Fig. 3·8. Their structural framing may be light, but it should be adequately braced.

When considering the way in which to place these monitors, one should decide whether he wants the windows to be parallel or perpen-

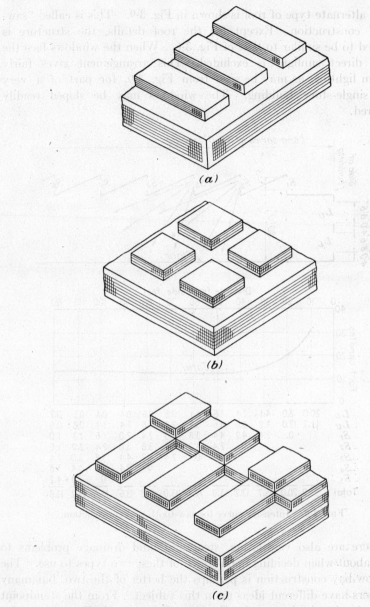

FIG. 3·8.   Possible arrangements of high-low-bay roofs.

dicular to the main aisles and column rows. The former may have advantages.

An alternate type of roof is shown in Fig. 3·9. This is called "saw-tooth" construction. Except for the roof details, the structure is assumed to be similar to that of Fig. 3·6. When the windows face the north, direct sunlight is excluded. This arrangement gives fairly uniform lighting, as may be seen from Fig. 3·9, for part of a very large single-story building. The windows may be sloped readily if desired.

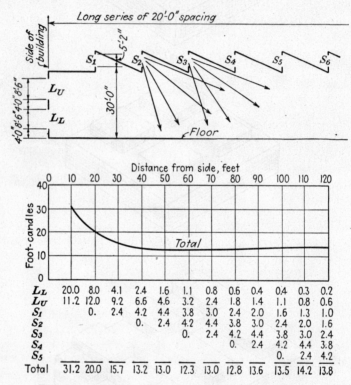

	0	10	20	30	40	50	60	70	80	90	100	110	120
L_L		20.0	8.0	4.1	2.4	1.6	1.1	0.8	0.6	0.4	0.4	0.3	0.2
L_U		11.2	12.0	9.2	6.6	4.6	3.2	2.4	1.8	1.4	1.1	0.8	0.6
S_1			0.	2.4	4.2	4.4	3.8	3.0	2.4	2.0	1.6	1.3	1.0
S_2				0.	2.4	4.2	4.4	3.8	3.0	2.4	2.0	1.6
S_3					0.	2.4	4.2	4.4	3.8	3.0	2.4
S_4						0.	2.4	4.2	4.4	3.8
S_5							0.	2.4	4.2
Total		31.2	20.0	15.7	13.2	13.0	12.3	13.0	12.8	13.6	13.5	14.2	13.8

Fig. 3·9.   Intensity curve for saw-tooth roof construction.

There are also ventilating, structural, and drainage problems to think about when deciding upon which of these two types to use. The high-low-bay construction is perhaps the better of the two, but many engineers have different ideas upon this subject. From the standpoint of illumination, both are very effective. The curves in Figs. 3·6 and 3·9 illustrate the uniformity of the lighting.

3·6 Details to Consider When Planning for Daylighting. Many things—large and small—should be considered before the plans

for the daylighting of a plant are finished. Special problems will
almost inevitably be present. Some general ones are mentioned here:

1. The surroundings outside a building must be considered because they
may shut off a large portion of the light that would ordinarily be relied upon, particularly that passing through the side windows. Such obstructions are other
buildings, tall trees (especially evergreens), and adjacent steep cliffs. The interference will depend upon the height, proximity, and reflecting quality of the
obstruction. Probably it will be slight if the distance from the side wall to the
object is from one to two times the height of the object. Light-colored bricks,
concrete, paint, or other materials for the sides of adjacent structures are beneficial, but dirt and weathering are likely to reduce their ability to reflect light.

2. When buildings have sections extending to one or both sides to form plans
shaped like the letters, E, F, H, U, and W, the various parts are likely to interfere
with the lighting of adjacent portions, especially in the case of multistory structures where the decrease in illumination of the lower floors may be considerable.

3. Large, overhanging eaves, if close to the tops of windows, will decrease
their effectiveness. This applies even more to wall windows alongside roofed
platforms. Glass placed in partitions more than about 25 ft. back from wall
windows will be of little benefit unless it covers most of the area of the partition.

4. Other questions are whether or not windows are to have operating (rotating) sashes. If so, which ones are to be operated? What are the types of operating equipment? How and from where are they to be operated? These
questions should be answered in advance so that the columns and bracing can
be made to avoid interference with the equipment and the sashes, the holes for
attaching the equipment can be provided, the operator arms will not project into
crane clearances, and operating chains and shafts will not be blocked off by
structural parts. Casement and double-hung windows are seldom used in factories except in offices, drafting rooms, and toilet rooms.

5. If continuous windows are to be used, the height and width of the panes
of glass, and the type and size of the sashes, should be selected in advance so that
the column spacing may be made in multiples of the widths of standard sashes.
This permits uniformity of details in the framework and the window arrangements, and it assists in working out a scheme that will not cause the columns to
interfere with the operating equipment for opening windows. This seemingly
small detail may become one of the factors to be used in establishing basic dimensions for the framing. It is better to adjust these matters at first than to
make special windows to suit the column spacing, or to have considerable complication in the framing of the wall. This was actually done in the case shown
in Fig. 3·4. If continuous windows are carried clear to the corners of a building,
the dimensions of the sashes should be considered when the wall lines and the
center lines of the corner columns are established.

6. The type of glass should be selected so as to give the best results. Clear
glass may be used along the north sides or where direct sunlight is not objectionable. Where bright spots and glare are undesirable, the glass should be trans-

lucent to prevent the passage of bright sunlight; it may be a special blue or other color to reduce the glare, or may have a roughened surface to diffuse the rays. In special cases, double panes with an air space between the two layers may be desired because of their insulating characteristics; in others, plexiglass may be advantageous because of its strength.

Control of the admission of direct sunlight is frequently desirable. In offices and many plants for light manufacturing, the use of venetian blinds or adjustable shutters is advantageous because the sun's rays can be shut out, while considerable light and air can still pass through. Exterior awnings, window shades, and rolling slat screens do not have this desirable feature to so great an extent. In southern regions where the summer sun is so bright and hot, large overhanging eaves will shade near-by windows and walls during the middle of the day, but they lack adjustability and give little help when the sun is low—the time when the rays penetrate far into the interior of the structure.

3·7 **Skylights.** At first thought, skylights seem to be advantageous because they are low, let in the direct sunlight, and require very little extra construction. When the sun is high, they admit the most light and tend to cause spotty illumination below them; when the sun is low, much less light passes through the glass because of the small area normal to the rays. The latter fact appears to indicate that skylights may be more desirable in sloping roofs than in flat ones. At least 25 per cent of the daylight, however, may come from the bright sky, not directly from the sun. This portion, therefore, is not affected so seriously by the inclination of the sun.

Special care must be taken to avoid leakage through and around skylights, particularly in regions of heavy snowfall. The panes may be broken unless they have short spans and are made of heavy, strong glass; for long spans of 5 to 6 ft., corrugated wire glass may be used. If a skylight is broken, the leakage may be harmful to expensive equipment or valuable materials. The glass should be translucent or rough in order to break up the sunlight and to avoid patches and streaks of brilliant light on the floor and machinery. Although economical in first cost, skylights should be studied carefully before they are adopted, to make sure that they constitute the best solution for the lighting problem. One design for their use in large, flat roofs is shown in Fig. 3·10.

Skylights may be especially useful when an existing structure is to be remodeled; e.g., when additional daylight is needed in one or more localized places and when the addition of monitors is impracticable or too expensive.

3·8 Planning for Cleaning Windows. Cleaning the windows in the roof of a high, single-story plant is a difficult task unless provisions are made to facilitate it. If washing them is difficult, they will seldom be cleaned; then their cost soon approaches wastefulness.

If monitors are used on a sloping roof, as in Fig. 3·4, a workman may be able to scramble along it to clean the outside of the glass. Unless

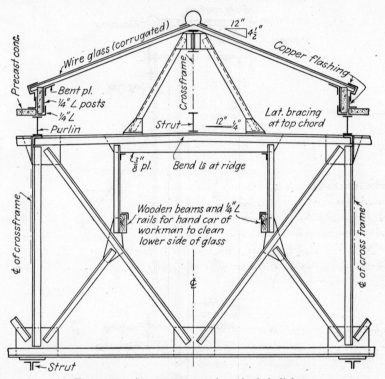

FIG. 3·10.   An arrangement for raised skylights.

walkways (catwalks) are provided along the inside or through the trusses below the monitors, washing the inside of the glass may be very difficult except when a workman can reach through open sashes to get at the inside of the fixed portions. If the windows are sloped or if skylights are used, washing the inside is generally more difficult than it is for vertical sash. The dropping of water on equipment and materials below may be very objectionable.

Since windows are used to admit light, cleaning (especially in the fall before the season of minimum daylight) is essential. If catwalks are installed to facilitate it, they may cut off part of the light even though they are made of open steel grating, thus partly defeating the general purpose. One way used to overcome this difficulty in the case of skylights is shown in Fig. 3·10. The trusses were designed to provide a central passageway under the skylight so that a special platform car could be dragged along on continuous timber rails. Of course, the

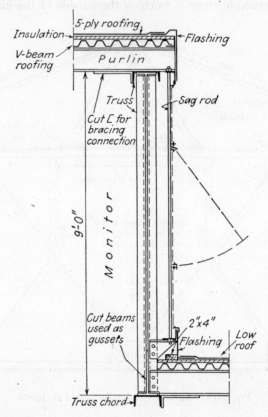

FIG. 3·11. Monitor framing for high-low-bay construction.

workman had to duck under the top chords of the trusses but, by standing on the car, he could wash the entire lower surface of the glass. Obviously, the outside could be cleaned from the flat roof.

One of the best arrangements seems to be high-low-bay construction with flat roofs. Figure 3·11 shows the details of a plant where the cleaning of the sash was planned for in the original design. By working on the low roofs when the operating sashes are opened moderately, a man can wash the outside of the glass, then the inside of the movable sash, and finally, by leaning over the bottom fixed portion, he can wash the inside.

3·9 Daylighting Multistory Buildings. Multistory buildings generally cannot utilize daylight so advantageously as single-story ones because they are often wide, columns and equipment cause obstructions that cut off the light to the interior, and the wall areas and heights are too small to permit the entrance of enough daylight to illuminate the interior properly. Obviously, the top floor is the only one that can be lighted through the roof. Therefore, multistory buildings should ordinarily be somewhat narrow if illumination by daylight is to be effective. The story heights should be large; preferably, the lower stories should be higher and have larger windows than the upper ones. Corridors, stairs, and elevators should be located centrally in order to leave the regions of best illumination for useful work. Unless light wells and courts are large in area, little light will enter the lower windows.

It is difficult ordinarily to avoid great variation in the intensity of daylight within multistory buildings. As an example, look at the curve showing the foot-candles from the windows along the left side of Fig. 3·2. Even with no obstructions, the intensity 40 or 50 ft. back from the windows is too small for work requiring good visibility, or else the illumination near the windows is too intense to give proper uniformity throughout the building. Many times, except when north light is utilized, shades or venetian blinds must be used to shut out direct sunlight near the windows to avoid excessive glare. This of course decreases the lighting of the interior still more.

Surrounding obstructions and the reflection from adjacent exterior surfaces are of relatively greater importance in multistory structures than in the mill buildings discussed in Art. 3·3. If a factory is to be built close to the property line, any clear space next door may be eliminated in the future when someone builds another tall structure on that property. Hence, the location of a multistory building with respect to property lines and in its relation to other structures and obstacles is very important from the standpoint of the utilization of daylight.

The reflecting qualities of the interior surfaces of multistory buildings are important. Smooth, clean, light-colored finishes assist greatly by reflecting the light back into the interior, as well as near the windows. In general, the ceilings should be as free as possible from projecting beams, the columns should occupy a minimum of the wall space, spandrel beams over windows should be shallow in order to increase the permissible height of the latter, and windows should be as nearly continuous as practicable. This means that wall-bearing construction with intermittent windows and large, intervening brick piers is disadvantageous from the standpoint of daylighting; steel and concrete-skeleton framework, with curtain walls supported thereon, are better in this respect. Of course, raising the tops of windows near to the ceiling benefits the daylighting; increasing the area of the glass by lowering the sills until they are close to the floor accomplishes little.

FIG. 3·12. A shop of the Northern Pacific Railway Co. at Brainerd, Minnesota, daylighted by means of glass-block walls and transverse high-low bays or monitors on top of the trusses. Architects, Toltz, King & Day. (*Courtesy of Owens-Illinois.*)

3·10 Glass Blocks. When daylight is desired without having ventilating sash, the use of glass-block panels in the walls may be advantageous. One such installation is shown in Fig. 3·12. These blocks are generally hollow. This gives the advantage of insulation and may be worth considerable in reducing heating costs during cold winter seasons and in improving the air conditioning in hot weather.

Glass blocks can be manufactured with a mat or rough surface which breaks up the parallel rays of light and produces a diffused light that improves the general distribution of the illumination. They deflect part of the rays so that the latter penetrate into the interior of a structure. Therefore, window shades and venetian blinds may be dispensed with sometimes.

Such panels must be cleaned frequently, just as windows should. Provision for doing this with reasonable facility is essential.

The construction features of glass-block panels are very simple, particularly when used with walls made of bricks, cement blocks, or other materials that are manufactured in individual units of such general type. They eliminate wooden or steel window frames that must be maintained; they are not easily broken. However, once they are installed, it is difficult to change the general scheme of construction. When glass-block panels are used in long buildings with steel or concrete framing, there should be enough expansion joints in the structure to make sure that shearing forces or deformations due to variations in temperature will not crack the glass. Furthermore, glass blocks should not be subjected to compression caused by superimposed loads.

In plants where air conditioning is essential and where strict control of the moisture and dust in the air must be had, this system of lighting should be investigated carefully before the general construction to be used is decided upon.

In order to determine the area of the panels required to produce a desired minimum intensity of illumination, one should secure the advice of the manufacturers of these materials.

3·11 Practical Details. In planning a structure with windows, endeavor to decide promptly upon the size of window pane to be used, being sure that it is a common standard one. Try to specify the same size throughout the plant. Decide also upon the material—whether wooden or metal sash; use standard sash sizes; and avoid an undue variety of types and sizes. Sketch the general window arrangement, then make tentative elevation or perspective drawings in order to make sure that the appearance is satisfactory and that it harmonizes with other construction at the plant. All too often this is neglected until such a late date that changes cause delays and even expense in revising plans. It is desirable also to determine at this time which sashes are to be movable, and whether they are to be top-hinged or center-pivoted. Be sure to locate all doorways at the same time so that the entire arrangement is coordinated.

Furthermore, study the architectural appearance, in order to determine whether or not the windows are to be set back from the surface of the wall and how much this recessing is to be. If not set back, they may cause a homely, walleyed effect, devoid of proper shadows, especially if they are intermittent. Make sure that the window heights, the elevations of the sills, the spaces between successive rows or tiers of windows, and the distance from the lintels over the top row to the eaves are all satisfactory.   Do not block expensive windows with crane girders or other heavy, longitudinal members.   Allow space over the upper windows for strong eave struts, stiff enough to avoid harmful deflections that might cause the sashes to bind or even to buckle.

In choosing the sizes of windows, be careful to avoid large units which, although possible, are difficult to handle and may be rather

Fig. 3·13.   A factory building that utilizes welded, rigid-frame steel construction for the supports of the saw-tooth roof and for the roof over the main aisle.   This building, having 200,000 sq. ft. of floor area, was completed for The Lincoln Electric Co. of Cleveland, Ohio, in 100 working days after orders were given to proceed. Notice the extensive window areas.

flimsy.   It is often wiser in the long run to use adequate, horizontal, intermediate supports, or vertical mullions, to stiffen the windows and to carry lateral wind loads to the main structural frame.

There are many practical details to consider, varying somewhat with the type of construction.   Illustrative details and typical construction are shown in the chapter dealing with the construction of walls.

On the whole, careful planning of all features, from the basic arrangement to the seemingly minor details, may make the difference between the economical, satisfactory daylighting of a plant and results that are annoying to all concerned.

Chapter 4

ELECTRIC LIGHTING AND POWER

4·1 Scope of Data. This chapter deals with some of the problems of artificial illumination by means of electricity insofar as they affect the planning of structures. Although the use of gas or other illuminants for industrial lighting is not extensive, many of the basic principles discussed for electric lighting are generally applicable to them. This chapter also gives some useful information about planning structures with due consideration for the provision of electric power because it is so intimately tied in with lighting.

The planning and designing of installations for electric lighting in new, large, industrial structures are of such great importance that they justify the services of capable engineers who are specialists in such matters; probably the improvement of lighting facilities in existing buildings is even more troublesome to accomplish. It is the author's purpose to discuss some things that the designers of structures should bear in mind and provide for in their planning so that the lighting system may be as efficient and economical as possible. Too often electrical engineers have to take things as they are and make the best of the situation.

Even in the best of designs, illumination of industrial plants by natural daylight should be supplemented by some artificial system if the results are to be satisfactory throughout the year for an ordinary 8 A.M. to 5 P.M. working shift; earlier and later shifts will be almost completely dependent upon this artificial lighting. Increase of efficiency, economy of production, easing of eyestrain, decrease of physical and nervous fatigue, minimizing of accidents, lessening of poor workmanship causing rejections, and greater contentment of personnel—all these things are benefits to be obtained from good illumination. Their constant and cumulative effects amply justify the expenditure necessary to provide an adequate installation. Not only is electric lighting excellent for general illumination but it is the best for securing local lighting of optimum quality, intensity, and flexibility—the last meaning

57

that it can be provided almost anywhere, at any time, and of any reasonable intensity.   This cannot be accomplished by daylight alone.

4·2 Physiological Considerations. When electric lighting is planned, it is more important to consider certain limitations of the human eye in the process of seeing than it is in the case of the diffused, rather uniformly distributed daylight of relatively low intensity discussed in the preceding chapter.   The two features to be considered here are the field of vision and glare.

Because man is inherently a predatory animal, his eyes, like those of the cat family, are in the front of his head so that he can concentrate upon what he is pursuing or is particularly interested in.   In contrast, consider the rabbit.   His eyes are on the sides of his head to enable him to see almost anywhere around him simultaneously.   Upon this ability to detect his pursuers in time probably depends, to a large extent, his very existence.

Figure 4·1 pictures the field of vision of the average man's eyes. The vertical angle of this field is far less than 180°, but the horizontal angle is near this amount, doubtless due in part to the elongated shape of the openings between the lids and to the lack of obstructions in the face alongside the eyes.   Although a man has at least blurred vision within this entire field, his clearest seeing is confined to about a 5° cone,[1] and he can see quite clearly within a 10° cone.   Outside of these, he can distinguish objects well enough to become conscious of their presence, especially if they move.   Almost automatically, he will move his eyes and perhaps his head to enable him to concentrate upon a moving object or a sudden bright light that appears in this outer field. A certain "perception time"—perhaps 0.2 to 0.3 sec.—is needed for him to see the object and to comprehend what he sees.   As shown in Fig. 4·1(b), the focusing of a man's two eyes upon an object gives him the ability to judge distances and to have a sense of depth in his field of vision.

The movement of a man's eyes to detect and see things that attract his attention, the focusing of the eye itself, and the changing of the size of the pupil to accommodate the eye to variations in the intensity of light—to a large extent these operations are more or less automatically controlled, yet their functioning is not unlimited.   The eyes will tire if subjected to too rapid and long-continued movements, too frequent and extreme variations of intensity, and too prolonged concentration upon

[1] HOWELL, W. H., "Textbook of Physiology," 14th ed., W. B. Saunders Company, Philadelphia, Pa.

seeing objects that are poorly illuminated or not properly contrasted
against their background.

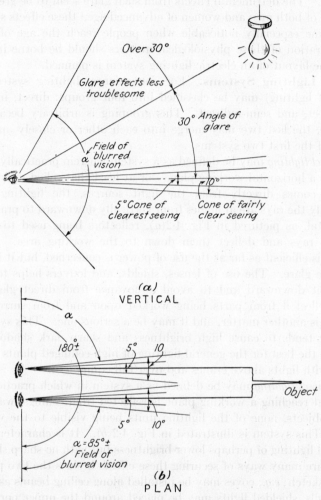

FIG. 4·1.   Cones of vision.

Another thing that tires the eyes is the glare from objects other
than the one looked at. Bare electric-light bulbs or very bright
luminaires seem to be especially troublesome if they come within about
30° of the axis of the cone of clearest vision, as shown in Fig. 4·1(a).
They tend to distract one's attention and to hamper clear seeing because

of the brightness of the light source compared to that of the object being looked at. Reflection from polished or white glossy surfaces does likewise. The detrimental effects from such glare seem to be greater in the case of both men and women of advanced age,[1] these effects starting to become especially noticeable when people reach the age of forty. Consideration of these physiological matters should be borne in mind when the layout of an electric lighting system is planned.

4·3 Lighting Systems. For convenience, lighting systems (or types of lighting) may be classified into four groups: direct, indirect, semidirect, and semi-indirect. This grouping is arbitrary because, in practice, the last two may merge into each other or closely approach either of the first two systems.

Direct lighting may be defined as a system wherein practically all the light on a horizontal working plane—or at least that relied upon in the design—comes directly from the light sources, the lighting units. Generally the rays are at angles from vertically downward to practically horizontal, as pictured in Fig. 4·2(a), reflectors being used to cut off upward rays and deflect them down to the working area. Such a system is efficient as far as the use of power is concerned, but it is likely to cause glare. The use of lenses, shields, and louvers helps to direct the light downward and to avoid annoyance from direct glare, but light reflected from parts being worked upon and from surrounding objects is another matter, and it may be a serious one. This system of lighting tends to cause high brightness and sharp dark shadows. It may be the best for the general lighting of high-ceilinged plants such as those with lights above cranes and over tall equipment.

Indirect lighting may be defined as a system in which practically all the light reaching a working plane is reflected from ceilings, walls, and other objects, none of the lighting units being visible to the workers' eyes. This system is illustrated in Fig. 4·2(b). It is characterized by diffused lighting of perhaps lower brightness but with no sharp shadows. There are many ways of securing these effects besides the two pictured in the sketch; *e.g.*, coves may be installed along ceiling beams as well as side walls, shielded lights may be placed around the upper portions of columns, or luminaires similar to the home type of movable floor lamp, which throws the light upward, may be used. Such a system is especially adaptable for offices, drafting rooms, and plants for light manufacturing; and it is well suited for use in multistory buildings. It is obvious that the reflecting surfaces should be light in color and clean,

---

[1] MARSH, BURTON W., Director, "Safety Traffic Engineering," American Automobile Association.

and of a texture that will diffuse the light rather than reflect it as smooth glass and polished metal surfaces do.   Such a system would be wasteful in a mill building with roofs supported by exposed trusses and having side walls with projecting columns and crane girders, because of the interference caused by these obstructions.   Furthermore, it would be wasteful when the interior surfaces cannot be kept clean.   Much of the light would also be lost through large windows.

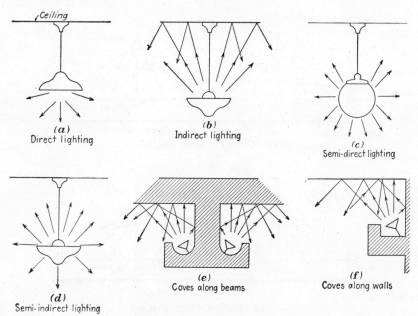

Fig. 4·2.   Types of lighting.

A *semidirect lighting system* is one in which the greater part of the light on a horizontal working plane comes directly from the lighting units, but nevertheless a substantial part comes by reflection from the inner surfaces of the room or from other objects.   One such type with an opalescent globe is shown in Fig. 4·2(c).   Although such luminaires produce a more diffused illumination than do direct-lighting units, yet they may be sufficiently bright to annoy workers when the globes are too near their working field of vision.

The *semi-indirect lighting system*, such as that shown in Fig. 4·2(d), provides appreciable light directly from the luminaires to the working plane, but the greater part of the illumination is produced by light reflected from the interior surfaces of the room and from its contents.

If the direct lighting is not more than approximately 25 per cent of the total and if it is of moderate intensity, this system is well adapted to use in offices, drafting rooms, and multistory buildings. It secures most of the advantages of the diffused lighting produced by the completely indirect system without being quite so extravagant in the cost of construction and power.

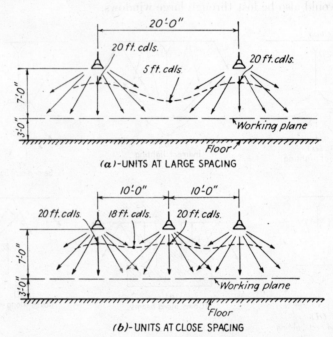

FIG. 4·3. Illustration of general effect of relative height and spacing of lighting fixtures upon intensity of illumination at working plane. (*Based upon data of General Electric Co.*)

4·4 General Lighting. One purpose of electric lighting is to provide general illumination. Consider the building shown in Fig. 3·3. Obviously, the central portion of the structure will be the first to need auxiliary lighting as the intensity of daylight dwindles; later the whole building will need it. Just as in the case of daylighting, the essential minimum foot-candles of illumination should be determined, and the lighting system designed accordingly. Obviously, it should have capacity enough to handle its full load during night operations, yet the wiring and switching should be so arranged as to give the desired flexibility in augmenting the daylight.

Table 4·1 Data Regarding Spacing and Height of Light Sources

Allowable spacing between light sources

Ceiling height (or height in the clear), ft.	Spacing between outlets, ft. — Usual	Spacing between outlets, ft. — Maximum (for units at ceiling) not more than	Spacing between outside outlets and wall, ft. — Aisles or storage next to wall	Spacing between outside outlets and wall, ft. — Desks, workbenches, etc., against wall, not more than	Approximate area per outlet (at usual spacings), sq. ft.
8	7	7½		3	50–60
9	8	8		3	60–70
10	9	9		3½	70–85
11	10	10½	Usually one-half actual spacing between units	3½	85–100
12	10–12	12		3½–4	100–150
13	10–12	13		3½–4½	100–150
14	10–13	15		4–5	100–170
15	10–13	17		4–5	100–170
16	10–13	19		4–6	100–170
18	10–20	21		4–6	100–400
20 and up	18–24	24		5–7	300–500

Mounting height of light sources

Direct and semidirect lighting units

Actual spacing between units, ft.	Distance of units from floor not less than, ft.	Desirable mounting height in industrial interiors	Desirable mounting height in commercial interiors
7	8	12 ft. above floor if possible—to avoid glare, and still be within reach from stepladder for cleaning.	The actual hanging height should be governed large y by genera appearance, but particularly in offices and drafting rooms, the minimum values shown in the second column should not be violated.
8	8½		
9	9		
10	10½		
11	11		
12	12		
14	12½	Where units are to be mounted much more than 12 ft., it is usually desirable to mount the units at ceiling or on roof trusses.	
16	14		
18	15		
20	16		
22	18		
24	20		

Semi-indirect and indirect lighting

Actual spacing between units, ft.	Recommended suspension length (top of bowl to ceiling), ft.
7	1–3
8	1–3
9	1–3
10	1½–3
11	2–3
12	2–3
14	2½–4
16	3–4
18	3–5
20	4–5
22	4–5
24	4–6

Courtesy of General Electric Co.

Because spottiness is to be avoided, the light fixtures of a direct or semidirect system should be reasonably far above the working plane and close enough together so that the light on any one point of the working plane will come from different sources and different angles. This is illustrated in Fig. 4·3. Table 4·1 gives data regarding the relationships between heights and spacings of light sources.

When a structure is planned, it is desirable to know the type of lighting system to be used, the general layout of the fixtures, the location and size of the electrical control room or switchboards, and the approximate sizes and locations of conduits. The pattern made by the system should have some symmetry and uniformity, should be an obvious and harmonious part of the structure, and should fit in with the framing.

When these plans are in the making, it is important to consider maintenance problems—the cleaning of luminaires and the replacing of bulbs. The fixtures in offices and multistory factories should be located so that they may be reached by means of stepladders, specially designed movable platforms, or ladders mounted on wheels. This is not so easy to accomplish in the case of high, single-story mill buildings in which the lights are attached to or near the roof trusses. Sometimes a workman may reach them by riding the crane bridges, by going along catwalks, or by riding on wheeled towers pushed along the aisles between machines, provided the lights have been located with this in mind. It is foolish to waste power burning dirty lights in dusty fixtures, the combination perhaps being only 60 to 75 per cent efficient. Yet, if cleaning them is dangerous and difficult, they will be poorly maintained. Although overhead lights might be suspended on pulley systems so that they could be lowered within reach of the floor, this is not usually practicable, and the multitudinous ropes and loops of wire are unattractive. Lights should be held firmly in a stationary position.

Sometimes light fixtures will control the clearance above a floor, *e.g.*, when it is desirable to have them below the bottoms of ceiling beams and roof trusses so that structural parts do not cut off the light. In offices and multistory buildings, the lighting system may affect various structural details and influence one's choice of framing schemes. Thus, suspended ceilings may be desired in order to have large, smooth surfaces; flat slabs and concrete columns with capitals may be wanted for similar reasons; large floor slabs with beams along the column lines or elsewhere may be most suitable when indirect-lighting units are to be installed along beam haunches. It may be desirable to arrange the ceiling beams to attain certain paneling so that the fixtures can be at the centers or other typical points of recessed areas, and the luminaires can be shielded by adjacent beams so that nearly horizontal rays will be intercepted and therefore cannot annoy workers some distance away.

Not all the light emitted by a lighting unit can be available to illuminate a working plane. That which passes out the windows, is absorbed by reflecting surfaces, or is deflected far away is not useful. The term "coefficient of utilization" denotes the percentage of light that actually (or, supposedly) reaches and is useful on the working plane. It is obvious that the shape of a room has an important effect upon the coefficient of utilization because of the relative area of walls compared to that of the floor. A glance at Fig. 4·3 shows that, if a room is narrow and the fixtures are high above the floor, a large part of the light will strike the walls first, only part of it being reflected therefrom. The matter of size and proportions of rooms is taken into account through the room index, for which data are issued by such manufacturers as the General Electric Co., whose handbooks containing such data should be secured.

In order to compute the intensity to be expected for any given case and to find the bulb sizes needed to produce a desired number of footcandles on the working plane, the following general procedure may be used:[1]

1. Find the room index.

2. Choose the type of system and fixtures that are to be used.

3. Assume a percentage reflection efficiency for the ceiling, and also for the walls: for the best white ceilings, assume 75 per cent; for darker ones and those that are not too well cleaned, 50 per cent; for those with dark, bare steel beams and trusses, 30 per cent—even this being optimistic. Assume that windows and doors reflect no light; furnishings and equipment may also cause large losses. When these things are considered, a 50 per cent factor for the walls is about as high as can be expected in a modern office with light-colored walls. For a well-kept warehouse or multistory factory it may be nearer 30 per cent; and for ordinary plants it may be only 10 per cent.

4. Using the room index and the other data from items 2 and 3, find the recommended coefficient of utilization.

5. Compute the area of floor allocated to each lamp, assuming it to be the square feet in the space bounded by the center lines between lamps or by the walls.

6. To allow for old bulbs, which are less efficient than new ones, and for dust on reflectors and reflecting surfaces, assume a maintenance factor generally about 70 per cent. It may be higher for clean, direct lighting and lower for indirect or semi-indirect systems when maintenance is poor.

[1] See "Illumination Design Data," General Electric Co., Nela Park Engineering Dept., Cleveland, Ohio.

7. To find the lamp lumens required, use the equation:

$$\text{Lamp lumens per outlet} = \frac{\text{ft.-candles} \times \text{area in sq. ft. per outlet}}{\text{coef. of utilization} \times \text{maintenance factor}} \quad (4\cdot1)$$

To find the foot-candles for a given lamp, use the following:

$$\text{Ft.-candles} = \frac{\text{lamp lumens} \times \text{coef. of utilization} \times \text{maintenance factor}}{\text{area in sq. ft. per lamp}} \quad (4\cdot2)$$

FIG. 4·4.   An excellent illustration of supplementary lighting.   There are fluorescent lamps in opaque reflectors below the eye level.   (*Courtesy of Matthew Luckiesh
of the General Electric Co., and the Architectural Record.*)

It is best to consult the manufacturers and competent engineers
about these matters of illumination.   Also consider the use of fluorescent
lighting as well as Mazda lamps.

4·5   Localized Lighting.   The problems of localized lighting to
supplement the general illumination are exceedingly varied, the best
solutions depending upon the needs of each special case.   The desired
results may be secured by batteries of overhead lights of the same type
as those for general illumination, by floodlights shining downward at
the desired angle, by lights within glass-covered panels in the ceiling
and walls, by adjustable luminaires on portable standards, or by specially shielded fixed lamps mounted on the frames of machines.   In

any case, the installation should be planned with proper regard to desired intensities, direction of rays, and reduction of glare.

In estimating the intensity of illumination from any given light source, first obtain from the manufacturer the distribution curve for

Fig 4.5. This plant was designed and built by the Austin Co. during the war for the manufacture of precision instruments and parts. The flat ceiling with acoustical tile, the diffused lighting from the recessed luminaires, and the wide spans between columns make this an attractive working area.

the reflector or unit to be used. In general, the intensity normal to a light ray is

$$\text{Ft.-candles} = \frac{\text{candlepower}}{(\text{distance in ft.})^2} \qquad (4\cdot3)$$

whereas the intensity on a horizontal plane is

$$\text{Ft.-candles} = \frac{\text{candlepower} \times \text{cosine of angle of light ray with vertical}}{(\text{distance in ft.})^2} \qquad (4\cdot4)$$

4·6 Planning Substations. Generally, electric power is brought to an industrial plant by means of high-tension overhead power lines or by subterranean cables. In a large plant, even one having its own generating station, the individual buildings consuming large quantities of power may have separate transformers in order to avoid the losses

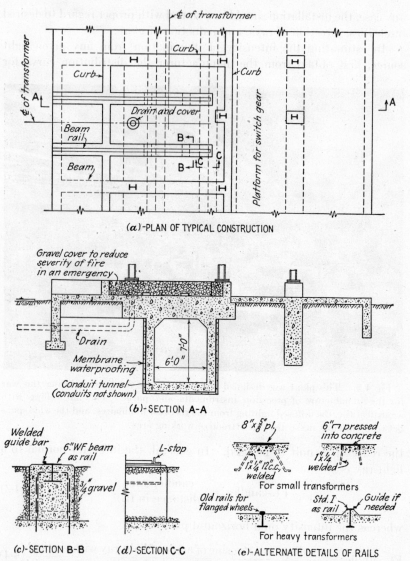

(a)-PLAN OF TYPICAL CONSTRUCTION

(b)-SECTION A-A

(c)-SECTION B-B   (d)-SECTION C-C   (e)-ALTERNATE DETAILS OF RAILS

Fig. 4·6. One arrangement for supports for transformers and superstructure
alongside a large industrial building.

that would occur in long low-tension lines.   These substations and their
appurtenances should be laid out in considerable detail during the general planning period, and the structure should be designed accordingly
if subsequent arguments and revisions are to be avoided.

The location of a substation is important.   It should be situated so as to minimize the length of cables to the electrical control room, switchboards, and equipment, but it must be where the power line can terminate conveniently in a dead-end tower.   One such arrangement is shown in Fig. 4·7.   Preferably, the transformers should be alongside railroad tracks or roadways so that they can be delivered to the substation easily

FIG. 4·7. The dead-end tower at D-C Substation No. 2, Morenci Reduction Works of the Phelps Dodge Corp., Morenci, Arizona.

FIG. 4·8. Substation at the concentrator, Morenci Reduction Works. Notice the platform onto which the transformers may be skidded for handling by railroad.

and replacements can be made quickly.   They may be inside a building but, because of ventilation and possible fire hazard, they are generally placed out of doors, generally within wire fences to protect against accidents, or even inside brick enclosures to guard against sabotage. Transformers are often supported upon steel-beam rails on concrete foundations so that they can be skidded or rolled from a platform area to their final positions under a structural framework holding the cables.

Special provisions should be made to protect the building against fire. These regulations are generally drawn up by the insurance companies. If the transformers are alongside a building wall, it should be made fireproof, with no openings except those protected by fireproof doors. Means should be provided for catching the oil in case of leakage or fire. One arrangement of transformers is shown in Fig. 4·7. Another is pictured in Fig. 4·8 where the low-tension cables pass through conduits racked on the inside of a tunnel to the control room, and the transformers are mounted on an elevated hollow-concrete platform so that the transformer supports are at flatcar level, and the space under the transformers is ventilated and is accessible for future alterations of, or additions to, the conduit layout. Obviously, a roof is a poor place for transformers because of the difficulty in handling them, the fireproofing of the structure, the catching of burning oil in case of a fire, and the making of costly structural supports.

Fig. 4·9. A power transformer in the New Jersey ventilation building of the Lincoln Tunnel. (*Courtesy of the Port of New York Authority.*)

A rather extreme case, pictured in Fig. 4·9, shows part of the transformer room near the bottom of the New Jersey ventilation building of the Lincoln Tunnel at New York City. This underground location was chosen because the space was available, and the high-tension cables came through the tunnel close to it. There is an access hatchway for installing the equipment from above. Valves in pipes that enter the fresh-air ducts of the tunnel provide ventilation for the transformer room. The construction is entirely fireproof, the access stairway is enclosed, and a large concrete duct leads from the room to the surface, this being a sort of chimney or smoke exit in case of fire. There are, also, spaces into which the transformers may be skidded during installation and repairing. When planning for transformers in an enclosed space like this, be very careful to make the layout such that a man would not be trapped and have to run around the equipment or dart through narrow spaces between transformers if an accident should occur when he is working on the transformers. Be sure, too, that the space is ventilated well and in a manner that will not cause the spreading of a fire.

4·7 Planning Electrical Control Rooms. For small installations, the switchboards and control panels may be exposed in the room where the equipment is located, somewhat as shown in Fig. 4·10. Provide space behind them for a man to work on the wiring, at least 2 ft. 6 in. of clearance; and provide proper access to it. It is also desirable to have room enough for future expansion in case more machines and

Fig. 4·10. Control panels and some of the electrical equipment in a control room.
(*Courtesy of the Phelps Dodge Corp.*)

circuits are added. In locating even these small units, try to place the panels where the operators can watch them easily and where they are easily and quickly accessible in case of emergency.

For larger buildings, it is desirable to have a central fireproof control room containing circuit breakers and switches for all major equipment, including the lighting. In determining the best location, consider many things: the space that is or can be made available; a short and direct run for the heavy cables and conduits from the substation to the control room; the minimum numbers and lengths of the distributing cables; the possibility of future additions and alterations; and convenience for the operators.

A control room should have at least one door high enough and wide enough to permit the installation of the largest panel board or other

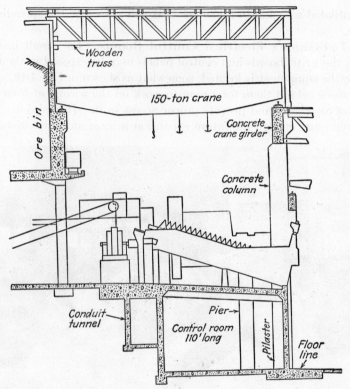

Fig. 4·11.   A centralized electrical control room and conduit tunnel placed under the floor at a point of change in floor levels.

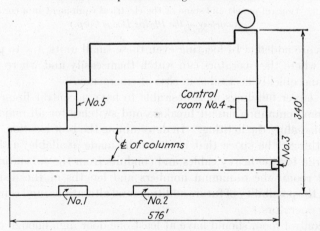

Fig. 4·12.   A plant with electrical control rooms decentralized.   This arrangement shortens the low-tension cables and provides flexibility of operation for various departments.

equipment without dismantling it.   Be very generous with these dimensions because the original equipment, and especially future additions, seem to have the habit of outgrowing the early estimates of sizes.   This also applies emphatically to the total floor area, aisle spaces, and ceiling height of the control room itself.

Generally try to give the electrical engineers more space than they consider to be their minimum needs. In several cases where this has been done, it has proved to be very fortunate; in others where extra leeway was not provided, it has caused hurried revisions of completed structural drawings on the one hand or a congested and unsatisfactory electrical installation on the other if the needs were not discovered until after the structure was completed. When computing dimensions for available space, generally assume that it is limited by the inside edges of pilasters, columns, beam haunches, and other obstructions.   Figures 4·11 and 4·12 show two very different arrangements of control rooms.   The locations and details in each case are especially adapted to the conditions peculiar to the respective plants.

Fig. 4·13.   Conduits leading out of the control room in the concentrator, Morenci Reduction Works.   (*Courtesy of the Phelps Dodge Corp.*)

When planning the control room, provide enough doors for the safe escape of operators or repairmen in case of a sudden fire.   Kalamein doors with panic locks, or sliding ones held open with low-melting-point devices so that they will close automatically, may be used, but the insurance requirements for such things should be investigated and adhered to.   Although it is important to provide adequate ventilation in the control room itself, this should be so planned that it will not automatically cause spreading of a fire.

4·8 Planning for Conduits.   A glance at Figs. 4·13 to 4·18 shows what a problem adequate provision for conduits may be, not only in the

Fig. 4·14. Conduits leading from a control room to various portions of the sixth floor of the New Jersey ventilation building of the Lincoln Tunnel. Notice how the steel beams had to be depressed to allow for the conduit crossings in the foreground. (*Courtesy of the Port of New York Authority.*)

Fig. 4·15. Conduits under the floor of the control room on the sixth floor of the New Jersey ventilation building of the Lincoln Tunnel. The structural floor is depressed to allow space for these conduits. (*Courtesy of the Port of New York Authority.*)

FIG. 4·16. Placing conduits from the control room to the pull chamber in the background for the future extension of the New Jersey ventilation building of the Lincoln Tunnel.   (*Courtesy of the Port of New York Authority.*)

FIG. 4·17. Conduits to fan motors and to location of control panel in the fore-ground, the sixth floor of the New Jersey ventilation building of the Lincoln Tunnel. (*Courtesy of the Port of New York Authority.*)

control room but in the rest of the structure. Generous provisions should be made for them in planning the structure itself. The structural designer should not expect that the electrical engineers can work out these complicated installations in time for him to know where every conduit is to be placed before the contract drawings for the framework of the building are made. He should consult with them and decide upon what type of conduit is to be used, what the maximum size may be, where the main runs are to be located, what spaces are to be allowed for the clearance of conduits in general, and how they are to be supported and protected. It is also desirable to plan an electrical installation so that the conduits may be revised and new ones added in the future without tearing out important structural parts. Specific locations and sizes of pull boxes and splicing chambers should be agreed upon in advance, too.

FIG. 4·18. Vertical bank of conduits in the New Jersey ventilation building of the Lincoln Tunnel. The offset was necessary because of an opening to be at the right. The two encased girders carry heavy columns in the upper portion of the structure. (*Courtesy of the Port of New York Authority.*)

In a single-story structure, trenches with covers may be built in the floor; if justifiable, conduit tunnels that can be entered by men may be built as shown in Fig. 4·11; overhead or wall racks may be used also. It is generally desirable to have conduits in or under the floor so that they come up to the machines somewhat as illustrated in Fig. 4·17. Figure 4·13 shows them emerging from under the floor of the long control room that is to be at the left, the general plan being somewhat similar to that of Fig. 4·11. The conduits are in trenches under the future floor at the right and will be encased in concrete. Here the conduits must be laid before the concrete work can be done. In a similar case, trenches were left in the concrete floors, and niches were provided in the retaining walls to be filled in

FIG. 4·19.   A bus-bar bridge at the plant of the Phelps Dodge Refining Co., El Paso, Texas.   A scale house is in the foreground.

FIG. 4·20.   This arrangement for excellent localized lighting was planned by A. H. Girard in cooperation with the industrial engineers of the International Detrola Corp.   (*Courtesy of Matthew Luckiesh of the General Electric Co., and the Architectural Record.*)

with concrete after the conduits were laid.   This often occurs some time after completion of the heavy construction.

In Figs. 4·14 to 4·18, the control room and conduit runs are in the upper floors of multistory, steel-frame buildings.   The beams and the structural concrete slabs were depressed generally from 12 to 18 in. to form trenches through the corridors to pull boxes or splicing chambers, and to other locations where large conduits or several small ones were to be installed.   After the conduit work was completed, these trenches

FIG. 4·21.   In this drafting room the luminaires are set in the long narrow panels between the beams.   (*Courtesy of the General Electric Co.*)

were filled with Aircrete (about 60 to 80 lb. per cu. ft.), and a monolithic mortar topping was added for the finished floor.   Cinder concrete, or even ordinary concrete, may be used similarly.

In such multistory construction as this, it is often advantageous to depress all steel beams sufficiently to allow at least 4 or 5 in. of concrete over their tops so that individual conduits to any machine or light box may be placed as needed without causing interference.   Figure 4·14 illustrates one case where this was done extensively and the conduits were buried in the structural concrete.   These conduits may terminate in the sides of the proper trenches so that their extensions may be coupled on later, if it is not desirable or feasible to install all of them at once before pouring the concrete.   Figure 4·17 shows conduits projecting above the floor line so that others in the control cabinet may be coupled to them.

In determining the clearance to be provided over the steel or in the trenches, consider conduit sizes, space needed for conduit crossings such as shown in Figs. 4·14 and 4·15, clearance for running the conduits under any top layer of reinforcing rods, and allowance for the cover required over the tops of the rods or the conduits themselves (perhaps 1½ in.). Such conduits running normally across the beams may do no harm to the slabs; if steel conduits, they may act as extra reinforcement. If they are nearly parallel to the beams, they should be placed near the

Fig. 4·22. This lighting system with its suspended-band arrangement provides excellent illumination at the machines. (*Courtesy of the General Electric Co.*)

center of the span of the slab, on top of the beams, or wherever they will not seriously weaken the shearing and bending strength of the slab. In Fig. 4·14, the slabs were made thick enough so that the diagonal conduits were not harmful. Furthermore, the slabs are strong enough to resist the shearing forces without the necessity of using bent reinforcement which would be a great nuisance—straight bars as negative reinforcement being far easier to place after the conduits are erected. Of course, in the case of reinforced-concrete buildings, the conduits may be placed easily if they are ready at the time the reinforcement is erected; otherwise, some of the latter may have to be taken out and reerected in order to place the former, because steel conduits cannot be pulled in like rubber hoses—a fact readily understandable after a glance at Fig. 4·16.

Vertical banks of conduits are generally necessary in multistory buildings. These take up considerable space. The framework should be offset or otherwise designed to accommodate them; or provisions may be made for holes in the floors, and niches or slots in the walls, so that the conduits may be installed later on. Provisions should be made

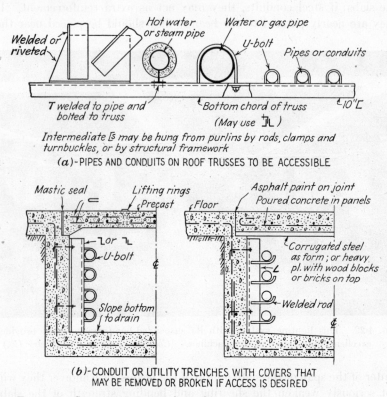

(a)-PIPES AND CONDUITS ON ROOF TRUSSES TO BE ACCESSIBLE

(b)-CONDUIT OR UTILITY TRENCHES WITH COVERS THAT
MAY BE REMOVED OR BROKEN IF ACCESS IS DESIRED

Fig. 4·23.   Some arrangements for making conduits reasonably accessible.

also for pull boxes, splicing chambers, and large-radius bends in these conduits. Even in Fig. 4·18, the conduits and the pull boxes for the cables were encased in concrete later.

When there is the likelihood that the building will be extended, the necessary conduits may be installed and closed with caps at the time of the original construction. Such a case is pictured in the background of Fig. 4·16, where a large pull chamber is built near the wall at the side of the building where the extension is to occur. When there is a real probability that the equipment will be moved or changed in the future, conduit systems buried in concrete are disadvantageous. Consider, then, the use of accessible trenches, utility tunnels, overhead racks, and centralized systems or main power lines and bus bars to which other connections can be added when needed.

If the designers of structures would foresee these important and necessary provisions for the accommodation of electrical work and provide these facilities in the first place, they would have better and probably more satisfactory structures, plus a lot of good electrical-engineering friends.

Chapter 5

VENTILATION

5·1 Introduction. Ventilation of industrial plants is important in almost all cases; its adequacy is vital in many instances. The planning of industrial structures should consider, and may be greatly affected by, features that are essential for its proper functioning.

The term "ventilation" will be used to denote the removal of vitiated, heated, or used air and its replacement by clean fresh air. This changing may be accomplished by means of natural forces or by mechanical equipment. The former will be called "airation"; the latter, "mechanical ventilation." Mere circulation of air without renewal and purification does not constitute ventilation in this sense.

The purpose of this chapter is to illustrate how ventilation is accomplished and how its effectiveness is estimated, and to show provisions that may be made for it in the planning of structures.

5·2 Number of Air Changes per Hour. The changing of the air is essential for the health and efficiency of the occupants of a structure because of their need for a renewal of the supply of oxygen, removal of obnoxious or harmful gases, elimination of dust, and avoidance of excessive heat. Ventilation is often measured by the number of air changes per hour, this being generally, but not necessarily, expressed in terms of the number of times that a volume of fresh air equal to the cubical contents of the inside of the structure is supplied during each hour. Although the admission of air may also be needed to produce draft in furnaces and chimneys, to supply blowers or compressors, and for special industrial purposes, these are not included in the term "ventilation" as used here.

The number of air changes required varies greatly. It may be estimated by calculation, experimentation, or experience under conditions similar to those in the plant to be built. In some cases involving crowded labor conditions, the ventilation may be determined from the maximum number of people who can be accommodated, assuming each one to require about 2,000 cu. ft. of fresh air per hour. In general, however, the number of air changes needed in an industrial plant will be controlled by the nature of the equipment and operations rather than by the number of employees.   Since the desired air changes may range from 2 or 3 to 20 or 30, this basic point of the design should be chosen with care and with the advice of competent people.   It is impracticable to recommend a figure for the air changes here because the processes, the cubical contents of a structure, the climate, and such matters vary too widely.

Seasonal variations may greatly affect the desirable air changes for any one plant, especially as far as the removal of excessive heat is con-

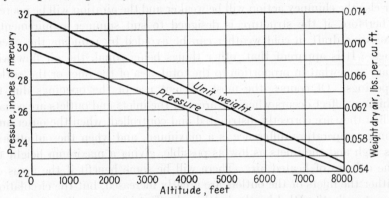

Fig. 5·1.   Weight of air and pressure at various heights.   (Temperature standard 70° at 0 altitude.   Each degree rise in temperature decreases the weight per cubic feet of air by approximately 0.22 per cent.)

cerned.   Therefore, in planning ventilation, provide facilities sufficient for the critical conditions of hot summer weather.   The requirements cannot, and generally should not, be looked upon as subject to exact determination.   Ventilation must be ample and conservatively generous without wastefulness, because it can otherwise cause great discomfort to and decreased production by the employees; it should also be flexible and capable of easy control to meet any and all probable conditions. If it is inadequate in any respect, the small saving made in construction costs will be insufficient to compensate for the discomfort when the time of great need arrives.

Airation in the winter involves the loss of heat from inside a structure.   When there is no heat-producing equipment used in the manufacturing processes, the attempt to conserve heat is likely to cause improper ventilation from the standpoint of oxygen supply and purity of the air.   This should be guarded against.

5·3   **Chimney Action.**   One natural force used in ventilating structures is the "chimney action" caused by heated air.   If a building contains furnaces, forges, or any other equipment that produces heat, the heated air rises and causes vertical convection currents. If it can escape through openings in the roof and if cool air from outside can enter the lower part of the building as the hot air escapes, there will be set up a circulation of air similar to that in a regular chimney. The activating force is the difference in weight between the heated air inside and the cooler air outside, this depending upon the difference in the temperatures of the two. Obviously, when the air outside is hot, as on a summer day, the inside temperature must be higher than it would be in cooler weather, or else the chimney action will be weaker and the airation will be poorer. Therefore, if the structure is designed to suit summer requirements, excessive draft in cold weather can be avoided by reducing the openings. It is apparent that, other things being equal, the air flow will vary somewhat in proportion to the total area of the inlet or the outlet openings. Of course, the most efficient use of the openings due to chimney effect occurs when the areas of the inlets and outlets are equal, when they are correctly distributed and controlled, when the outer and inner temperature difference is a maximum, and when the outlets are as high and the inlets as low as possible, giving a maximum height to the column of heated air. There will be some benefit if the areas of either the inlets or the outlets are greatly increased, but the circulation is naturally throttled by the bottleneck effect of the smaller of the two. One must remember that the quantity of air leaving a structure must be equal to that entering it. Figure 5·2 illustrates some of these principles.

When the sources of heat are at localized spots, it is advisable, as far as the chimney effect is concerned, to place the outlets in the roof as nearly over these sources and as high as possible. It is not desirable to force the hot air to travel far along under the roof before it reaches an outlet. The cool air can flow along the floor more easily unless the source of heat is altogether too far from the inlets. In no case should the cool draft be uncomfortable or unsafe for the men working in the building.

The amount of heat absorbed by flowing air in Btu per minute may be, according to E. W. Conover[1] of the Detroit Steel Products Co.,

$$H = 0.0175QD$$

where H = Btu per minute
Q = cu. ft. of air per minute
D = temperature difference between outgoing and incoming air

If the production of heat per minute can be determined, one can get an idea of the volume of air required for a given difference D. This can

[1] *Engineering News-Record*, July 31, 1941.

then be compared with the volume of the structure. Of course, in a large building with a few localized sources of large quantities of heat, it is best to design the structure to handle these points as individuals rather than to think of the problem in terms of the volume of the entire building.

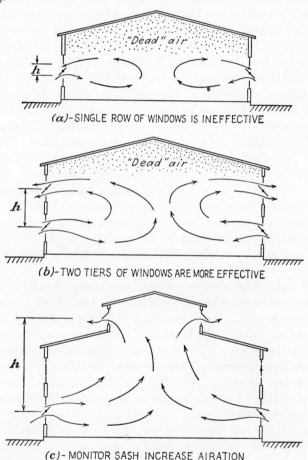

(a)-SINGLE ROW OF WINDOWS IS INEFFECTIVE

(b)-TWO TIERS OF WINDOWS ARE MORE EFFECTIVE

(c)-MONITOR SASH INCREASE AIRATION

Fig. 5·2. Convection currents within a building.

At sea level the weight of air can be assumed as 0.076 lb. per cu. ft. at 60°F. The rate of decrease of weight per cubic foot per degree Fahrenheit rise in temperature is about 0.00166 lb. per cu. ft. The decreases in weight of air for various heights above sea level are shown in Fig. 5·1.

From the differences in weight of the heated and unheated air, the moving force may be approximated.   The quantity of air moved by this force or head is proportional to the square root of the head, but it also decreases as the resistance to flow through the openings becomes greater. Since the pressure of the cooler outer air is greatest at the bottom inlets, whereas it is least at the top outlets, intermediate openings between the top outlets and bottom inlets may merely tend to "kill" the draft.

When a building covers a large area, the central portion may be poorly ventilated by the circulation that is caused by temperature difference alone.   Part of this may be due to ineffective inlet capacity, or the fact that the inlets are so far away that the air entering them passes out elsewhere before it can reach the central region.   Making this latter portion higher, as in Fig. 3·8(c), may help to remedy this.

The permissible minimum difference in temperature D between the air outside a building and that within it is the critical one for design. Thus, the magnitude of the natural forces producing airation will be least when the ventilation is needed most—in the summer.   What D should be depends upon the health of human beings, not merely upon the magnitudes of these air forces.   In a climate where the air temperature outside is frequently 90°F., a value of 20° for D is likely to be altogether too large. D equal to 10° would mean 100°F. inside the building, and this is certainly all the workers ought to be obliged to stand.

5·4   Wind.   The chimney action previously discussed must be depended upon during calm days.   When the wind blows, the condition changes considerably.   Wind sets up pressures and suctions that tend to move the air through the building if the proper openings for ingress and egress are provided.   Therefore, the chimney effect and wind effect will operate simultaneously.   On the other hand, the wind may vary in direction and intensity.   The effects of wind in any direction should be studied, and the building should be so designed that the wind will improve the ventilation.

The action of wind upon a building on level, clear ground is pictured in Fig. 5·3.   If this building is closed tightly, the wind must pass over and around it, somewhat as shown by the arrows.   The windward side AB will be under pressure, the leeward side CD will be subjected to suction, the sides BC and AD, also the roof FG, will be under suction, too.   This is because of the inertia of the air streams.   If the width of the building is great enough, the leeward portions of the sides and roof may be subjected to pressure because the air streams will be forced back against them.   Mr. Conover states that the extent of the suction areas at such points as BJ and FK of Fig. 5·3 "is a function of the

obstructing face. On the other hand, the distance is independent of
the velocity of the wind. The velocity of the wind determines the
intensity of the suction only." This indicates that the effectiveness of
the wind is greatest when it is perpendicular to the long side of the

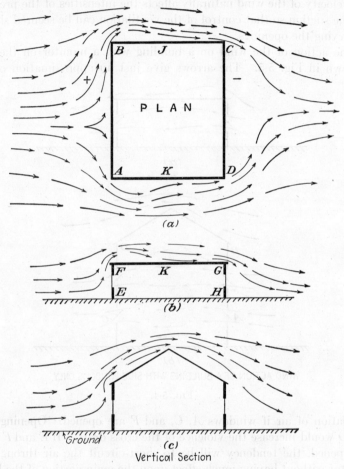

(a)

(b)

(c)
Vertical Section
WIND CURRENTS AROUND AND OVER A BUILDING
FIG. 5·3.

structure. It appears also that the extents of the suction areas along
the sides and roof vary with the width and height of the windward side
of a building until the former is nine times the latter,[1] after which the
height controls them.

[1] Detroit Steel Products Co., "Industrial Airation by the Fenestra Method."

Next, assume that the windows on both sides of a building are opened. As shown in Fig. 5·4, the wind will blow in the windward side, pass through the building, and then go out the leeward side. The actions of pressure and suction combine to produce the flow of air. The velocity of the wind naturally affects the intensities of the pressure and the suction so that control of the ventilation can be secured simply by varying the openings.

The action of the wind on a building with a monitor on the roof is shown in Fig. 5·5. The arrows give just an approximation of the

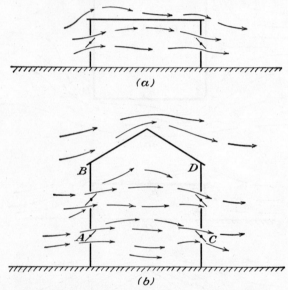

(a)

(b)

WIND ACTION OF A BUILDING WITH SIDE WINDOWS ONLY

Fig. 5·4.

circulation of air if windows A, C, and F are opened. Opening of B and D would increase the violence of the cross draft. If E and F alone are opened, the tendency will be to short-circuit the air through the monitor without having much effect upon the main portion of the building. If E is opened along with A, C, and F, it may decrease the flow of air from A to F, and it may even tend to produce some downdraft. It certainly will do the latter if F is closed. It should be noted also that the monitor becomes less effective when the wind is parallel to its windows; in fact, the windows at the ends of the building will be the most useful ones in such a case. Furthermore, since the suction effect is greatest at the windward end of the monitor in this case and since there may be pressure on the windows farther to the leeward, there may even be a backdraft in the building causing air to move toward the

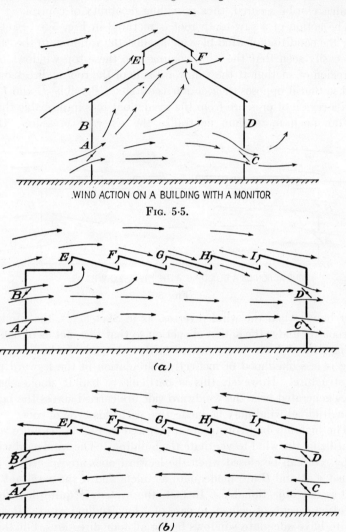

WIND ACTION ON A BUILDING WITH A MONITOR

Fig. 5·5.

(a)

(b)

WIND ACTION ON A SAW-TOOTHED ROOF

Fig. 5·6.

monitor windows at the windward end. At any rate, the air entering through the windows in the end of the structure is likely to be short-circuited out the near end of the monitor, whereas the far end of the building may be poorly ventilated. It is advantageous to have the window operators so arranged that almost any desired combination of openings can be secured, thus providing flexibility of control.

The action of a saw-tooth roof is pictured in Fig. 5·6. Sketch (a) is for the condition of wind blowing against the windows in the "teeth." It is easily seen that the wind coming into these top windows beyond the region of suction at the windward side of the roof is directed downward so that it opposes their action as outlets. Possibly H and I might be in a region of pressure from the inside, but it is improbable that this will do much more than neutralize the external pressure. On the

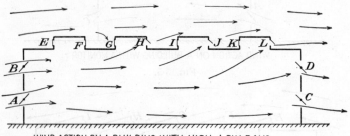

WIND ACTION ON A BUILDING WITH HIGH-LOW BAYS

Fig. 5·7.

other hand, when the wind reverses, as in Sketch (b), the windows in the roof are under the action of suction so that they act as outlets. By closing H and I, the air is carried farther through the building so that there is less likelihood of ineffective circulation in the leeward part of the structure. However, this is particularly bad if smoke, heat, or fumes generated near the windward side are carried across the building. A longitudinal wind may be ineffective with this type of roof.

The high-low-bay construction pictured in Fig. 5·7 is more suitable for utilizing the wind to ventilate the building. The windward windows in the roof can be closed when the leeward ones are opened; E can be opened if A and B are inadequate as inlets and if the resultant downdraft is not objectionable. In fact, the system is quite flexible in its operation except, of course, in case of a longitudinal wind. It is desirable to have adequate windows facing all four directions, but this may be difficult to accomplish unless the monitors are built like intermittent boxes on the roof, or when an arrangement similar to Fig. 3·8 is used.

All the preceding discussions show that it is wise to consider the direction of the prevailing winds, especially the summer ones, when deciding upon the direction of the axis of a building and the type of roof construction. The designer should consider these prevailing winds when he lays out an industrial plant to make sure that the portions of the plant that produce smoke, obnoxious gases, and heat are not directly windward of the parts that he is being so careful to airate properly. The records of the U. S. Weather Bureau contain data about these winds, some of which are given in Table 5·1.

Table 5·1 Average Velocity and Direction of Prevailing Winds for Summer Months

State	City	June Mph	June Dir.	July Mph	July Dir.	August Mph	August Dir.	Average Mph	Average Dir.
Ala.......	Birmingham	5.4	S.	5.1	S.	4.8	S.	5.1	S.
Calif......	Los Angeles	5.0	W.	4.8	W.	4.7	W.	4.8	W.
Fla.......	Miami	7.5	S.W.	7.1	S.W.	7.4	S.W.	7.3	S.W.
Ill........	Chicago	15.0	S.W.	12.0	S.W.	12.0	S.W.	13.0	S.W.
Ind.......	Indianapolis	9.2	S.W.	8.4	S.W.	8.0	S.W.	8.5	S.W.
Iowa.....	Des Moines	7.1	S.W.	5.9	S.W.	6.2	S.W.	6.4	S.W.
Mass.....	Boston	9.3	S.W.	8.4	S.W.	9.2	S.W.	9.0	S.W.
Mich.....	Detroit	9.9	S.W.	9.5	S.W.	9.2	S.W.	9.5	S.W.
Mo.......	Kansas City	9.1	N.	8.1	N.W.	9.1	N.W.	8.8	N.W.
Neb......	Omaha	7.8	S.W.	6.8	S.W.	7.5	S.W.	7.4	S.W.
N.Y......	New York	13.0	S.W.	13.0	S.W.	14.0	S.W.	13.3	S.W.
N.Y......	Albany	6.7	S.	6.3	S.	5.9	S.	6.3	S.
N.C.....	Charlotte	5.3	S.W.	4.9	S.W.	4.7	S.W.	5.0	S.W.
Ohio.....	Columbus	9.5	S.W.	8.6	S.W.	8.5	S.W.	8.9	S.W.
Ore.......	Portland	5.9	N.W.	5.9	N.W.	5.5	N.W.	5.8	N.W.
Wash.....	Seattle	8.1	S.	7.3	N.	6.6	N.	7.3	N.
Wis.......	Milwaukee	9.3	N.E.	8.4	N.W.	10.4	N.W.	9.4	N.W.

5·5 Airation Computations.[1] A few basic assumptions applicable to airation problems but not stated in preceding articles are given here because they apply with and without wind. They are the following:

1. Other things being equal, the volume of air exhausted through a roof of any type will vary as the area of the openings. Adjustable louvers are, of course, equivalent to operating sash of the same net clear area except for the greater resistance of the air passing through the slats.

2. The difference in temperature between the air inside and outside of a building decreases as the quantity of air flowing through the building increases.

3. The shape of a monitor roof—whether peaked, flat, or inverted V-shaped —has no appreciable effect if the monitors and openings are the same otherwise.

4. It makes negligible difference in most cases whether monitor windows are horizontally pivoted at the center, top, or bottom (or even if they are pivoted

[1] The data given in this article are based upon those issued by the Detroit Steel Products Co. in "Industrial Airation by the Fenestra Method."

vertically). The same statement applies to vertical windows compared to sloping ones. The chief requirement is that the movable areas and the angle of opening are equal. Furthermore, opening a window more than 75° from the vertical gains little.

5. Obstructions in front of windows should, of course, be minimized; *e.g.*, crane girders and trusses hamper the flow of air if close to and across the openings. Partitions inside a building, even those with doors or screened openings in them, interfere greatly with the movement of air, particularly the fresh air from the inlets. Furthermore, tall buildings, or cliffs close to a structure may reduce the beneficial effect of the wind; they may even cause downdrafts on the roof when conditions are suitable.

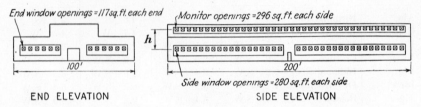

FIG. 5·8.   Elevations of a small factory.

The approximate methods explained herein for computing the number of air changes in a given structure under specific conditions seem to be sufficient for practical purposes. They assume that the window openings are unobstructed and that the wind is blowing horizontally against the building. Good judgment is essential in determining what margin of safety is needed to allow for imperfect conditions. Such problems are generally those of testing a given or assumed structure to see whether or not the resultant airation is satisfactory. As an illustration, the building of Fig. 5·8 will be analyzed for various conditions.

The number of air changes per hour N, resulting from flow caused by temperature difference alone, is computed as follows:

1. Assume a temperature difference equal to 10°F.
2. Assume that all movable sashes are fully open.
3. From Table 5·2 for $h = 17$ ft., $D = 10°$, and equal openings, find by interpolation that $Q = 121$ cu. ft. per min. per sq. ft. of opening.
4. Find the total inlet area $= 2 \times 117 + 2 \times 280 = 794$ sq. ft. Total outlet area $= 2 \times 296 = 592$ sq. ft. The larger exceeds the smaller by $794/592 = 1.34$. Having an excess of inlets (or outlets) will increase the flow somewhat above that occurring if both were equal to the lesser of the two. Hence, from Fig. 5·9, find 13 per cent increase to add to the exhaust through the outlets as computed from item 3. Therefore, $\Sigma Q = 1.13 \times 121 \times 592 = 80,800$ cu. ft. per min. or 4,848,000 cu. ft. per hr.

5. If the volume of the building is 410,000 cu. ft., this gives $N = \Sigma Q/V = 4,848,000/410,000 = 11.8$ air changes per hour.

Next, compute the air changes in this same building for a wind of 5 mph blowing perpendicular to the long side. A typical calculation may be made as follows:

Table 5·2 [Q = **Cubic Feet of Air Flow per Minute per Square Foot of Inlet or Outlet Opening (Inlet and Outlet Openings Equal)**]

h = height of outlet above inlet, ft.	D = Temperature difference, °F.							
	5°	10°	15°	20°	25°	30°	40°	50°
5	46	66	79	93	104	114	130	145
10	66	93	114	131	147	160	184	204
15	81	114	139	160	179	196	225	250
20	95	131	160	185	207	227	259	288
25	106	147	179	208	231	253	290	324
30	114	160	196	226	253	276	317	354
35	124	173	211	244	272	298	343	383
40	133	185	227	261	291	319	367	410
45	141	196	240	278	309	338	389	433
50	149	208	253	293	326	356	410	456
60	160	228	278	321	356	391	450	500
100	210	293	360	415	462	504	580	646

1. Assume that all lower sashes are fully opened but that those in the ends of the building are ineffective.

2. Assume that the leeward monitor sashes are opened but that the windward ones are closed to prevent short-circuiting the air through the monitor.

3. The total inlet area = 280 sq. ft.; total outlet area = 280 + 296 = 576 sq. ft.

4. The velocity of the wind is 5 mph or $5 \times 88 = 440$ ft. per min. Obviously, there will be eddies and interruptions of direct flow when the wind blows against the building so that the volume of air passing through the openings will be less than the area of the minimum openings (inlets in this case) times the velocity of the wind. Therefore, applying the correction factors in Table 5·3, find $\Sigma Q = 280 \times 440 \times 0.60 = 74,000$ cu. ft. per min., or 4,440,000 cu. ft. per hr.

5. Therefore, $N = 4,440,000/410,000 = 10.8$.

Similarly, when the wind is blowing diagonally (perhaps at 45°) against this building, $N = 397 \times 440 \times 0.35 \times 60/410,000 = 9$. When the wind blows lengthwise of the structure, $N = 117 \times 440 \times 0.50 \times 60/410,000 = 3.8$. This assumes that the monitor windows are ineffective as outlets, although the portion near the windward end may be subjected to some suction. Hence, the minimum area used is that of one set of end windows, and the 50 per cent figure taken from

Table 5·3 is that without a monitor because, in this case, the latter does not cause any appreciable increase in suction areas when the wind is parallel to it. From these computations, it may seem desirable to install windows in the ends of the monitor for ventilation purposes, depending upon the needs of the situation.

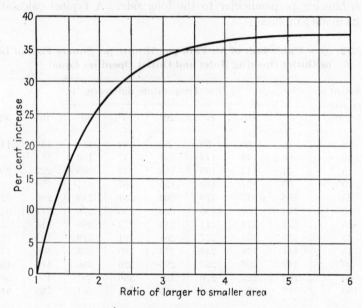

Fig. 5·9.   Curve showing percentage increase of volume of air flow when inlets and outlets are unequal.

Table 5·3   Correction Table

(The Percentages Shown for Buildings with Monitors Are Larger than for Buildings without, as Monitors Create Greater Flow by Putting Greater Area in Suction)

Direction of wind	Without monitor		With monitor	
	Perpendicular	Diagonal	Perpendicular	Diagonal
Percentage of flow	50	30	60	35

Under normal conditions, both wind and temperature differences will combine to cause flow of air in the building, but the number of air changes will not be so great as the sum of those previously computed because the faster movement of air caused by the help of the wind will result in less difference in temperature and, consequently, less flow due to it.   These combined effects may become very complex, but experience seems to indicate that it is sufficient to add the separate flows and apply to their sum the correction factors shown in Table 5·4.

Table 5·4   (Apply Percentages in This Table to Give Combined Flow)

When TD is   0%, W 100%, use 100%
When TD is   10%, W 90%, use 91%
When TD is   15%, W 85%, use 86%
When TD is   20%, W 80%, use 82%
When TD is   25%, W 75%, use 77%
When TD is   30%, W 70%, use 73%
When TD is   35%, W 65%, use 68%
When TD is   40%, W 60%, use 64%
When TD is   45%, W 55%, use 59%
When TD is   50%, W 50%, use 55%
When TD is   55%, W 45%, use 59%
When TD is   60%, W 40%, use 64%
When TD is   65%, W 35%, use 68%
When TD is   70%, W 30%, use 73%
When TD is   75%, W 25%, use 77%
When TD is   80%, W 20%, use 82%
When TD is   85%, W 15%, use 86%
When TD is   90%, W 10%, use 91%
When TD is 100%, W 0%, use 100%

For the case of a 10° difference plus a 5-mph wind perpendicular to the long side, N for Fig. 5·8 may be computed as follows:

1. Assume that the inlet area for computing the effect of temperature difference alone is that of the lower windows on the windward side and both ends, 280 + 2 × 117 = 514 sq. ft. since the leeward lower windows serve as outlets and the windward monitor ones are closed.   The outlet area is 296 + 280 = 576 sq. ft.

2. From Table 5·2, Q per sq. ft. of opening = 121 cu. ft. per min., as before.

3. The inlets constitute the minimum area.   Hence, 576/514 = 1.12 excess of outlets.   From Fig. 5·9, about 3 per cent is to be added to Q from item 2. Therefore, $\Sigma Q = 1.03 \times 121 \times 514 = 64{,}000$ cu. ft. per min. $N = 64{,}000 \times 60/410{,}000 = 9.4$.

4. Combining ΣQ from item 3 with that caused by the normal wind previously computed, gives

	Cu. ft. per min.	Per cent
Temperature difference............	64,000	46
Wind.........................	74,000	54
Sum.........................	138,000	100

Therefore, total flow = 138,000 × 0.59 = 81,000 cu. ft. per min., by the use of Table 5·4, and $N = 81,000 \times 60/410,000 = 11.9$.

Great accuracy in such calculations of air flow should not be expected. The computations give a reasonable scale for the answers, but one should be conservative in designing important plants, perhaps using a safety factor of 2, calling the assumed air changes equal to half the computed values. Worthy of remembrance is the fact that the number of air changes required and the acceptable temperature difference are chosen arbitrarily. When proper adjustability is provided, the operators can easily throttle the air flow by changing effective window openings; they cannot readily increase the capacity of the system when critical conditions show it to be inadequate.

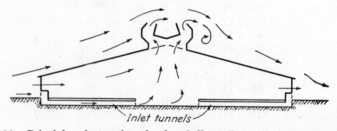

Fig. 5·10.   Principles of operation of a clamshell ventilator with fresh-air tunnels to deliver cool air to center of structure.

The number of operating sashes, their areas, and their positions are important matters. These analyses may help one to determine what his decisions should be. Ordinarily, if there are enough windows for adequate daylighting, they can be sufficient for airation. A structure should be designed in the first place so that window-operating equipment can be installed without hitting bracing and vital members, the sashes can be opened as wide as intended, and the circulation is not throttled by obstructions. In large buildings the provision of adequate inlets may be so difficult as to affect structural design. One extreme case is pictured in Fig. 5·10 where a "clamshell" is incorporated in the roof, and inlet tunnels extend from the outside to the central portion of the structure.

Its adaptability to both daylighting and airation seems to make the high-low-bay construction of Fig. 5·7 more suitable than that of Fig. 5·6 for large buildings. The difficulties of using skylights as ventilators in inclement weather, and the fact that they may not cause effective suction areas under the action of the wind, handicap their extensive use when good airation is desired.

5·6 Roof Ventilators. Special ventilators have been developed for installation in the roofs of industrial buildings to take the place of operating sashes and to avoid dependence upon the direction of the wind. One type of ventilator is shown in Fig. 5·11. It is a cylindrical metal

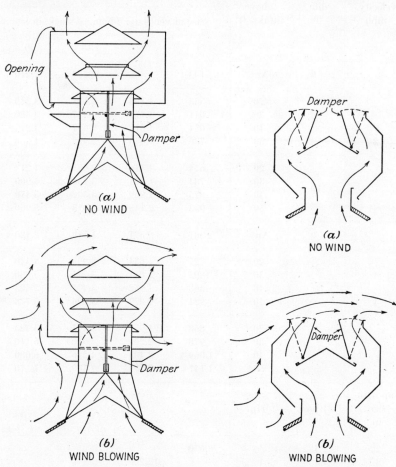

FIG. 5·11.   Action of cylindrical ventilator.

FIG. 5·12.   Action of slotted or streamlined ventilator.

shell designed to be effective in a breeze from any direction; it may have a damper to throttle its action during cold weather or high winds; and it may be equipped with a motor-operated fan if desired. In calm weather it causes airation the same way as other roof openings of equal throat area and at the same height. When fans are included, they

Table 5·5   Capacity of Cylindrical Ventilator, Cubic Feet per Minute

Wind velocity, mph	Temp. diff., °F.	Height above intake, ft.	Area of ventilator stack, sq. ft.			
			3.14	7.07	12.57	19.63
			Size of ventilator (diam. of stack, in.)			
			24	36	48	60
	0	Any	193	435	774	1,210
	5	20	533	1,198	2,131	3,330
		30	611	1,375	2,447	3,820
		40	674	1,516	2,697	4,213
2		50	730	1,643	2,922	4,568
	10	20	674	1,516	2,697	4,213
		30	784	1,764	3,136	4,900
		40	875	1,969	3,502	5,470
		50	953	2,145	3,815	5,960
	0	Any	387	871	1,548	2,420
	5	20	727	1,634	2,905	4,540
		30	805	1,811	3,221	5,030
		40	868	1,952	3,471	5,423
4		50	924	2,079	3,696	5,778
	10	20	868	1,952	3,471	5,423
		30	978	2,200	3,910	6,110
		40	1,069	2,405	4,276	6,680
		50	1,147	2,581	4,589	7,170
Fan diam. size, in.	Rpm	Hp				
22	1,425	½	5,050			
32	1,150	1	....	12,200		
42	850	1½	....	....	20,000	
54	720	7½	....	....	....	44,250

give great flexibility to a ventilation system, and they provide positive movement of a given quantity of air per minute, even during the hottest, calmest weather.

A streamlined ventilator is pictured in Fig. 5·12. It is designed to provide more area of opening than is available in cylindrical ventilators

Table 5·6   Velocity of Discharge through Streamlined Ventilators

Capacity = lineal feet per minute × square feet of area of ventilator stack opening.

Temperature difference, °F.	Height of ventilator above intake, ft.	Wind velocity	
		2 mph Lineal feet per minute	4 mph Lineal feet per minute
5	20	152	208
	30	176	231
	40	193	249
	50	209	265
10	20	193	249
	30	225	280
	40	250	306
	50	273	329

of the same cost.   However, it does not have the advantage of equal effectiveness for any direction of the wind, nor is it readily adaptable for fan installations.

When roof ventilators are used in combination with monitor windows, both will act together on calm days, but the former may have little effect because of their relatively small area.   Both will operate simultaneously if the wind blows, provided the windward sashes are closed; if the ventilator fans are running when the monitor sashes are open, the latter will be likely to permit the air to short-circuit through the fans.   When a building contains a few scattered sources of large amounts of heat, it is feasible to install ventilators with fans over these units as a special precaution and for use during peak periods.   When the fans are running, the operating sashes in the monitors in the vicinity can be closed so that fresh air is drawn from other portions of the structure, and the hot air will be drawn through the ventilators.

Ventilators with and without fans are especially useful in plants when the opening of windows is not permissible.

The size, type, and position of ventilators should be determined before the structure is designed; then the framework can be made to accommodate them.   The dead load of a ventilator and the overturning moment caused by wind acting upon a large cylindrical ventilator may require special purlins under the ventilator—perhaps with light bracing to steady the purlins laterally.   Large monitor ventilators like that of Fig. 5·10 are naturally important features affecting the design of a roof and the bracing system of a building.

5·7 Mechanical Ventilation. When a building contains several stories, the ventilation situation for each floor is somewhat like that shown in Fig. 5·4. When the wind blows, the cross circulation may be satisfactory if it is not too drafty. Under other conditions, it may be necessary to install a power-operated ventilation system, frequently in-

Fig. 5·13. This building has a saw-tooth roof with panels of glass blocks for daylighting and an excellent system of ducts for uniform ventilation of the extensive area. The bays are 25 ft. wide; the spacing of the duct openings 33 ft. This ventilation system is in the plant of the International Business Machines Corp. at Endicott, New York. It is the product of the Anemostat Corp. of America.

corporating it with the heating plant, although fans may be placed in some of the windows to produce the circulation. The details of such ventilation and air-conditioning systems are too extensive to illustrate fully here.

The essential parts of a mechanical ventilation system are or may be the following for single- or multistory structures:

1. A central power-operated fan, or smaller units at separated locations.
2. An inlet duct. Part of the air may come from out of doors and part by

ducts from within the building if recirculation is desirable.   Unless partial recirculation is permitted, the loss of heat is likely to be a serious burden on the
heating system during the winter.

3. An air washer in the inlet duct to clear the air of dust and to humidify it.
Equipment to produce chemical purification may be used if needed.

4. A duct system to the points of distribution of air in the building.

5. A return-duct system if recirculation is used.

6. A heating unit or units may be installed somewhere in the system if it is
used for heating the building in addition to ventilating it.   Correspondingly, air-
cooling equipment may be used to control the temperature during hot weather.

When forced circulation is to be provided, it is very important to
decide upon it and to plan the system in detail so that it can be incorporated in the original design of the building.   In this case the ducts
can be concealed by building them in the walls, partitions, and floors,
and the system can generally be laid out more efficiently and satisfactorily.   When a designer tries to install such a system in an old or
completed building, he has to make the best compromise that he can
between satisfactory operation, appearance, and cost.

Some different principles, systems, and data that may be used in
planning the duct system are the following, assuming that the fans and
heaters are in the basement:

1. Place all ducts in the outer walls, with outlets and inlets for recirculation
in the walls also.   The air in the supply ducts is likely to be chilled in the winter.

2. Place all ducts in inside partitions or at inner columns.

3. Place supply ducts in inside partitions or at inner columns, but locate return ducts in outer walls.

4. In winter weather the heating of the air will assist the circulation in the
supply ducts because of convection, whereas the reverse occurs when cooled air
is supplied in the summer.

5. Since condensation of moisture is likely to occur in the ducts under conditions that cause chilling, provisions for drainage must be made.   Furthermore,
corrosion of the ducts must be guarded against.

6. The ducts may have a constant cross section with varying air velocities.
In this case, the dampers can be regulated to give equal flow of air per vent by
using small openings near the fan and increasingly larger ones as the ends of the
duct lines are approached.

7. The ducts may have varying cross sections, the area being in proportion
to the number of vents served between the point in question and the end of the
run.   This system is not very flexible in operation.

8. The elbows in ducts should be made with large radii to avoid harmful eddies near the inner corner.   When the ducts are large, the use of fins or diaphragms as in Fig. 5·14 helps to minimize disturbances in the air stream.

9. Because of frictional resistances to flow along the surfaces of the ducts, round or square cross sections are most efficient; flat, thin ducts are not desirable as far as friction is concerned.

Before locating outlets and returns, one should think carefully over the question of just what circulation is desired in the rooms. Some points to consider in this connection are the following:

1. When warm air is discharged near the ceiling, it will fall as it cools and as it is displaced by incoming warmer air, producing a downward circulation.

2. When warm air is introduced near the floor, it tends to rise at once and displace cooler air, the warm air thus tending to collect near the ceiling.

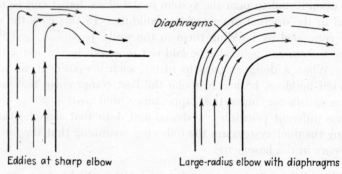

Eddies at sharp elbow   Large-radius elbow with diaphragms

Fig. 5·14.   Elbows in duct system.

3. When outlets for warm air are near the ceiling and when inlets to return ducts are under them and near the floor, the forced circulation works in the same direction as the convection currents due to chilling of the air supplied to the room.   However, the circulation on the far side of the room is likely to be weak compared to that near the openings.

4. When the warm air enters near the ceiling and the inlets to the return ducts are near the floor on the opposite side of the room, the circulation of the air is likely to be more uniformly distributed.

5. When the inlets for warm air are near the floor and the return inlets are over them near the ceiling, the convection and forced draft tend to short-circuit the system and confine the circulation to the air near that side of the room.

6. When the warm air enters near the floor and the return inlets are near the ceiling at the opposite side of the room, the tendency is to cause a draft up the first wall and along the ceiling, short-circuiting the system to a certain extent.

7. Various improvements can be made by using more than one inlet and outlet arrangement if conditions justify so many ducts.

8. Strong downdrafts or lateral movements of cool air may be injurious to occupants.

9. The use of the regular duct system for air conditioning in the summer re-

verses its action as far as the relation of warm and cool air is concerned. Therefore, it may be worth while to install dampers and cross connections in the main
ducts in the basement so that the entire system may be interchanged if desired.

10. All inlets and outlets should be controlled by dampers that can be adjusted to suit conditions.

11. The opening of windows may interfere greatly with the operation of the
system. Hence, the layout should be arranged so that only the appropriate
ducts need be used in mild weather when all that is required of the system is the
replacement of air far from the windows.

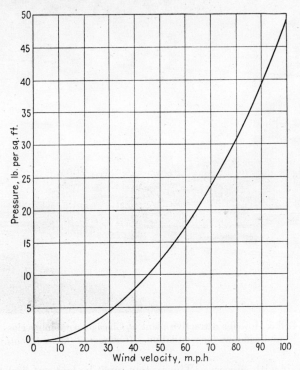

Fig. 5·15. Wind force at various velocities.

The capacity of the heating plant and the air-cooling unit, the number of changes of air per hour, the sizes and arrangement of ducts, the
type of circulation to be used—these are questions to be settled by
competent engineers. Each particular case should be considered by
itself, and the system should be designed accordingly.

Dust collectors, ducts to supply air to special equipment, suction
systems to remove fumes, and other installations of this general type are
frequently necessary or desirable. When, where, and how they are to

be installed are questions to ask before a building is designed. Cyclones, fans, motors, and even ducts may be surprisingly large so that they cannot be conveniently set in odd corners, hung from beams, or placed between trusses. Adequate spaces should be allocated to them, holes left in floors and walls for future installation of the ducts, and adequate supports provided. However, data for these things cannot be picked

Fig. 5·16.   Bell & Howell's attractive plant at Chicago, combining glass blocks for light and windows for ventilation.   (*Courtesy of Owens-Illinois.*)

out of the air with success. The system must be laid out first to ensure its proper operation and the adequacy of the structure. The owners and mechanical engineers should, therefore, see that the necessary layouts are made soon enough and carefully enough so that they need not be changed after the structure is designed or built.

The principal points to emphasize here are the importance of ventilation in industrial plants; the effect that provisions for its proper functioning may have upon the type, shape, and details of the structures; and the economy and satisfaction that generally result when the original plans are made to accommodate all these things.

Chapter 6

ROOFS

6·1 Introduction. The planning of important structures requires the designer to think about so many different things that it is difficult to determine which of many interrelated features should be decided first.

After the general style, shape, and size of a building have been selected to suit the requirements of the site and the equipment, and after it has been decided to make the framing of steel, concrete, or wood, what should be the next step? One might try to lay out the general framing scheme, but sooner or later he will realize that he cannot proceed far until he has determined in considerable detail what the roof, floors, walls, and partitions are to be made of, and what their general construction will look like. It is therefore advisable to determine these parts quite completely in the beginning because they are prerequisites for the design of the main framing; they are not just minor details.

For this reason, this chapter and the two following ones are intended to assist the reader in his selections of the particular construction to be used for each part. Many varieties of construction are now in use for roofs, floors, walls, and partitions,[1] and still others are likely to be developed. Some of them will be illustrated here, but it is impracticable even to try to include all useful types in these three chapters. The data given are for the purpose of showing some types, illustrating certain details, and suggesting construction that may be suitable for the specific case that the reader may be studying.

Seldom are the types of construction to be used for roofs, floors, walls, and partitions independent of each other, or of the style and material of the structural framework. Nevertheless, there is generally considerable freedom of choice within certain practicable limits. The designer should select tentatively the desired construction for each element of the building, make sure that all parts will harmonize and fit together to form a satisfactory structure, and then work out the typical details to be used.

[1] Additional useful data may be found in "Architectural Construction—The Choice of Structural Design," by Theodore Crane, John Wiley & Sons, Inc., New York.

6·2 Desirable Qualities. For what qualities or characteristics should a designer look when he is planning a roof? Here lightness, strength, waterproofness, insulation, fire resistance, cost, durability, and low maintenance charges are of prime importance. Without a good, tight roof, the usefulness and value of a building may be greatly impaired. There is, however, considerable overlapping in practice so that one cannot draw absolute lines of demarcation between roofs to be used on this or that type of structure.

A few comments regarding the desired qualities previously listed are the following:

1. *Lightness.* The desirability of light weight is especially great in the case of long-span roofs. For purlin spans under 15 or 16 ft. and for trusses less than 40 ft. long, the sizes of members may be controlled largely by advisable minimum sections, or, at least, the increase in the cost of the framework because of larger dead loads will be slight except in the case of timber framing. The designer must be careful to avoid letting his desire for lightweight roof construction make him negligent of the other characteristics that may be important, too. He should remember to fasten down such roofs as well as to hold them up, because suction during gales may lift them.

2. *Strength.* There is generally considerable uncertainty regarding the intensity of live loads for which roofs should be designed. Flat roofs in snowy climates may actually have to carry at least 40 lb. per sq. ft. of horizontal projection; when surrounded by parapets, they may be loaded even more heavily. Although unit weights vary greatly, one may assume that 1 ft. depth of hard, dry, wind-blown snow weighs 10 lb. per sq. ft.; if a cold rain falls upon such snow, the load may be increased from 25 to 50 per cent before there will be enough drainage action to take off the excess water, even when the roof has a moderate slope. If the inlets or scuppers are filled with ice, the load upon flat roofs with parapets may become relatively heavy. Sloping roofs having a pitch of 3:12 or greater may accumulate extensive snowdrifts on the leeward side, but water falling subsequently will drain off to a large extent.

It seems desirable to design a roof for the following minimum live loads, stated in terms of pounds per square foot of horizontal projection:

a. 40 for roofs having 4:12 slope or less in snowy climates; 50, if flat roofs are surrounded with parapets 3 ft. or more high.

b. 30 for all roofs in regions where the winters are moderate.

c. 20 for all roofs in the far South and Southwest.

Besides uniformly distributed live loads, it is advisable to provide for the effect of a 200-lb. man walking around on a reasonably flat roof during construction and maintenance operations or for the purpose of removing snow. Therefore, this feature may need special consideration in case the roof is to be made of weak and brittle materials.

The effect of wind loads on sloping roofs of industrial buildings should generally be computed on the basis of the following pressure, pounds per square foot, of vertical projection:

a. 20 for buildings less than 50 ft. high.

b. 30 for structures 50 ft. or more in height.

c. 40 for structures in regions where tropical hurricanes and tornadoes are expected.

On the other hand, in cases of combined dead, live, and wind loading, a designer may be justified in permitting the theoretically computed unit stresses in the materials to exceed by as much as 30 per cent those ordinarily allowable for dead load and live load, or dead load and wind load alone. However, the combination should not result in members that are weaker than those for dead load plus live load, or dead load plus wind load. In fact, skimping the assumed live load to be used for design purposes may save relatively little money. The failure of a roof is practically inexcusable.

3. *Waterproofness.* The attainment of waterproofness of a roof is frequently dependent upon the common sense and good judgment used in working out the details of construction and drainage. Obviously, the roofing or covering itself must be watertight, or able to shed the water. The following five general types of roofing are used:

a. Built-up Bituminous Membranes. These are usually made of layers of roofing felt or fabric coated with asphalt or tar. A series of layers or plies is built up by lapping successive layers, thus obtaining a large, continuous, waterproof sheet of excellent durability. Frequently, this type of roofing is covered with small gravel while the bituminous material is soft. This is done to provide a surface that will resist wear and will not become too soft and sticky under a hot sun; the gravel does not add to the waterproofness. When such roofings are likely to be walked upon frequently, it is advisable to cover them with tiles laid in asphalt, or with some other suitable material. Such built-up roofing is especially advantageous for flat roofs.

b. Prefabricated "Pilot" or Other Bituminous Roofing Papers. These are generally low-priced but relatively short-lived. As it is difficult to keep the joints tight, they are not used on flat roofs. These roofings are easily and cheaply applied, but the material is readily damaged by workmen walking on the roof, by wind, branches of trees, and ice.

c. Metallic Sheets. These may be noncorrodible materials like copper and aluminum, or they may be "tin" or galvanized steel. In some cases, small sheets or strips may be soldered at lapped joints to form continuous membranes of large area; on sloped roofs, the batten type may be used. They should, however, be fastened down securely to prevent vibrating in the wind, or even being ripped off, and they should be provided with frequent contraction joints so that they will not be ruptured by tensile stresses produced by low temperatures. For this, vertical ribs or soldered, upstanding joints are suitable if planned so as to avoid interference with drainage. Nails holding down a copper roofing should be copper also in order to render long service.

d. Shingles.   These may be made of wood, slate, bituminous material, asbestos-cement, or even terra-cotta tile.   Since they are laid with staggered joints and large laps that, of themselves, are not watertight, they are for use on sloping roofs only.   Because of the sizes and types of industrial structures, shingles are not used extensively except for minor buildings.

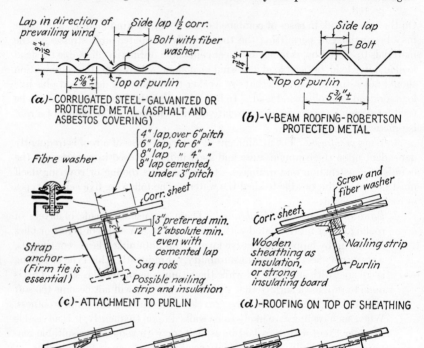

Fig. 6·1.   Details of some corrugated roofings and their attachments.

e. Corrugated Sheets.   These may be copper, aluminum, galvanized iron or steel, asbestos-protected metal, or transite.   Unlike the materials previously described, corrugated roofings need not be laid on some form of sheathing or supporting medium; they are designed to span from one purlin to another.   Since the joints between adjacent sheets are lapped but seldom made watertight, these sheets are basically a sort of shingle, and hence should not be used on roofs having a slope of less than about 3:12 unless the laps are cemented.   The fastenings must be firm and durable, and the structure should be so designed that workmen can get at the connections to install them properly.

In the case of any of the preceding roofings, except corrugated sheets, it is important to provide a strong, stiff support (sheathing) so that deflections under load will not be harmful. For example, if wooden sheathing is used under a

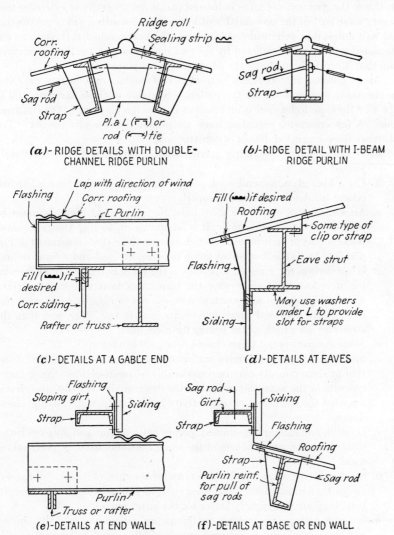

FIG. 6·2. Details of pitched roofs with corrugated roofing.

built-up bituminous roofing, or even under a sheet-metal one, the boards or planks should be tongued-and-grooved so that, when a man steps on one board, it will not deflect while its neighbor remains stationary, thereby tending to rupture or loosen the roofing. It is also important to make sure that shrinkage of wooden sheathing, deflections of abutting beams, and movement of expansion joints will not cause the roofing to rip apart.

4. *Insulation.* Adequate insulation of roofs is beneficial in two ways. For instance, the roof areas of large industrial plants are generally so extensive that a very large part of the unwanted heat losses in cold weather will occur through the roof unless it is well insulated; similarly, the heat conducted through an un-insulated roof and then radiated by the roof may be so great under the summer sun that it seriously increases the discomfort of employees.

Many different materials can be used as roof insulation; some can serve also as sheathing and supports for the roofing. Selection of these materials and of the way they are to be used is an inherent part of the planning of the construction. A few comments regarding some useful materials are given below. The sketches show suggested details of construction.

a. Wooden planks have fairly good insulating qualities if they are tightly jointed.

b. Cork, fiber glass, mineral wool, and the many "insulation boards" are excellent insulators when used properly.

c. Air spaces, too, may have great insulating value, but they also must be used correctly. For example, it is advantageous to trap the air in small pockets that are not interconnected, such as those cases illustrated in Fig. 6·5(d). An "attic," or an air space between the roof and a hung ceiling, is excellent in the summer, especially if the space is ventilated; in the winter, it is less effective because the transfer of heat through the ceiling warms the adjacent air, which in turn escapes or rises by convection currents to the roof and there delivers its heat to the latter, and then the cooled air goes back to the ceiling for more heat.

d. Stone concrete is not to be classed as a good insulator.

e. Special lightweight concretes with porous aggregates or with admixtures that produce porosity may be considerably better insulators than ordinary concrete of the same thickness, but the designer should insist upon learning what the coefficient of conductivity is for specific materials and thicknesses.

f. Gypsum and similar fine-grained, porous materials are usually even better insulators than are products of the same thickness made of portland cement.

g. Steel and most other metallic sheets and shapes are, of course, "radiators" rather than insulators. Even when covered with asbestos or similar coatings, they are but slightly better for the latter purpose.

h. Built-up bituminous roofings, roofing paper, asbestos or asphalt shingles, and slate should not be counted upon as adding much to insulation.

Condensation is a matter to consider as part of any study of an insulation problem. The moisture in warm air inside a structure will condense on surfaces if they are cool enough to chill the adjacent air below the dew point. This may cause objectionable dripping, peeling of paint, and rusting of steel. It is a difficult problem to overcome. Even when hung ceilings are used under a roof, with bat or bulk insulation on top of the plaster or whatever material is used, the moisture may condense in the insulation and cause metal lath and other steel-work to rust. Insulation applied directly to the underside of metal or masonry roofs may become partly saturated. It, as well as the structural roof, should be a material that will not soften, deteriorate, or cause flaking under such conditions. The attachments of such insulation to any overhead construction should be noncorrodible if moisture conditions are likely to be bad.

As a general rule, it is desirable to place most insulating materials on top of a structural roof if the former are stiff and strong enough, and if they are suitable for the direct application of the roofing.

How much insulation to use, and what kind, are matters for the exercise of good judgment in each case. The additional cost of adequate insulation is usually only slightly more than that of a skimpy, unsatisfactory job.

5. *Fire Resistance.* The ability of a roof to resist fire from without and within the structure is so important that an engineer should consider the hazards very carefully before he uses combustible materials in the construction of roofs of important structures. Heavy timber framing with tight, thick sheathing and devoid of "kindling wood" is often so slow burning that it is suitable for various structures; wood may also be treated with chromated zinc chloride or other chemicals that retard its combustion greatly.

The designer should remember that large, flat, tight, horizontal surfaces made of wood will not burn easily; similar surfaces in a vertical or steeply sloping plane will burn more readily. If the air cannot circulate easily so as to provide an adequate supply of oxygen, combustion will be retarded. Exposed platforms, open construction composed of small members with free circulation around them (such as stairways), wooden partitions and floors without fire stops to prevent the flow of air, vertical shafts, and hatchways—these are the kinds of construction that may endanger the safety of a wooden building. Therefore, wooden sheathing on a roof may not be too great a fire hazard if the supporting framework is incombustible, and if the contents of the building are not highly inflammable.

On the other hand, bare steel, although incombustible, is not fireproof but may soften and yield when heated sufficiently. Concrete of adequate proportions will endure considerable heat unless it becomes badly spalled by the effects of heating and then chilling by cold water, or unless the heating effect lasts long enough to dehydrate the cementaceous compounds. Bricks, tiles, and even ordinary plaster on metal lath are, of themselves, fire-resistant to a considerable extent. Most of the ordinary roofings, except wooden shingles and bituminous coverings, will not burn easily, if at all.

6. *Cost.* Naturally, everyone is and should be interested in securing economical construction. The roof areas of some industrial plants are literally measured in acres. It therefore behooves the designer to study carefully what are the real costs of various types of roofs, considering the roof itself, the supporting structure, and even the foundations in some cases. For example, a heavy roof may be cheaper per square foot than a suitable lightweight one, but the cost

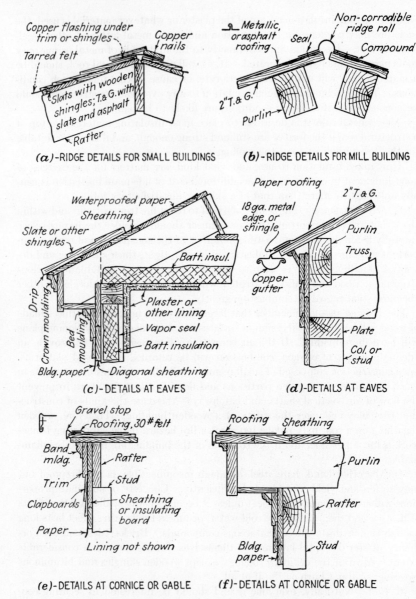

Copper flashing under trim or shingles
Tarred felt
Copper nails
Slats with wooden shingles; T.&G. with slate and asphalt
Rafter

(a)-RIDGE DETAILS FOR SMALL BUILDINGS

Metallic, or asphalt roofing
Seal
Non-corrodible ridge roll
Compound
2"T.&G.
Purlin

(b)-RIDGE DETAILS FOR MILL BUILDING

Waterproofed paper
Sheathing
Slate or other shingles
Batt. insul.
Drip
Crown moulding
Bed moulding
Plaster or other lining
Vapor seal
Batt. insulation
Bldg. paper
Diagonal sheathing

(c)-DETAILS AT EAVES

Paper roofing
2"T.&G.
18 ga. metal edge, or shingle
Purlin
Truss
Copper gutter
Plate
Col. or stud

(d)-DETAILS AT EAVES

Gravel stop
Roofing, 30# felt
Band mldg.
Rafter
Trim
Stud
Clapboards
Sheathing or insulating board
Paper
Lining not shown

(e)-DETAILS AT CORNICE OR GABLE

Roofing
Sheathing
Purlin
Rafter
Bldg. paper
Stud

(f)-DETAILS AT CORNICE OR GABLE

Fig. 6·3.   Some details of wooden roof construction.

of long-span framing and piled foundations may actually make the heavy roof more expensive.   When the spans are small and other loads are heavy, this matter of roof weight may be negligible.

Ease of erection is an important item affecting the cost of a roof. Naturally, it is very easy to erect a corrugated metal roof or one composed of precast concrete or gypsum planks which can be rested on and clipped to the structural framework. Wooden planks can also be spiked down quickly; when they are used with steel framing, bolted nailing strips will be needed. These prefabricated parts serve as platforms to support the workmen as the erection progresses. On the other hand, concrete (or gypsum) cast in place on forms is usually expensive because of high labor charges, the cost of form materials, and the hoisting or pumping of the concrete, and its subsequent distribution and finishing.

7. *Durability and Low Maintenance.* The durability of a roof is generally dependent upon the longevity of the roofing or the flashings, unless the designer has made a very unwise choice of the materials and details of the roof construc-

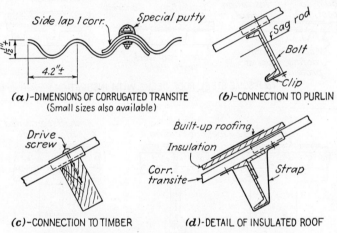

(a)-DIMENSIONS OF CORRUGATED TRANSITE (Small sizes also available)   (b)-CONNECTION TO PURLIN

(c)-CONNECTION TO TIMBER   (d)-DETAIL OF INSULATED ROOF

FIG. 6·4. Some details of corrugated transite roofing.

tion. When its importance is considered, he can see how utterly foolish it would be to use a poor surfacing on an otherwise excellent roof. Water must be kept out if the roof is to provide the optimum service. Keeping this water out is not only a question of using the most advisable roofing for the particular case, but much depends upon provisions for drainage, the quality of the flashing, and the prevention of abuse. Walking upon roofs, shoveling of snow, and chopping of ice are not operations that are recommended for any ordinary roofing.

The cost of the material of a roofing is only one part of its total cost, but the durability of that material may control the service life of the initial construction. The labor charges seldom vary greatly regardless of whether the materials are good or poor. Hence, use only the best materials because the cost of repairs and replacement will otherwise more than offset any saving in the original cost. As an example, assume that one is debating the relative merits and costs of a galvanized sheet-metal roof vs. those of a copper one. The initial cost, the expenditures for repairs and painting, and the cost of replacement must be combined

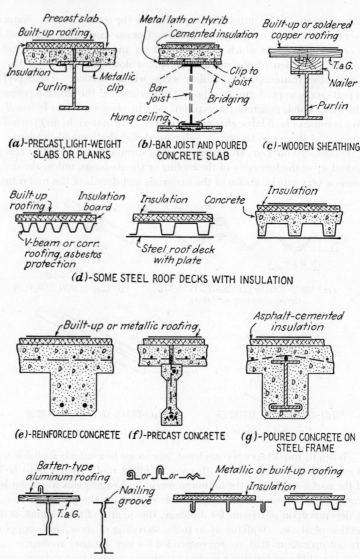

(a)-PRECAST, LIGHT-WEIGHT   (b)-BAR JOIST AND POURED   (c)-WOODEN SHEATHING
SLABS OR PLANKS   CONCRETE SLAB

(d)-SOME STEEL ROOF DECKS WITH INSULATION

(e)-REINFORCED CONCRETE   (f)-PRECAST CONCRETE   (g)-POURED CONCRETE ON
                                                    STEEL FRAME

(h)- STRAN-STEEL JOISTS   (i)- STEEL ROOF DECK

FIG. 6·5. Types of construction adapted especially to use with flat and slightly
sloping roofs.

over a period equal to the desired life of the structure in order to judge relative
costs properly.

6·3 Flashing. The junctions of roofing at valleys and ridges; its
connections to parapets, walls, chimneys, pipes, and other projections;

its junctions with gutters, scuppers, and downspouts—all are points where leakage is likely to occur. The details of these connections should be designed and installed carefully. The flashing should be of the best noncorrodible material.

Some mistakes made in planning the details of flashing and in performing the work in the field are the following:

1. Using poor material, or metal of inadequate thickness.
2. Placing the flashing on rough, pliable, or irregular surfaces which may cause it to rupture.
3. Failure to make joints between pieces of flashing watertight.
4. Failure to provide for thermal shrinkage and expansion. These situations may be overcome by placing upstanding ribs, downward crimps, or lapped (shingle) joints at frequent intervals (perhaps 30 to 40 ft. apart). If this is not done, the tensile forces caused by shrinkage in cold weather may tear the flashing or pull it away from other parts. Often this effect is difficult to avoid.
5. Puncturing of flashing with nails at points where water can enter.
6. Attaching flashing by means of corrodible nails. Copper ones are desirable.
7. Providing insufficient lapping of flashing on slopes.
8. Providing insufficient extension of flashing under shingles or other roofings, and inadequate laps over the tops of adjoining, lower surfacings.
9. Failure to lap flashing adequately into built-up roofing—not merely under the roofing or pasted on top when the slopes are flat.
10. Stopping flashing too low when adjoining parapets, chimneys, walls, and projections, provided clogging of drains or the formation of ice can cause the water to accumulate.
11. Failure to back up flashing with strong supports so that workmen who step on it or accidentally kick it—as when they are washing windows—will tear or displace it.
12. Attempts to secure fancy architectural effects by shingling gutters and ridges, and by omitting the flashing in order to save a little in the cost of the structure.
13. Attempts to "paste" the flashing onto chimneys and brickwork instead of bonding it into the masonry.
14. Covering nailheads with a dab of roofing cement, and then forgetting to maintain it. Soldering over them is better when it can be done.

The details in Figs. 6·2 and 6·6 show some ways of installing flashing, but it is impracticable to try to illustrate all usual and possible arrangements.

6·4 Drainage. The planning of the drainage system of a roof should be done when the first studies of the general features of the roof are made. Thereafter, the exact slopes and elevations can be established easily.

It is sometimes very difficult to provide adequate drainage facilities later if they were neglected in the first place.

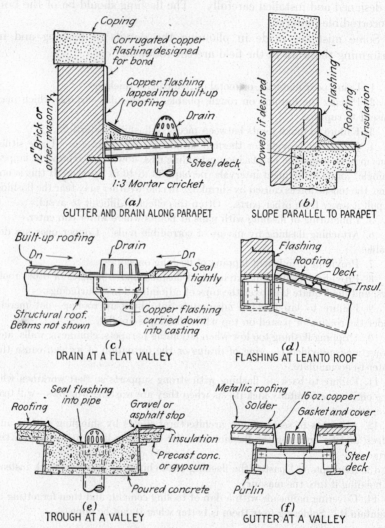

FIG. 6·6.   Details of parapets, gutters, and flashing.

Obviously, good judgment is one of the primary requisites when planning drainage.   What are the climatic conditions, the size and shape of the roof, and its construction?

It is possible to make flat roofs so that they are level; if desired, trusses and beams may be cambered.   In general, however, it is advisable to plan for sufficient slope to prevent water from actually lying in puddles on the roof for any protracted time. Slopes of as little as ⅛ or ¼ in. per ft. are sufficient for this, except during periods of ice and snow. In such times, melting snow tends to hold water so that slopes of as much as 1 or 2 in. per ft. will not drain readily. On this account, provisions should be made to avoid the overflowing of water, during such periods, into skylights, monitor and saw-tooth windows, and any other openings in or near the surface of the roof. Remember that the inlets may be frozen up, and the accumulated weight of water may overload the roof if it is trapped behind parapet walls or in valleys where it can be impounded. As a general rule, scuppers through parapets are objectionable because of the staining of the building by water that is blown against it. As a safety measure, however, a scupper that is located above the usual water line will serve as an overflow if the regular drains do not function properly.

The following suggestions are for consideration when one is planning the drainage of large flat roofs:

1. When there are no interfering projections in the roof, a one- or two-way slope may be used. A four-way or pyramidal roof will generally cause needless complications of the roof framing. When level parapets are used, the sloping ends of the roof can be concealed behind them; when level eaves are desired, the roof over the end bays can often be warped from the first interior column line to the edge of the structure.

2. With high-low-bay or saw-tooth construction, a roof may be sloped in a direction along the high bays, keeping high and low roofs parallel.

3. When it is desirable to slope the main roof of high-low-bay construction crosswise of the monitors, one of the systems shown in Fig. 9·11 may be used. When a building is very long, it may be possible to cut the high bays into units about 100 ft. long with a low bay between their ends, build a "cricket" along the high side of the monitor, and use the low bays as drainage channels.

Even with flat roofs, water may be collected by gutters at the eaves and then carried by downspouts, if they are designed correctly. It is sufficient to assume that the maximum rainfall is not greater than a rate of 1 in. per hr. When gutters are planned, the illustrations in Fig. 6·6 and the following suggestions may be helpful:

1. Use noncorrodible materials because the cost of maintenance and replacement is so relatively great.

2. Place gutters on a slope of ¹⁄₁₆ to ⅛ in. per ft. (0.5 to 1.0 per cent) to secure proper flow.

3. Use gutters that are large enough in cross section to hold the necessary water without spilling over or impounding the water sufficiently to have it back

up over the flashing.   In determining sizes, consider the width of roof area draining to a gutter.

4. Avoid long, continuous slopes of gutters unless intermediate outlets or downspouts are used—perhaps 50 to 100 ft. apart—or unless the size of the gutter is proportioned accordingly.

5. Provide strong and closely spaced supports for all gutters, and use in troughs material of sufficient thickness to avoid sagging and lateral buckling between supports.   Gutters in valleys and behind parapets should be backed up continuously by sheathing or other materials so that they will not be damaged if a workman steps in them or kicks against their sides.

6. Avoid carrying gutters on continuous slopes around corners because of the tendency of the flowing water to spill over the outer edge.   It is desirable to have a high point in the grade, or to have an inlet, at such a corner.

7. Make certain that gutters can be cleaned easily of leaves, paper, and debris that may lodge in them.

8. With steep roofs, consider snowslides and their tendency to clog and damage gutters, also to endanger persons below.   Snow guards may be desirable.

The details of outlets for drainage systems of roofs are also important.   Obviously, these outlets should carry away the water as fast as the gutters take it to them.   In planning these outlets, the designer should think about the following features:

1. Be sure that flowing water will not "jump" past the outlet.   Therefore, side openings in gutters may be ineffective unless the gutters are streamlined into them.

2. Gutters should be warped or dished downward around bottom outlets so that the water is directed longitudinally into the pipe rather than across it.   This also helps to create sufficient depth and pressure to expedite the entrance of water into the pipe.

3. Scuppers and other forms of side outlets that dump the water off the edge of a roof are undesirable because water blown by wind against the building and the splash from the water hitting the ground will stain the walls.

4. Pipe downspouts that conduct the water to the ground should have a long-radius elbow at the bottom to avoid objectionable splashing.   Even then, scouring may be severe unless a paved drainage ditch is provided.

5. Long headers and storm-water drains that collect water from a series of other pipes should have a slope of about 2 per cent.   The pipes should enter the large header from above or at an angle of 45° downward, the Y entering so that the incoming water flows in the same general direction as that already flowing in the header.

6. Inlet openings should have removable, noncorrodible screens of some sort to keep large objects out of drainage piping.

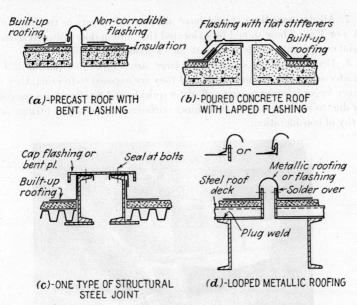

(a)-PRECAST ROOF WITH BENT FLASHING

(b)-POURED CONCRETE ROOF WITH LAPPED FLASHING

(c)-ONE TYPE OF STRUCTURAL STEEL JOINT

(d)-LOOPED METALLIC ROOFING

FIG. 6·7.   Details of some types of expansion joints.   (Drainage to be away from joint.)

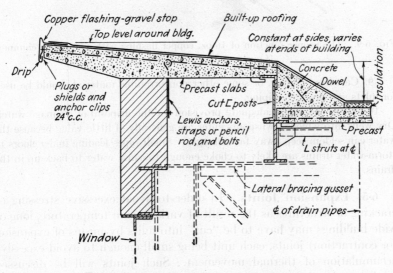

FIG. 6·8.   A detail of an overhanging cornice.

7. All drainage lines should have adequate cleanouts in the form of plugs in Y's or T's.   These should be so located that a man does not need scaffolds or special equipment in order to get at the cleanouts.

8. Drainage piping should be of large size.   Pipes less than 3 or 4 in. in diameter are generally inadequate.   If they are exposed to freezing, they should be even larger in order to carry off water quickly and to allow for some constriction due to icicle action on their inner surfaces.   Long-radius fittings are also worthy of consideration.

Fig. 6·9.   The proper junction of 16-oz. copper flashing with a masonry chimney.
(*Courtesy of American Brass Co.*)

9. Cast-iron, copper, or some other noncorrodible material should be used for inlets and drainage piping.

10. There should be adequate provision for the disposal of drainage water. Dry wells into which downspouts enter are generally of little value because the water can seldom seep away fast enough.   Small pipes leading under floors to storm-water drains are likely to choke enough to cause water to back up in the drains.

6·5 Expansion Joints.   In order to avoid excessive stressing or cracking of structures as the result of variations in temperature, long or wide buildings may have to be "cut" into units by means of expansion (or contraction) joints, each unit being small enough to avoid excessive accumulation of thermal movement.   Such joints will be discussed further under the various types of construction, but special details are generally necessary where they cut through the roof.

The movement to be provided for at an expansion joint in a roof is seldom more than ± ½ to ¾ in., yet it may be difficult to permit this movement without leakage.   As a general rule, it is advantageous to have such a joint at a high line or the summit in a roof so that water drains away from it. When proper gutters and flashing are used, an expansion joint may be at a valley; this, however, invites failure of deforming parts and leakage from the overflowing of gutters. A contraction joint crossing the line of flow is also to be avoided. In planning the drainage of a large roof, select the locations of expansion joints before the slopes and the drainage system are determined.

FIG. 6·10. An installation of copper gutters and downspouts. (*Courtesy of American Brass Co.*)

At a summit, the roofing should be raised enough to prevent overflow into the joint if drains become clogged or constricted. The opening should be capped with proper flashing. This flashing may be folded

FIG. 6·11.   View of batten style of aluminum roofing on the dome of the Cincinnati Union Terminal.   (*Courtesy of the Aluminum Co. of America.*)

upward to use the accordion principle to accommodate the movement without admitting the water, or it may lap over one side and be so arranged that it sheds water and permits the roof to slide under the flashing. If the fold of continuous flashing is downward, dirt and ice may collect in it so that a closing of the joint during a rise in temperature will create pressure and rupture the material.

An expansion joint at a gutter may be made of continuous material which forms both flashing and gutter and which bends to accommodate the movement of the joint. Nevertheless, fatigue, clogging, and ice are likely to cause trouble eventually. When a slip joint is used, the gutter should be stationary upon supports that are connected to one side so that all motion occurs in the space where the flashing overlaps the gutter, otherwise chafing may cause holes in the latter. However, clogging of the gutter may cause overflowing and leakage.

6·6   Special Details. Each designer is likely to have his own ideas regarding the best materials and details for use in the roof of a given structure at a specific location. It is inadvisable and impossible for anyone to make specific recommendations and to state that one material is best or that such and such details should be used. The illustrations are merely for the purpose of showing types of construction that might be employed. Still further suggestions are given in other chapters.

Chapter 7

FLOORS

7·1 Introduction. The selection of the type of construction to be used for the floors in a building and the choice of the materials composing them are basic decisions that should be made early in the general planning, especially when the structure is a multistory one. What the owner wishes to have, what the designer prefers to use, the kind of material that has been selected for the framing, the style of framing desired, the load to be carried, the service to be performed, fire resistance, architectural appearance, weight, and cost—all these are matters that affect such decisions. With floors, as with roofs, the variety of materials and construction that are good and serviceable is vast—so extensive that all cannot be illustrated here.

Sometimes the best procedure, when the floors of a structure are being planned, is to choose a type that seems to be the most desirable one, then to arrange and proportion the supporting framework accordingly; in other cases, the reverse may be advisable because there may be an obviously preferable framing scheme to which one type of floor is especially well adapted.

In the first case, the general type of construction desired for the structure as a whole, the magnitudes of the loads to be carried, and the use to which the building is to be put may be such that a few varieties of floor construction are automatically the most worthy of consideration. In the second, the selection may be influenced by the desire for long-span framing to minimize the number of columns, the need of securing light weight in order to reduce the loads on the foundations, the preference for flat rather than beamed ceilings, and the preference for steel or concrete, or even for wood.

The cost of a floor is, of course, a matter to be investigated with care because of the great area that is generally involved. The unit price of the flooring itself, including material and labor, is one item, but the cost of the supporting framework, the foundations, maintenance, and even of insurance are other items to be included when estimates of

relative costs are made.   The effect upon clearances or upon the height
of the structure may be of some importance, too.

7·2 Concrete Floors.   When a building is to be made with
reinforced-concrete framework, it is logical to have the floor slabs an
integral part of the beams and girders, or of the columns in the case of
flat-slab construction.   Such floors, when properly made, are strong
and durable, but they are heavy.   They should be, and generally are,
reinforced so as to be continuous across beam after beam in order to
avoid localized cracks at the beams, these cracks being caused by tension in the tops of the slabs.   Most concrete floors are poured in place
on forms, hence simplicity, uniformity, and the possibility of the reuse
of forms are items for the planner to consider when he wishes to mini-

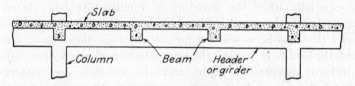

FIG. 7·1.   Reinforced-concrete slab-and-beam floor.

mize the cost.   Seldom are precast slabs as desirable for floors as they
are for roofs.

Figure 7·1 pictures the ordinary slab-and-beam floor.   This type
may well be used for heavy loads and for beam spans of 20 ft. or more.
The slabs are relatively shallow (usually 4 to 8 in. thick), and their
spans seldom exceed 10 ft.   Whereas long-span slabs would be heavy
and relatively limber, the T-beams provide depth and stiffness, with
large leverage for the steel.   These beams generally frame into cross
girders along the column lines or rest upon walls.   The slabs, beams,
and girders should be made continuous in order to avoid tensile cracks
over the supports.   Such a floor is deeply paneled, and the large headers
are likely to be important in matters of clearance and story heights.
When there are large, moving live loads, there is little distribution of
load laterally from one beam to another; hence each part must be
designed for the most severe condition that may affect it.   One great
advantage of this type of floor, however, is the fact that the framing
can be varied and adapted to almost any condition and dimension, and
openings may be provided through the slabs without seriously weakening
the structure.

Another type of concrete floor is shown in Fig. 7·2.   Here a system
of beams is built along the column rows, and long-span, heavy, flat slabs

fill in the spaces between the beams, thus forming deep but large paneling. This type simplifies the formwork, and perhaps the reinforcing also. The slabs are reinforced in both directions so that the loads are carried by all the beams bounding a bay. The effects of heavy, concentrated, moving live loads are thus spread around excellently except when the load is close to one of the beams, in which case it has little effect upon the bending moment in the slab. These thick slabs may be used for fairly heavy loads, such as trucks, and for spans up to 20 ft. or

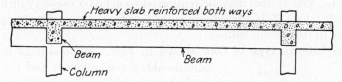

Fig. 7·2.   Reinforced-concrete floor with beams along column lines.

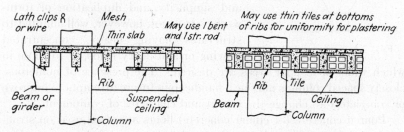

Fig. 7·3. "Tin-pan" floor slab.　　　　Fig. 7·4. Hollow-tile-and-concrete floor slab.

thereabouts without excessive deflections. They may be useful for short-span bridges and viaducts, for heavy truck aisles over basements, and for heavily loaded warehouses and factories. Both beams and slabs should be designed as continuous members over intermediate supports. Of course, making large holes through such slabs probably will be detrimental to their strength; however, small holes about 2 ft. square may be provided safely at the corners of the bays. Chopping large holes through and burning off the reinforcement of such a floor after it is built are things that make the designer figuratively tear his hair, although the safety factor used in conservative designing has been known to "hold the structure up" in some such cases.

One modification of the large, flat-slab idea is the "tin-pan" construction illustrated in Fig. 7·3. This is primarily a deep slab reinforced in one direction, and having part of the concrete omitted in order to save weight; it is basically a series of miniature T-beams poured on thin steel forms. Such a floor is intended for light loads and spans up to about 20 ft. Lateral distribution of concentrated loads will be improved by cross ribs. This type of floor may be made two-way with rectangular, intermittent recesses instead of long, inverted troughs. A hung ceiling attached to the bottoms of the T-beams will provide a flat lower surface when desired for use in offices and high-class buildings.

Hollow terra-cotta tiles, lightweight concrete, gypsum, and wood fiber and cement blocks may be used in a long-span slab as pictured in Fig. 7·4. The system may be reinforced to act as a one-way or a two-way slab. One of its advantages is the fact that plaster may be applied directly to its bottom surface.

The flat-slab type of floor shown in Figs. 7·4a and 7·22 is used

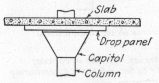

considerably for warehouses and for some multistory factories. It provides a maximum of vertical clearance, a flat ceiling, and simplicity and duplication of form-work. It is not, however, well adapted to structures having heavy, concentrated moving or stationary loads, or to those in

Fig. 7·4a.   Flat-slab floor.

which wide, open floor areas are desired. The presence of numerous, closely spaced columns may be a handicap in future attempts to improve or completely to change the layout and character of equipment.

Poured concrete (or cinder concrete) floors are often used on structural-steel framework. When the steel beams are left bare, as in Fig. 7·5, the structure is not really fireproof, but this arrangement provides lighter, cheaper construction than when the beams are encased as pictured in Fig. 7·6.

A few points to consider in the planning of concrete slabs on bare steel are the following, referring to Fig. 7·5:

1. Place the bottom of the slab flush with the lower surface of the top flange of the beam, as shown in Sketch (a). This clinches the steel and provides lateral support for the top flange. Sketch (b) shows how this simplifies formwork. However, special care should be used to keep all the beams flush-top.

2. When the beams cannot be at one level, the slab may be thickened in places, as pictured in Sketch (c), or the slab may be haunched downward, as in (d). In the latter, it is advisable to have some kind of mechanical anchor on top of the beam flange to clinch the concrete to it if the beam needs lateral support.

3. When adequate anchors, like those in Sketches (e), (f), and (g) are used, the combination will form composite beams. In these beams, the concrete assists in resisting compression, thereby stiffening and strengthening the member compared to the bare steel alone. Provision for the transmission of longitu-

dinal shear is essential. Sketch (h) shows a simple type of anchor that may be used when lateral steadying alone is desired.

4. When anchorage of any kind is used on top of steel beams, the designer must be careful to avoid having them ripped off, and having the anchors cause

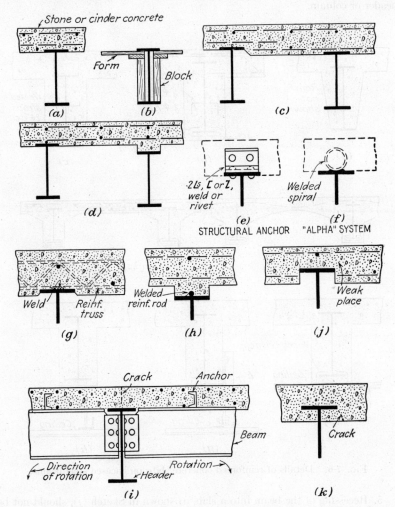

Fig. 7·5. Details of reinforced-concrete slabs on bare steel beams.

cracks in the slabs near the ends of the beams. With simply supported steel beams, an anchor may be used safely near the middle of a span, or even in the central third of the beam; when anchors are near the ends of the beams and when the slab runs continuously across the header, as shown in Sketch (i), deflection of the simply supported beams will almost inevitably cause the anchors to yield or the slab to crack, depending upon which is the weaker.   For truly composite beams, the slab should have a joint over the header, or else the steelwork and the slab should be made continuous over or through the supporting member, whether header or column.

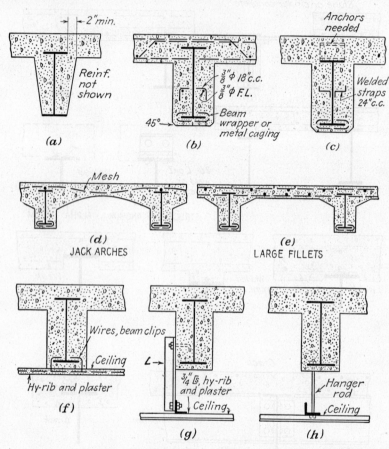

FIG. 7·6.   Details of reinforced-concrete slabs on encased steel beams.

5. Recessing of the beam into a slab, as shown in Sketch (*j*), should not be excessive because this weakens the shearing resistance of the slab.   It also decreases the ability of the slab to carry negative bending moments (tension on top) across the beam, and this tension should be provided for if cracks over the beam are to be avoided.   Filling in slivers of concrete as pictured in Sketch (*k*) has psychological effect only, and the extended pieces may break off and drop upon persons below.

Encasement of the steelwork of floors is illustrated in Fig. 7·6, about which the following comments are given:

1. Encasement of the web of the beam with the bottom flange bare, as pictured in Sketch (a), does not make truly fireproof construction; nevertheless the exposed steel will not heat up rapidly unless the fire is intense. The bare flange is useful for the attachment of hangers for pipes, conduits, and equipment.

2. The haunching should be about 2 in. wider on each side than the top flange of the beam in such an arrangement as (a) and (b). This allows room for getting the concrete past the edges of the slab forms and permits reactions from the loads on the slabs to bear down on the encasement and the bottom flange of the beam.

3. Any concrete encasement of the bottom flange should be tied on with small bent rods or by means of wire mesh, as illustrated in Sketch (b). Some form of anchors or through rods should also mechanically hold together the two halves of the encasement of a web.

4. Placing the top flange of a steel beam near the bottom of the concrete slab, as in (c), is less desirable than raising it nearer the top, as in (b). The latter facilitates concreting and has less tendency to break the slab away from the steel along the top flange.

5. Long, plain steel beams, encased as in Fig. 7·6, are likely to have the elongation of their bottom flanges cause the breaking of the bond between the steel and the concrete, thereby causing localized, noticeable cracks about 4 or 5 ft. apart in the latter. The author has designed long-span, encased, riveted, plate girders with cover plates and rivets almost the full length of the bottom flanges. These rivets provided enough mechanical bond to prevent large, localized cracks.

6. Encased steel beams may be designed as composite beams, provided the principles mentioned previously in connection with Fig. 7·5 affecting longitudinal shearing resistance are adhered to.

7. Curved lower surfaces of slabs may be used, as in Sketch (d), when the moments and shears from heavy loads require it, but the formwork is usually more expensive than for straight surfaces. Making large fillets for the same purposes, as pictured in Sketch (e), also increases the cost of forms.

8. The use of 45° chamfers at corners, as in Sketch (b), is almost necessary to avoid ragged edges and spalling of corners when the forms are removed.

9. When beamed ceilings are not desirable, hung ceilings may be suspended from the beams as shown in Sketches (f), (g), and (h). The hanger rods (or small structural shapes) should be so thick that corrosion will not endanger the safety of the ceiling.

10. Special problems arise when spandrel beams supporting walls are encased. Some possible arrangements are shown in Fig. 8·13.

7·3 Finish of Poured-concrete Floors. The finishing of the top of a concrete floor is a matter requiring excellent workmanship and the use of proper materials. What these are to be depends largely upon the use for which the floor is intended.

Finishing the floor with a steel trowel generally causes the surface to be so smooth that it is likely to be slippery. The mortar is also flushed to the top so that shrinkage may cause crazing—tiny, irregular, checkered cracking.

The use of a wooden float for finishing concrete floors generally produces a granular surface. Aluminum crystals or other durable grits may be worked into the top of the concrete to augment its nonskid qualities; this is especially useful in the case of stair treads.

Many special patented materials and methods of construction are used for the purpose of improving the nature and durability of the surface of concrete floors, and to adapt them to special uses. If any one of these were undoubtedly best for all purposes, the present keen competition between them could not exist because that one would be used almost universally. The author has specified and used many different surfacings, and he knows that he or anyone will meet criticism as soon as he tries to discuss this subject. However, the following points are mentioned for the reader to ponder:

1. A concrete floor may be monolithic. In that case, the surface must be finished within perhaps 2 to 6 hrs. after the concrete is placed, and no adjustment of level, grade, texture, marking, or jointing can be made subsequently. This is sometimes inconvenient, and the finished surface may be damaged as the result of later construction operations; at least it will need to be protected.

2. A floor may have a separate topping. In that case, the structural slab is roughly screeded to a surface about 1 in. below the desired finished one. When convenient, the top surfacing can be added and completed. This is an advantage when machinery or other equipment is to be placed on the floor and when the surface is to be made to meet various requirements of elevation, slope, and pattern. One should be sure that any topping added, after the shrinkage of setting has occurred in the main slab, will not crack because of its own subsequent shrinkage. He should also be satisfied that there will be sufficient bond to keep the topping from loosening and peeling off.

3. Various materials are used to harden floor surfaces. Some are chemicals that increase the density and waterproofness of the concrete; some are special aggregates and mixes to provide density and resistance to wear; others are at least partly metallic but are for the same purposes.

4. The repairing of a worn, rough, concrete-floor surface is difficult indeed. Therefore, careful planning to obtain the optimum service from a concrete floor is well worth while. When the floor is subjected to the grinding action of steel-tired wheels, the scraping of sliding objects, the spilling of acids, and excessive and rapidly changing variations of moisture and temperature, then special surfacings

are probably desirable.　An ordinary concrete surface is likely to disintegrate if subjected to such service conditions.

The top of a badly worn concrete slab may be chipped off so that a topping can be applied to resurface it.　This is usually a costly process and is likely to damage the floor slab seriously.　In some cases, a floor may be cleaned and slightly roughened for the application of an extra topping; this, however, is likely to cause difficulties incident to the raising of the floor's surface.　It is usually very difficult to make an ordinary portland-cement mortar topping stick to an old concrete floor; some mixtures of asphaltic[1] or other binding materials may be best, but one should be sure that bituminous materials will neither soften nor dry out.　No new topping should be applied until the old floor has been cleaned with great care.

When floor slabs needing repair are on the ground, it is probably cheaper to break them up and to replace them completely.　This procedure is generally impracticable when the floors are self-supporting, monolithic, reinforced-concrete construction, and when they are carried on encased structural-steel framework. Hence, the original design and construction must be as nearly perfect for the required service as one can make it, if subsequent maintenance costs are to be minimized.

5. Painting of concrete floors with ordinary oil paints is likely to cause them to be slippery, and the durability of the coating may be very unsatisfactory. One should consult the manufacturers regarding special paints that are more serviceable.

6. Covering of structural concrete with renewable surfacings of the following materials may be helpful:

a. Wooden blocks set in mortar or on a sand cushion provide a fairly resilient surface that is advantageous around machinery, and in places where workmen must stand continually.

b. Paving bricks set in mortar are useful when there is considerable vehicular traffic to be borne.

c. Tiles of various types are both attractive and serviceable in offices, washrooms, and locker rooms.　Terrazzo coverings are also very suitable for such service.

d. Asphaltic materials are useful when certain chemicals are frequently spattered or dripped upon a floor.

e. Linoleum cemented to the concrete is excellent for use in offices, corridors, and places subjected to pedestrian traffic.　It should not, however, be used on floors that are laid on the ground where dampness may cause it to loosen or disintegrate.

f. Hardwood floors attached to sleepers embedded in the floor or in a cinder-concrete fill over it are useful in offices and in special cases where a wooden surface is desirable.　The wood, however, should be supported continuously, and it should be nailed down thoroughly.

g. Steel gratings may be embedded in concrete in order to provide a metallic

[1] Stone-hard is one such commercial product.

wearing surface. The concrete, however, may become pitted between the bars so that the floor is rough and noisy, and parts of the floor not polished by traffic may become rusty.

h. A lightweight concrete with a mortar or other suitable topping placed on top of the main slab may be advantageous when conduits and other small utility accessories are to be covered up.

7. Whatever surfacing is used should have the qualities of compressive strength so that it will not become dented, resistance to abrasion so that it will not wear off, toughness so that it will not shatter under impact, waterproofness to prevent the seepage of water, chemical stability so that it will not disintegrate, attractive appearance so that it is not objectionable to the occupants of the structure, and a quality of surface that is safe for the intended use. In one plant that was investigated recently, the concrete floors near the elevators were found to have been worn down at least an inch by reels of wire that were rolled over them.

In a three-story factory 450 ft. long, built at least 30 years ago, the floors were designed for a light live load. Now the owner wishes to install new and heavier equipment. The weakness of the floor has proved to be an almost insurmountable barrier to his plans, and measures to reinforce it are either ineffective or altogether too costly. Thus, the owner has a large building that is no longer useful. This illustrates how important it is to make the floors of a structure adequate for any probable service, not merely for the original purpose alone.

7·4 Lightweight Concrete Floors. Ordinary portland-cement concrete with natural sand and gravel or crushed stones as aggregates is heavy—about 150 lb. per cu. ft., including the reinforcement. Therefore, engineers have devised means of securing almost the same serviceability by the use of lighter construction. A few of the materials that can be used with portland cement for the making of lightweight monolithic floors are the following:

1. Lightweight aggregates such as cinders, Haydite, and burned clay products yielding concretes that weigh approximately 100 to 120 lb. per cu. ft.

2. Chemicals that cause the set concrete to have a very porous structure; *e.g.*, Aircrete weighing from about 60 to 100 lb. per cu. ft.

As a general practice, these lightweight concretes are used in the floors of steel-frame buildings rather than in those of reinforced-concrete construction. In the former case, the saving of steel in tall, long-span buildings may be considerable; in the latter, the need for high strength in the framework may necessitate the use of stone concrete throughout, and it may be too troublesome to try to make some parts of one kind of concrete and others of another quality when the construction is to be monolithic. There may be conditions where the spans are short and the loads are small enough to permit the use of precast-concrete floor joists or beams with the lightweight concrete slab poured on top of the joists after their erection.

These lightweight concrete floors are generally covered with some type of masonry topping, wooden surfacing, linoleum, or other suitable wearing material.

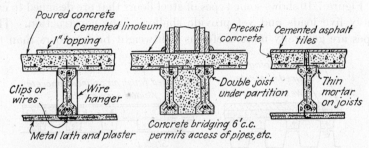

FIG. 7·7. Precast-concrete joists for fireproof floors.

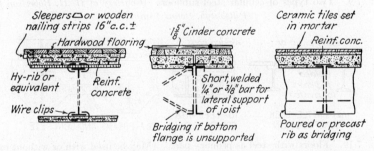

FIG. 7·8. Some examples of steel-bar joists and concrete floors.

7·5   Steel Floors.   There are several types of steel floors, and floors with steel parts to carry the loads, where concrete or some other material serves as a filler to close up the spaces and to form a suitable surface.

Bare steel plates are frequently useful for platforms, floors that are subjected to the wear of metallic wheels, floors that are heated severely or subjected to the spatter of molten materials, parts of floors that may have to be dismantled and reerected frequently, and for the flooring on hatch covers that must be strong and light in order to facilitate handling them. Checkered floor plates are rolled with various patterns, the purpose being to secure a nonskid surface. This is an important feature because flat steel is slippery when wet or greasy.

Steel gratings are used frequently instead of solid plates because, for the same weight of steel per square foot, the former are stronger and stiffer. However, the designer should not forget that dirt and small objects dropping through the openings of the grating may be objectionable or even hazardous; furthermore, the passage of smoke, gases, and hot air through them may be disadvantageous. Closing the openings in gratings by filling them flush with concrete or mortar is seldom satisfactory because the latter may eventually drop out unless the grating provides a mechanical lock for the masonry.

Figure 7·10 shows some types of steel floors that are designed to carry heavy live loads and yet provide shallow, light construction. These types are generally more useful as lightweight bridge floors than they

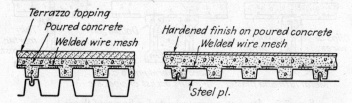

FIG. 7·9. Two types of cellular steel subfloor. (*Courtesy of H. H. Robertson Co., Pittsburgh, Pennsylvania.*)

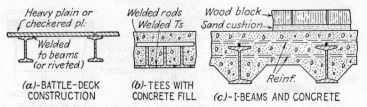

FIG. 7·10. Floors with steel as primary part. (May be used with or without extra wearing surface.)

are as working floors in industrial plants because they are relatively costly per square foot of floor area. On the other hand, Fig. 7·9 illustrates some types of steel floor construction that are designed especially for industrial purposes. A hung ceiling with Vermiculite plaster may be used for fire protection.

The combinations of structural floors and finished surfacings shown in Figs. 7·7 to 7·13 have been selected to illustrate a wide variety of each. Naturally, many other combinations can and should be used when they best suit one's purposes.

7·6 Wooden Floors. For very light manufacturing and for offices, the ordinary wooden-joist floor may be desirable. The joists may be supported on brick walls, timber framing, wooden beams, or even steel beams, but, in any case, the spans are relatively short and the load-carrying capacity is small. It is also possible, and sometimes feasible, to use welded bar joists or precast-concrete ones instead of timber, thereby making a floor that is less combustible than an all-wood one, although these members do not render the structure fireproof. However, in such cases, special care should be exercised to secure positive attachment between the wooden flooring and the joists. In most

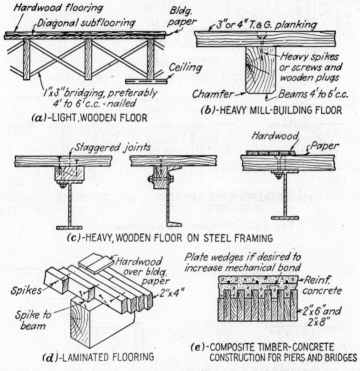

Fig. 7·11.   Some examples of wooden floors.

instances, wooden floors are used for industrial purposes when the structures are the heavy, mill-building type of timber framing, and they are very serviceable.

For some steel-frame, multistory factories, the use of heavy tongued-and-grooved planking for floors may be advantageous, or the flooring may be laminated. These are illustrated in Fig. 7·11. Such floors are relatively light, fire-resistant, and strong. Another great advantage is the fact that equipment may be shifted easily and attached at almost any point, conduits and piping may be rearranged, holes may be cut when necessary, and, in short, the flooring may be adapted to almost

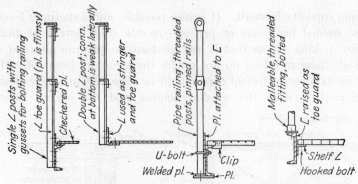

(a)-CHECKERED PLATES AND GRATING USED FOR PLATFORMS

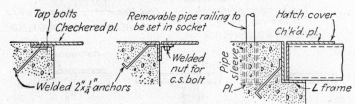

(b)-CHECKERED PLATES SUPPORTED   (c)-HATCH DETAILS AND RAILING
ON CONCRETE   FOR USE WHEN HATCH IS OPEN

Fig. 7·12.   Platforms and miscellaneous details.

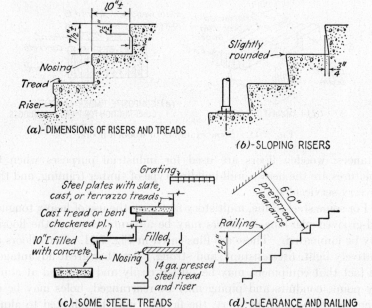

(a)-DIMENSIONS OF RISERS AND TREADS

(b)-SLOPING RISERS

(c)-SOME STEEL TREADS   (d)-CLEARANCE AND RAILING

Fig. 7·13.   Some information about stairs.

any reasonable alterations without the difficulties and the cost that such changes entail when they must be made in a concrete floor.

Any wooden floors that are not over a basement should have adequate provision for ventilation to avoid their decay.   A series of screened openings with a total area of about one-tenth the perimeter of the floor times one may be suitable for ventilating floors not over 40 ft. wide; for more extensive floors, the openings should be larger.   Of course, in cold climates such floors should be insulated properly.

7·7   Floors Laid Directly upon the Ground.   Because of the rotting of wood and the rusting of bare steel, floors laid directly upon the ground are generally made of concrete; at least, the base slab is so

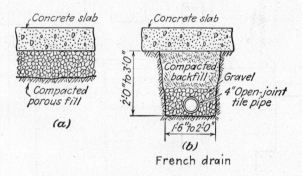

Fɪɢ. 7·14.   Underground drainage.

made.   Building such floors requires far more than merely dumping some concrete on the ground and then finishing off the top.

Drainage of the soil under the slab is generally one of the first essentials.   A 6- to 12-in. layer of compacted cinders, gravel, or coarse sand directly under the concrete, as shown in Fig. 7·14(a), or at some lower level, is generally desirable.   This prevents capillary action from drawing moisture up close to the concrete.   This is especially helpful in cases where freezing temperatures might otherwise cause the formation of ice lenses under the floor, thereby making the latter heave, crack, or settle.   However, this porous material is useless if the ground water cannot drain away easily because the layer otherwise serves as a sump to collect water, instead of disposing of it.

French drains, as pictured in Fig. 7·14(b), are usually necessary whenever the ground is low or the soil is clay, hardpan, or other relatively impermeable material.   A few feet of coarse sand or gravel fill will serve the same purpose, provided the water has a sufficiently low point into which it can drain.

A system of French drains should be planned so as to intercept the flow of ground water at the edges of a floor, or even outside the foundations. The piping should be connected to one or more points of discharge, using a slope of at least 0.25 to 0.50 per cent. For large areas of wet soils, drains may be needed in rows about 25 to 50 ft. apart. A herringbone pattern with a main line and laterals may be suitable. In

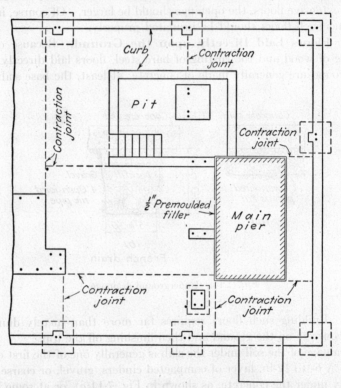

FIG. 7·15.   Floor and foundations at a lime-burning plant.

any case, the backfill in the trenches, and any filled ground under the floor, should be compacted thoroughly in order to avoid harmful local settlement.

Floors of basements, pits, and trenches that are necessarily below the ground-water level at some or all times will almost inevitably leak unless they are waterproofed adequately. This subject will be discussed more fully in Chap. 13, but, for floors alone, the reader is cautioned to avoid possible heaving caused by the water pressure underneath a floor.

Shrinkage is a matter to consider when concrete floors of large area poured on the ground are being planned. The deformation may be only about ¼ to ½ in. in 100 ft., but this can cause objectionable cracking. Some ways to avoid harmful cracks are the following:

1. Divide the floor into blocks or strips which can be poured alternately, letting the first pours attain much of their shrinkage by setting a few days before pouring the intervening sections. Further shrinkage is likely to open up the junctions (construction joints), but probably no one will see it. Finishing these alternate sections to proper level and grade may be difficult because they cannot be lined up easily.

2. Pour the floor monolithically, then, before it has reached its final set, cut it into blocks by means of special tools which will form dummy joints or planes

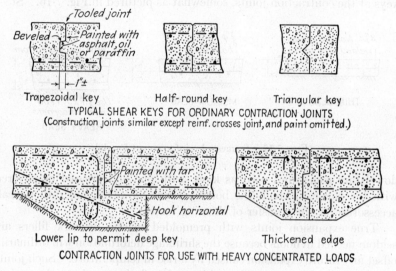

Trapezoidal key   Half-round key   Triangular key

TYPICAL SHEAR KEYS FOR ORDINARY CONTRACTION JOINTS
(Construction joints similar except reinf. crosses joint, and paint omitted.)

Lower lip to permit deep key   Thickened edge

CONTRACTION JOINTS FOR USE WITH HEAVY CONCENTRATED LOADS

Fig. 7·16. Shear keys in slabs.

of weakness. It is to be hoped that the shrinkage cracking will occur along these joints. The coarse aggregate may make this tooling difficult, and the reinforcement may prevent the desired localization of the cracks.

3. Pour one strip or block of floor, then strip the edge forms the next day; paint the edge with cutback asphalt, oil, or any material that will break the bond of concrete placed against it; pour the adjoining floor sections; and complete the remainder similarly.

4. Reinforce the slab sufficiently to have the shrinkage taken up in "unnoticed" hair-cracks. This may be accomplished if the area of the rods in any one direction is at least 0.25 per cent of the normal cross section of the slab.

When planning the jointing system of a concrete floor placed on the ground, remember that sections more than 20 to 40 ft. long may develop intermediate cracks. When a floor area is cut up by pits, pilasters on foundations, intermediate column footings, miscellaneous trenches, or machinery foundations, the joints should be planned so that they will be located at bootlenecks and other major changes of section where cracking is likely to occur. One example of such planning is shown in Fig. 7·15. Reinforcement extending through construction joints interferes with shrinkage deformation at the joints. If this steel is decreased to about 50 per cent of the main reinforcement, the former will probably yield, although there is a question as to the advisability of having rods pass through the joint.

Floors carrying heavy electric or motor trucks should have shear keys at the contraction joints, somewhat as pictured in Fig. 7·16. Steel

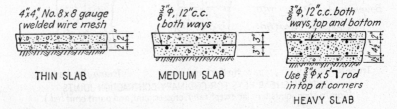

FIG. 7·17. Suggested reinforcement for slabs.

dowels are sometimes used as keys, with one end greased or covered with tar paper to break the bond. These, however, are rather weak accessories for the transfer of shearing forces.

True expansion joints with premolded mastic or cork fillers are seldom needed in floors because the shrinkage deformation will ordinarily offset any future expansion caused by a rise in temperature. Such joints are useful, however, around machinery foundations and at other points where it is desirable to isolate the floor from the other concrete.

An unreinforced-concrete floor will probably crack sooner or later. Heavy wire mesh and light reinforcement are useful for resisting shrinkage as well as for carrying loads. Figure 7·17 presents some suggestions for the reinforcement of these concrete floors. A slab not over 6 in. deep is too thin for the use of two layers of reinforcement. If one layer is used alone, should it be near the bottom or the top? If the former, the slab may crack on top because of negative bending moments over hard spots in the subgrade that do not settle as much as adjacent areas; if the latter, the slab is not strong in distributing wheel concentrations, hence tensile cracks may occur at the bottom but, fortunately, no one will see them unless the concrete is broken clear through. Some engineers place a layer of reinforcement in the middle of these thin floors as a sort of compromise, intending that the concrete will have sufficient bending resistance in either direction.

Should these floor slabs be supported on foundation walls, column piers, and machinery foundations, or should they be isolated therefrom? The following points should be considered in this matter:

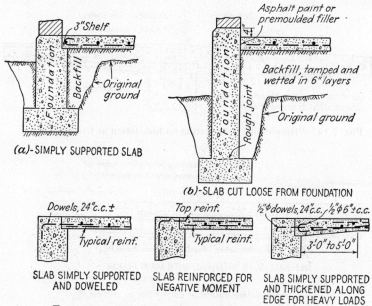

Fig. 7·18. Junctions of concrete floors and foundations.

1. If a floor is supported on shelves as shown in Fig. 7·18(a), there is no danger that the soil will cause the slab to settle with respect to the adjacent main structure.

2. When the edge of a slab is supported, settlement of the fill or ground under it may cause the slab to crack unless it is adequately reinforced.

3. Placing a floor on shelves, and doweling it into the foundation walls, helps the latter to resist overturning moments.

4. Raising the main foundations about 4 in., as shown in Fig. 7·18(b), and cutting a floor loose from the heavy construction are useful when the floor must be placed on fill and when it may settle a little, because the settlement is not noticed, except at doorways and similar points.

5. When a slab rests on shelves, there is a question as to how to reinforce it for local loads because the distribution of these loads between the shelf and the soil is uncertain.

6. In some cases, such as low platforms and inaccessible spaces, it may be economical to backfill the space, then to pour the slab on the fill in lieu of forms,

even though the span of the slab is short and its edges are supported upon walls. Here the slab should be reinforced to act as a self-supporting one.

Trucks entering into buildings cause especially severe stresses in the floor slabs at the doorways. It is frequently desirable to use "barn-door" panels at these points. As shown in Fig. 7·19, these panels are heavily

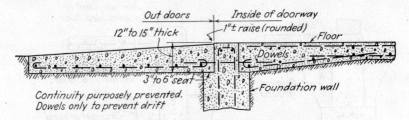

FIG. 7·19.   "Barn-door" slabs resting on foundation at truck doorway.

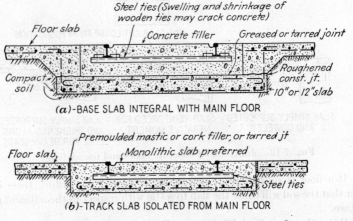

FIG. 7·20.   Details of railroad tracks in concrete floors.

reinforced slabs designed to carry the truck loads from the foundation wall to the main ground area beyond the wall. If the foundation wall does not extend under the doorway, frost action may heave the pavement.

Some people ask if it is satisfactory to pour a new concrete floor directly upon the top of an old, broken one. If this is done, the new slab is likely to develop cracks at the same points as those already existing in the underlying floor. Heavy reinforcement will help to avoid this, but soft soil, water, and frost (if freezing occurs) may still cause trouble. Shrinkage joints in the new floor will almost certainly be ineffective unless the new slab is isolated from the old one by means of tar paper or a substantial, intervening layer of sand.

When floors are, for all practical purposes, extended out of doors to form paved areaways, the conditions become far more severe than those existing under shelter. Then it is important to provide for surface drainage as well as for ground water, to design the pavement to resist weather as well as loads, and to provide numerous expansion joints if the plant is in a region of large and rapid variations of moisture and temperature.

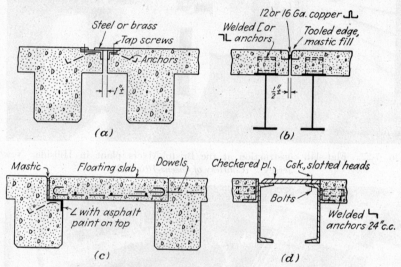

FIG. 7·21.   Some details of expansion joints in concrete floors.

In some cases, floors laid directly on the ground are made with asphaltic materials, or even of soil stabilized with cement, somewhat as is done in the case of highway pavements. These, however, are not classed as high-type floors, although they may be exceedingly useful.

7·8 Expansion Joints. When expansion joints are provided through the roof and framing of a multistory building, they must be used in the floors, too. If they are not, nature will soon provide them in the form of cracks, unless the floors can stop the functioning of the joints. The details to be used vary with the type of floor, and the locations of the joints should be planned so that they serve their purpose without setting up objectionable shearing stresses in the structure.

Complete and independent supports for adjacent moving portions may be most desirable; some details of such joints are shown in Figs. 7·21(a) and (b). On the other hand, when there are heavy live loads

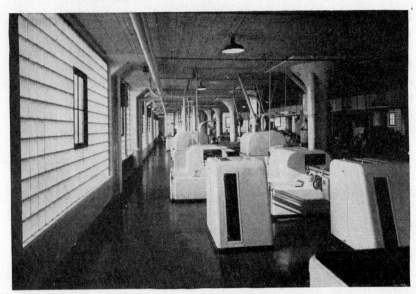

FIG. 7·22.   Flat-slab construction at the Bristol-Myers plant in Hillside, New Jersey.   (*Courtesy of Owens-Illinois.*)

FIG. 7·23.   An installation of Irving subway grating and "vizabledg safsteps" in a power plant.   Notice the use of pipe handrailing.   (*Courtesy of Irving Subway Grating Co., Inc.*)

moving across an expansion joint, the relative deflections of the beams may, if the spans are long, cause a shock against the floor when the wheels hit the unloaded portion.   Since any transfer of shearing forces between the beams requires strong, expensive details, it may be advisable to use some such devices as those pictured in Figs. 7·21(c) and (d).

Adjacent portions of the floor at an expansion joint may be carried upon one common support if the flooring at one side can slide upon this member.   However, any sliding joints are likely to develop considerable frictional resistance, and reinforcement should be provided to resist the resultant tension.   Such joints are likely to clog up, too, so that pressures cause spalling of the concrete.   As a general rule, the more simple the construction and the more positively it can work, the better will be its service.

Chapter 8

WALLS AND PARTITIONS

8·1 General Features to Be Considered. Some important factors that influence the selection of the materials and construction of walls for buildings are the following:

1. *Architectural Appearance.* Although the shape of an industrial building may affect its aesthetic value considerably, the exterior walls are generally the features that determine whether or not its appearance is pleasing. Of course, along with the texture, color, and pattern of the exterior surface of the wall material must be included the pilasters, paneling, and any other elements that contribute to the total effect of the ensemble. For example, a high, long, blank wall almost certainly will be unattractive regardless of the nature of the surface of the material of which it is made. Shadow lines, vertical and horizontal offsets, changes in color and texture, arrangement of windows, and the details of the trim are some means whereby an architect may skillfully enhance the appearance of a structure. Architectural elevations and perspective drawings are extremely useful in helping one to determine and to judge what are the best answers to these problems.

2. *Cost.* The cost of the material used for the solid portions of the exterior walls is usually a relatively small part of the total cost of a building; the difference in cost of one desirable material over that of a less desirable one is still less important. Nevertheless, the aesthetic effect produced by the structure is permanent and will continue long after any reduction of initial expenditure is forgotten. On the other hand, 12-in. brick walls naturally cost more than corrugated metal or transite coverings. The engineer should consider all important features, then make his choice upon the basis of value received, both real and intangible.

3. *Suitability.* Associated with these matters of appearance and cost should be that of the general suitability of the wall material for the structure in which it is to be used, and that of its harmony with neighboring structures. It is difficult to define the former quality because of the varying uses to which structures may be put, the climate of the region, the availability of materials, insulating properties, and the different kinds of construction that may be desirable and practicable. For instance, a 60- by 200-ft. building with walls of neat yellow face brick may appear out of place among buildings with corrugated metal siding, not because the new building of itself is unsightly but because it emphasizes

146

the difference between the new and the old. It is even more self-evident that a building with corrugated, galvanized metal siding may appear incongruous when set among others having attractive walls of red bricks, concrete, or stucco.

4. *Durability.* Of itself, a wall covering need not last longer than the rest of the structure, or the purpose for which the structure is built. The former situation seldom arises except in the case of buildings with combustible frames and roofs but with fireproof walls; in general, the durability and weather-resisting qualities of the walls and roof determine the useful life of the building. The latter—the purpose for which a structure is built—has a way of changing as time goes by. Many a "temporary" structure erected years ago is still functioning, or its owner wishes that it would continue to do so. Hence the use of cheap, temporary wall coverings is likely to prove costly in the long run on account of maintenance charges and replacement in order to continue the building in unintended service. Good, durable materials are usually worth their cost.

5. *Strength.* Aside from wall-bearing structures and those erected in regions that are subjected to earthquakes, the strength of wall materials is seldom critical unless the structural supports are improperly designed, or the walls are too thin and tall. Resistance to wind should be provided for, and buckling of thin walls under their own weight should be prevented. It is the structural frame rather than the wall itself that should generally be relied upon to hold a thin, flimsy wall in place.

6. *Weight.* The weight of a wall may be especially worthy of consideration when continuous windows are used, because the lintels and any spandrel beams must carry to the columns all the wall loads supported by these members. Heavy brick or masonry walls may therefore add considerably to the cost of the framing. Even in other cases, lightness is often advantageous.

7. *Resistance to Fire.* Combustible materials, such as wood, may be well adapted to use as walls except for the hazard of fire; incombustible materials like steel and transite may be fire-resistant although not truly fireproof. The inherent dangers and the risks involved should be studied in each case before anyone makes his selection of the material to be used. The taking of chances may be justified or even necessary in some cases, but the individual who makes the decision should be willing and able to carry the responsibility. The statement, "I'm sorry," does not go far in the compensation for loss of life and property.

It is difficult for one to illustrate and compare all—or even nearly all—possible types of wall construction. In this chapter the endeavor is to give the reader considerable information by showing several common types of wall construction used in industrial buildings, together with illustrations of suitable structural framing and details. This is done largely by means of drawings. By studying these illustrations, the reader can see how the type of wall construction adopted will be one of the starting points for the planning of the structural frame of a building. The sequence of the types of wall discussed in this chapter is based largely upon their light weight rather than upon their relative desirability.

Insulation of roofs, considered in Chap. 6, is also important in wall construction.   The principles previously explained are not repeated here but some of their applications and illustrations of possible arrangements are given.

A large amount of development and experimental work is being carried on with the object of securing lighter, cheaper, and better walls than those that have hitherto been in common use.   These will be especially important in tall, multistory buildings; lightness alone is not so important in factory buildings.   Even in the case of industrial structures, the use of prefabricated panels may bring about considerable changes in one's ideas of suitable construction.   With the cost of labor so high, there will be great incentives to encourage inventors and manufacturers to develop and produce new procedures and new materials. However, it is inadvisable to attempt to illustrate here many of these possible developments.

8·2 Corrugated Metal and Transite.   As a lightweight covering for walls, corrugated metal and corrugated transite may be used.   It is possible to utilize either of these materials, especially transite, in the form of flat sheets, but, if they are thin, they should be fastened to some type of sheathing or to closely spaced supports.   If this is not done, the thin metal particularly will bulge, bow in, vibrate in the wind, and be generally weak and unsatisfactory.   The advantage of corrugating the sheets is the attainment of considerable stiffness and strength for the amount of material used.   The corrugations may differ in size and detail, whereas the sheets in all cases can be applied as panels or overgrown shingles, generally having the corrugations running vertically.   The spacing of the horizontal supporting members will depend upon the gauge of the material, the strength of the sheets as vertical beams, the locations of sills and lintels of windows and of the tops of doors, the lengths of sheets that can be obtained and handled, the positions of special members such as eave struts and some horizontal bracing, and the logical subdivision of limited wall areas into panels.

The metallic sheets may be made of plain steel, galvanized or tinned steel, steel coated with asphalt and asbestos or similar protective coverings, copper, and aluminum.   The transite is primarily a pressed mixture of portland cement and asbestos.   It is heavier and more brittle than the metallic coverings but is generally more durable than the corrodible metals, and it has more insulating value than metals possessing large conductivity.

Some methods of attachment of these corrugated sheets are illustrated in Fig. 8·1; others may be equally suitable.   Some of the principles to be considered in the planning of a structure with corrugated siding are the following:

1. Arrange the details so that the siding will shed water. This may require special flashing or other details at eaves, gables, doors, windows, and foundations. Some illustrations are found in Fig. 8·2.

2. Place horizontal splices at the supporting members—girts, struts, etc. Generally these splices should lap about 4 in.

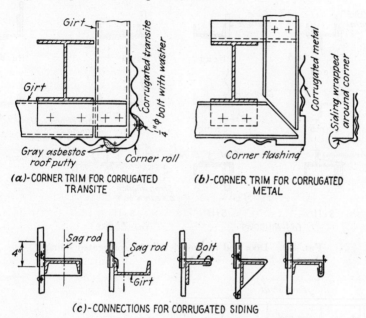

(a)-CORNER TRIM FOR CORRUGATED
TRANSITE

(b)-CORNER TRIM FOR CORRUGATED
METAL

(c)-CONNECTIONS FOR CORRUGATED SIDING

Fig. 8·1. Some details of corrugated siding.

3. Make vertical splices so that they lap properly; 1½ corrugations may be sufficient.

4. Connect, or "stitch," all sheets at splices and elsewhere closely enough to avoid any separation of sheets that may cause leakage of water blown by the wind, or objectionable draftiness. Special premolded metallic or asphaltic sealing strips are manufactured to close up openings where corrugated sheets terminate against plain surfaces.

5. The bottoms of sheets adjoining foundations should generally be held by a girt about 1 ft. above the foundation because it is difficult to attach the corrugated materials to concrete and masonry. It is inadvisable to seal the siding into a slot in the foundation, because of the likelihood of the corrosion of metal or the cracking of transite. It is often desirable to have a slight curb along the top of a foundation to help keep wash water and dirt away from the siding.

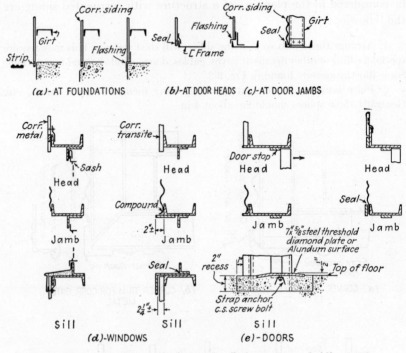

(a)-AT FOUNDATIONS   *(b)*-AT DOOR HEADS *(c)*-AT DOOR JAMBS

(d)-WINDOWS   *(e)*-DOORS

FIG. 8·2.   Door and window details for corrugated siding.

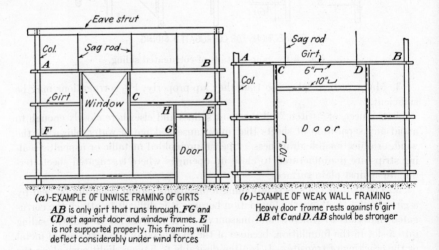

(a)-EXAMPLE OF UNWISE FRAMING OF GIRTS

AB is only girt that runs through. *FG* and
CD act against door and window frames. *E*
is not supported properly. This framing will
deflect considerably under wind forces

(b)-EXAMPLE OF WEAK WALL FRAMING

Heavy door frame rests against 6"girt
AB at *C* and *D*. *AB* should be stronger

FIG. 8·3.   Wall framing for corrugated siding.   Careful planning is essential.

6. Uniformity of pattern produced by splices is desirable if a patchy effect is to be avoided.

7. The trim or flashing at corners, windows, and doors should be such that the completed structure has a neat, workmanlike appearance. If the windows and doors look like missing sheets with glass and sash in their stead, the structure may be definitely unattractive. If the sashes and doors are practically flush with the siding, the structure may look walleyed, whereas recessing of these parts may produce shadow lines that add much to improve the appearance.

FIG. 8·4. A small pump house with corrugated siding. Although small, this structure illustrates many of the details of such construction. (*Courtesy of the Phelps Dodge Corp.*)

8. The attachments of the siding should be such that they are accessible for the removal and replacement of the sheets without tearing other parts to pieces, should this replacement become necessary. Thus, brickwork, sheathing, plaster, and insulation should not be constructed inside the completed siding without considering this feature. Wooden sheathing, plywood, and suitable insulating boards may be attached outside the girts by fastening them to nailing strips; then the corrugated siding may be nailed to them.

Of course, metallic siding—and sometimes transite, too—may cause objectionable radiation of heat in summer and loss of heat in winter. Although not so serious as in the case of roofs, these walls may still need insulation. When climatic conditions are severe, however, this may justify further study of the whole problem of the best materials and construction for the given case.

Walls made of such units as corrugated sheets have considerable adjustability. For example, in a large mill building with heavy cranes, the deformations and vibrations of the structural framework might crack a rigid wall covering, whereas the joints between the sheets, and the springing of the corrugated material usually permit these small motions to occur without harm.

Fig. 8·5. This structure illustrates the use of corrugated transite siding on a terminal building of the Pacific Intermountain Express. (*Courtesy of Johns-Manville.*)

Pressed steel and aluminum panels of various types are also suitable for wall coverings. These are mostly troughed or boxed sections that can be used with or without insulation. Their installation is somewhat similar to that of corrugated metal, although attachment by direct bolting and by welding may be used in some cases.

8·3 Wooden Walls. Wooden sheathing may be used under metallic coverings, asphaltic papers and shingles, asbestos-cement shingles, and stucco but, aside from the last, such construction is seldom used for the walls of industrial plants. Such sheathing is often used, however, as a covering or as a base for one of the various types of wooden surfacings when conditions of size, use, cost, and available materials make it desirable.   The sheathing may be attached to steel framework by means of bolts or nailing strips, but it is more likely to be used when the main structure itself is made of wood.

Some of the ordinary types of wooden sidings are shown in Fig. 8·6. For tightness, insulation, and strength, it is desirable to place the covering over tongued-and-grooved sheathing placed diagonally at 45°.   It is also generally desirable to place a layer of tough, fibrous, waterproofed paper or electrolytic copper foil or aluminum foil on the sheathing before the siding is applied.   The maximum tightness is secured if the ends and edges of these sheets are lapped and sealed with waterproof glue or special cement.

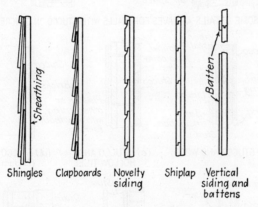

Shingles   Clapboards   Novelty   Shiplap   Vertical
                          siding   siding and
                                                battens

Fig. 8·6.   Some types of wooden siding.

When the inner surface of the sheathing is permanently exposed to view, the question of appearance may make it desirable to place the sheathing vertically or horizontally, with suitable diagonal bracing members.   For offices and structures in which smooth, neat walls are desired, the inner surfacing may consist of metal lath and plaster, wood, plywood, or specially prepared materials manufactured for such purposes.

8·4 Stuccoed Walls.   As used here, the word *stucco* denotes a mortar composed of sand, portland cement, a little lime, and water, all applied as a sort of plaster.   This is in contrast to *gunite*, which is a portland-cement mortar applied by means of a pneumatic gun.   Both materials may be used for linings and coverings if desired, but stucco is by far the cheaper and the more common.

A very rich mix is likely to have more shrinkage cracks than a leaner one, and the stucco itself seldom needs to act as more than a coating that does not carry loads.

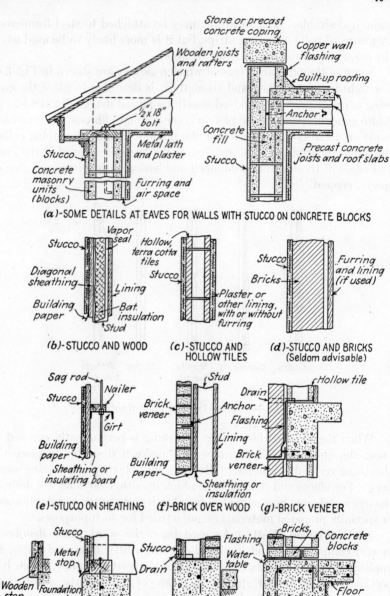

(a)-SOME DETAILS AT EAVES FOR WALLS WITH STUCCO ON CONCRETE BLOCKS

(b)-STUCCO AND WOOD   (c)-STUCCO AND HOLLOW TILES   (d)-STUCCO AND BRICKS (Seldom advisable)

(e)-STUCCO ON SHEATHING   (f)-BRICK OVER WOOD   (g)-BRICK VENEER

(h)-SOME DETAILS OF WALLS AT TOP OF FOUNDATIONS

FIG. 8·7.   Walls with coverings of stucco and brick veneer.

Stucco may be used as an exterior wall surfacing in combination with various materials. Some illustrations of such construction are the following, most of which are pictured in Fig. 8·7:

1. A stucco surfacing over wooden sheathing as in Sketch (b). A strong, fibrous, waterproof paper or membrane of some type is desirable over the sheathing; all its joints should be lapped and cemented if it is to be weatherproof. A galvanized welded-wire mesh, lapped at joints and securely fastened at frequent intervals, is essential. This reinforcement should be set out from the backing sufficiently to ensure its complete embedment in the stucco, otherwise it may eventually corrode seriously. Bat insulation may or may not be used, depending upon climatic conditions.

2. A stucco surfacing on some type of insulation board. This construction should be similar to that with wooden sheathing.

3. A stucco surfacing on hollow tiles as in Sketch (c). This may be applied directly to the tiles if the bond is adequate. In wet, cold climates, mesh reinforcement in the stucco may still be beneficial; and the problem of leakage may need special attention.

4. A stucco surfacing on brickwork as in Sketch (d). This construction is similar to that used in the case of hollow-tile walls, but the covering of good brick construction with still another surfacing seems to be wasteful.

5. A stucco surfacing with heavy mesh on sheathing or insulation attached to steel girts as in Sketch (e). This forms a diaphragm which should span from girt to girt and be supported thereby. Of course, this construction should be used alone only in mild, dry climates; even then, its use is not recommended because of the flexibility of the framework, and the probability of cracking the stucco. Stucco should be placed with a backing of some kind, even if the latter is temporary; otherwise the work is difficult, and the reinforcement is not covered properly to resist corrosion.

When planning stuccoed walls, one should remember that stucco is a hard, brittle material; it shrinks during setting; it expands with a rise of temperature; and it contracts when chilled. Therefore, if it is applied to a framework and sheathing that deform excessively or unequally with respect to itself, the stucco is very likely to crack severely.

It is important to make the junction of stucco with window and door frames, corner trim, eaves, and gables so that water cannot leak behind the stucco. Calking the junction at the sides and flashing over the tops of door and window frames may be advisable. It is also essential to make sure that water will not get through the stucco where it meets the foundation.

Stucco may be painted with special materials; it may also—and more advisably—be tinted by the addition of coloring matter in the mortar itself, or by the application of a colored cement wash. Ordinary oil paints should not be applied unless they are recommended and guaranteed by the manufacturer.

8·5 Hollow-tile Walls. Walls made of hollow tiles are strongest if made with the cells of the tiles placed vertically, and the joints well mortared. If built in this way, they are generally strong enough for ordinary curtain-wall construction. They should not be used as bearing

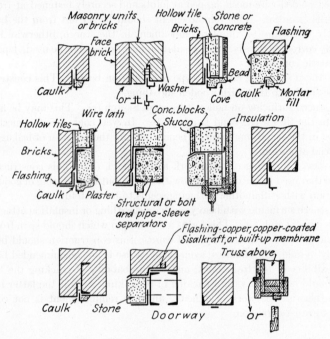

FIG. 8·8. Some examples of lintels.

walls unless the cells are filled with concrete, in which case the advantage of their light weight and the insulating value of the air spaces are lost. Many tiles will still be strong enough if placed with the cells horizontally, but, when the holes are vertical, they help greatly in conducting any leakage or condensation water down to exterior outlets that should be located at the bottom of the wall or at the floor line.

Because of appearance, as well as weathering, a stuccoed covering— or a veneer of brickwork mechanically anchored—is usually applied on the exterior surface of a hollow-tile wall; for aesthetic reasons plaster, wood, ceramic tiles, or some specially prepared lining should be used on the inside. Some suggested construction is shown in several of the accompanying illustrations.

8·6   Walls of Bricks and Concrete-masonry Units.   In many cases, bricks—and concrete blocks, too—are very satisfactory for use in the construction of walls.   They are strong, durable, prefabricated units that can be erected easily.   Bricks generally present a pleasing appearance and can be obtained with various qualities, colors, and textures. On the other hand, they are heavy.

The quality of the mortar and the excellence of the workmanship used in its construction are likely to control the strength, waterproofness,

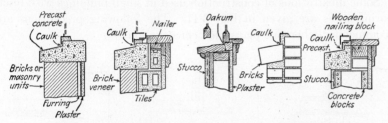

Fig. 8·9.   Details of some construction of window sills.

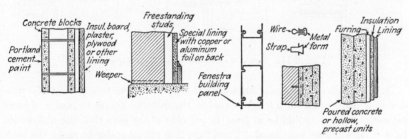

Fig. 8·10.   Some miscellaneous types of wall construction.

and durability of a brick wall.   The bricks themselves are generally manufactured under well-supervised and -controlled conditions; this should, but may not, be equally applicable in the case of the field work.

Brickwork should be constructed with completely filled joints, and the bricks themselves should be placed in accordance with some predetermined pattern that gives adequate *bond; e.g.,* crossing of joints by adjacent bricks so as to knit the work together.   These conditions apply to curtain walls that are supported by spandrel beams from floor to floor as well as to those which are used to carry superimposed loads.

Bearing walls made of bricks, and those built of concrete blocks and similar materials, may be suitable for small buildings and for multistory structures that approximate the office-building and apartment-house type of construction.   When the floors are supported upon steel beams, bar joists, precast-concrete joists, and wooden beams, these members

may be erected easily as the walls are built.   The masonry work may
then be carried on from floor to floor, using the previously erected floor
framing as a working platform.   This is likely to result in considerable
saving of money because of the avoidance of costly scaffolding outside
the walls.   Furthermore, the floor slabs may be poured after the floor
framing above them is in place, thus ensuring a minimum of damage to
the completed floor, as well as eliminating the cost of temporary coverings
over the floors.

Some illustrations of construction used in small buildings with brick
bearing walls are given in Fig. 8·11.   The following precautions are
recommended when one plans such construction:

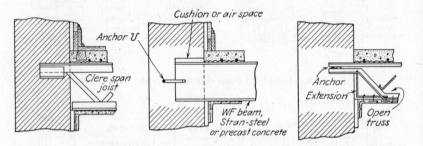

F ɪɢ. 8·11.   Some wall-bearing brick construction.

1. The ratio of the area of brickwork in a horizontal section through the windows (or doors) and for a length equal to the distance center to center of piers
between windows should be at least 40 per cent of the area that the wall would
have if no windows were used.   Even then it is not desirable to make the piers
too thick and narrow.

2. The clear height of a wall should not be excessive.   Building codes should
be consulted for data regarding such details.   Of course, there should be a floor
or roof at the top, to which the wall is connected so that lateral pressures against
the walls may be resisted by the floor or roof, and the forces carried down end
walls, partitions, bracing, or other lateral supports.   Cross walls or pilasters
naturally stiffen such masonry walls.

3. If a wall must resist lateral forces applied to its top or side, or both, without other construction to provide a lateral support for the wall, then it should be
designed as a vertical cantilever with combined compression and bending.   No
tension in the brickwork should be permitted unless the latter is reinforced.
Such cantilevered, plain brick walls should be studied with extreme skepticism.

4. Stiff, strong lintels over openings are especially important and should have
adequate bearing areas at their ends.

5. The thickness of a pier used between openings and made thicker than the
wall itself should not exceed about 1½ to 1⅔ times the thickness of the wall.

Curtain-wall construction is often used for brick walls of important industrial plants. Here the brickwork is a filler and is supported both vertically and laterally by the framework of the structure. When the spandrel beams are faced with bricks on the outside, it is best to make the wall thick enough so that its center of gravity will be somewhat back from the edge of the vertical support. This generally requires

FIG. 8·12. Welding made possible with development of an unusual modern design for this plant making bicarbonate of soda. The plant has a number of 250-ton concrete bins like that under construction in the rounded corner, which is entirely supported by welded framing. The Austin Co. is the designer, fabricator, and builder. Notice the cantilevered erection outriggers for supporting the scaffolds for the masons. (*Courtesy of The Lincoln Electric Co., Cleveland, Ohio.*)

12-in. walls. It is also important to see that the brickwork is steadied by, and is tied to, the spandrel beams and columns sufficiently to transmit to them all probable lateral forces. Scaffolds for the use of the masons may be hung from the top of the completed framework, as shown in Fig. 8·12. Figure 8·13 illustrates some details of spandrel beams supporting brick walls.

In reinforced-concrete construction there is a real question as to whether or not the spandrel beams should be covered with a veneer of bricks. This should be decided upon the basis of architectural appearance as well as of economy.

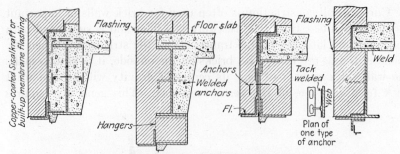

(a)-COMBINATIONS OF SPANDREL BEAMS AND LINTELS

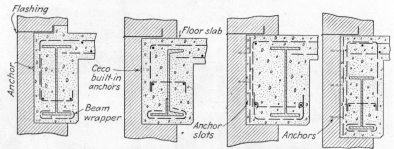

(b)-EXAMPLES OF ENCASED STEEL SPANDREL BEAMS
(Reinforced-concrete spandrel beams may be similar in general arrangement)

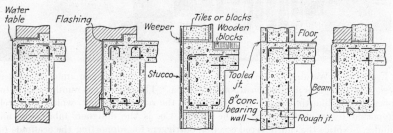

(c)-EXAMPLES OF POSSIBLE DETAILS OF SPANDREL BEAMS IN REINFORCED-CONCRETE CONSTRUCTION

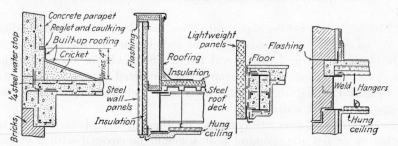

(d)-MISCELLANEOUS SPANDREL AND PARAPET DETAILS

FIG. 8·13.   A few of the many varieties of spandrel beam and wall details.

The junction of brick walls with columns is likely to be a trouble-some point. The following are some illustrations of possible details:

1. The columns may be set back to clear the wall as shown in Fig. 8·14(*a*). In this case, the connections of spandrel beams may become complicated, and mechanical anchors are required between the brickwork and the columns; on the other hand, diagonal bracing and struts can be kept clear of the brickwork. Obviously, the embedment of a sloping diagonal in brickwork is difficult and unsatisfactory.

2. A column may be set back 4½ to 5 in. from the face of the wall as shown in Fig. 8·14(*b*) so that the outer layer of bricks will clear column splices, rivet heads, and bolts. Unless the wall is at least 12 in. thick or is corbeled at the column, the wall cannot grip the column satisfactorily. The brickwork may be brought

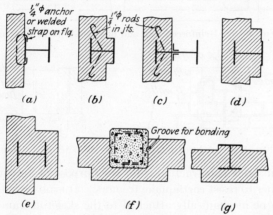

FIG. 8·14.　Encasement of columns in masonry walls.

in against the columns as shown in Figs. 8·14(*b*), (*c*), and (*d*); or the column may be encased completely as illustrated in Sketch (*e*). The last is usually unnecessary except in offices, cafeterias, lounge rooms, and other places where its improved appearance is advantageous. The bare steel flange may even be desirable when bracing, pipes, ducts, beams, trusses, and equipment are or may in the future be fastened to the column. In such construction, heavy brick walls at least 12 in. thick may be sufficient for the bracing of the outer flanges of the columns unless openings in the walls weaken the brickwork too much.

3. When the architectural treatment of a structure calls for pilasters or buttresses projecting from the face of the main wall at the columns, the latter may be set with respect to the surface of these projections, as shown in Figs. 8·14(*f*) and (*g*).

Brickwork may be reinforced with steel so as to act somewhat like reinforced concrete although, of course, it is limited in strength and usefulness. High parapet walls, and others that are not braced at their tops, may have pilasters or buttresses reinforced as vertical cantilevers, and the walls between them may be reinforced as horizontal beams. Some construction of this nature is shown in Fig. 8·15. Another is illustrated in Fig. 8·16, this being a case where the walls support the roof loads through trusses that rest upon reinforced-brick pilasters. In the case of low structures, this construction may be feasible and economical where one does not wish to trust the lateral stiffness of plain brick walls that are held in place by gravity only. Another use of rein-

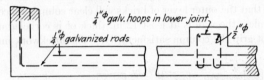

FIG. 8·15. Reinforced wall and pilasters of brick masonry.

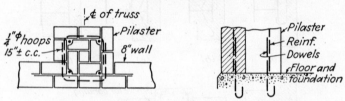

FIG. 8·16. A brick pilaster reinforced to act as a column.

forcement in brick construction is for the purpose of knitting the brick-work together to resist earthquake tremors. It is obvious that the walls should also be mechanically attached to the skeleton framework of the structure. One method of doing this is by means of welded anchors on the columns, or by ties as in Fig. 8·14(b).

When planning reinforced brickwork, one should consider the joints and the way the bricks will be laid up. In horizontal joints, the sizes of rods should not exceed ¼ in., as otherwise the joints will become too thick. It is desirable also to have these small rods galvanized because bond stresses are generally small, whereas corrosion and staining might be harmful. As shown in Fig. 8·16, vertical reinforcement should be located so that the rods occur at points of continuous vertical jointing, or where the bricks can be notched or have their corners clipped without undue labor. This is especially troublesome at splices, e.g., where the main reinforcement overlaps dowels embedded in the foundations. Obviously, the rods should be thoroughly encased in mortar.

Solid brick walls alone are not good insulators. Sweating at the inside surface during cold weather is also to be avoided. Furthermore, the heat capacity of heavy walls may retard the rate of warming up a room on a winter morning, and it may similarly cause a room to remain hot for some time after the walls have once become heated by the summer sun.

One way to remedy these disadvantages is to build the walls so that they are of the hollow-cavity type. The brickwork should be carefully bonded together; corrodible metal ties should not be trusted for this. The air spaces should also have drains (small tile or other pipes, or split tiles) at their bottoms in order to remove any leakage and condensation. Special bricks with holes through them may, if laid properly, serve partly in remedying insulation and condensation troubles.

It is not customary to insulate brick walls of industrial plants except for offices, multistory buildings for some types of manufacturing, and other cases of special nature. Some suggestions for such construction are pictured in Figs. 8·7(d) and 8·10. In any case, the materials should be resistant to moisture and vermin, and there should be means for draining away any accumulated moisture.

The prevention of leakage of moisture through brickwork is a matter deserving thoughtful study. The proper mortaring of all joints is one helpful feature; flashing is another. Some details of brick-wall construction have already been illustrated. All such details should be studied carefully in advance so that the main structure can be planned to suit them.

There are many conflicting ideas about how to install flashing and even about the best materials to use. Flashing may be especially desirable under copings, at window heads, at floor lines, and above steel spandrel beams—even above concrete ones. Whether the flashing is copper, felt and asphalt, or some other material, care should be used to avoid planes of weakness in the walls, and to see that the walls are supported properly and that lateral shearing forces can be resisted.

Incidentally, horizontal surfaces of brickwork left exposed to the elements are likely to disintegrate at the joints. This should be remembered when chimneys, parapets, platforms, areaways, and perhaps even window sills are planned.

The deflection of beams and its effect upon curtain walls should be considered. Of course, heavy concrete floors should be poured and made self-supporting before the walls are built up to them, thus permitting the dead-load deflection to occur; otherwise, if the top joints are mortared completely, the beams try to shift their loads to the walls. In the case of future live loads, this tendency will exist unless mastic is used in the top joints. When heavy machinery causes vibrations, it may be advisable to isolate part of the floor from any solid, or nearly solid, curtain wall. If this is desirable, remember that the brickwork should not be against and bonded to the encasement of the beam, or to the beam itself, because it will try to transmit shearing forces.

Many of the features that have been mentioned concerning brick walls are applicable to walls composed of concrete blocks, stone masonry, precast concrete, cinder-cement blocks, and other prefabricated masonry materials.

8·7 Concrete Walls. Poured concrete may be used for walls of industrial plants, especially when the general construction is made of reinforced concrete. These may be load-bearing or curtain walls, and, to a certain extent, they possess characteristics that are similar to brick construction except that the construction does not have multitudinous joints, the material can be reinforced to resist tension, and the concrete must be poured against forms. Provisions should be made for insulation and avoidance of condensation.

Provision should be made, too, for shrinkage and thermal deformation of concrete without harmful cracking. Brickwork, with its multitudinous joints, can take up a certain amount of deformation by means of unnoticed hair-cracks at the joints, whereas concrete must crack unless the deformation can occur (preferably unseen) at the specific points or lines that are provided for that purpose.

Construction joints—both vertical and horizontal—are needed to limit the lengths, heights, and volumes of individual monolithic pours. The vertical ones may be used as part of a system of crack control; the horizontal ones are for construction purposes only since the force of gravity presses the parts together regardless of shrinkage and thermal action. Dummy joints and planes of weakness may be installed for the purpose of localizing cracks. The locations of all joints should be planned carefully in advance. This subject of poured-concrete construction will be discussed more fully in Chap. 11.

In order to minimize costs, concrete curtain walls may be built of precast units that are poured in forms on the ground or elsewhere and then erected as large blocks or tiles with mortared or sealed joints. It is probable that hollow, cellular panels will be manufactured in order to decrease the weight of the walls and to improve insulating qualities. It is obvious, however, that any large precast units are difficult to handle in the field, and, if a great variety of sizes and shapes is to be avoided, a building must be planned to utilize a specific product made to certain dimensions, or to a limited variety of them. Much thought will undoubtedly be given to such details as the provision of lateral steadiness, anchorage or keying of units, avoidance of leakage, exterior and interior finish, vertical supports, light weight, ease of erection, and sizes and thicknesses consistent with durability.

Concrete walls may be solid with furring strips and insulation or plaster on the inside, as illustrated in Fig. 8·10. Another possible method is the use of vertical, ribbed construction somewhat similar to tin-pan floors, having the insulation and lining attached to the edges of the ribs.

8·8 Expansion Joints. Whether or not to provide expansion (or contraction) joints in buildings, and where to put them if used, are troublesome questions, especially when bricks, concrete, and stucco

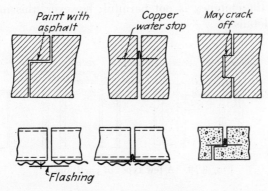

FIG. 8·17. Some principles for the planning of expansion joints in walls.

having considerable shearing strength and brittleness are used. The foundations of heavy buildings are not quickly affected by changes in weather, and generally frictional and shearing forces keep them from sliding back and forth with thermal variations. On the other hand, the walls and framing may be affected both quickly and positively by such changes. Undoubtedly, large stresses or cracking of the structure will result if too great an accumulation of deformation and of accompanying stresses occurs.

Expansion joints should be provided at intervals sufficiently close together to avoid harm to the structure. These joints may be from 100 to 200 ft. apart, depending upon the type of and the material used in the building. They should cut clear through the structure, including the foundation, preferably in one plane or with only minor irregularities that do not cause serious resistance to movement. They may well be at offsets and other architectural features that conceal them or minimize their visibility because cracks are likely to occur at changes of section. They should be both weatherproof and lightproof. Some principles of expansion joints in various walls are illustrated in Fig. 8·17.

Structures whose walls and partitions will permit the deformation of the framework without injury to themselves and to the latter may be made in long, continuous units, but the complete elimination of expansion joints in structures over 250 ft. long should be questioned seriously.

When a chimney, or hot-air duct, is to be incorporated in a concrete or masonry wall, the localized expansion is likely to cause cracking of the wall. It is often advisable to plan the construction so that the expansion of the chimney is not harmful; however, this may involve troublesome details.

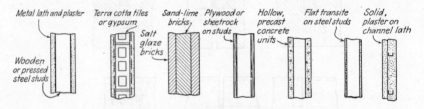

FIG. 8·18.   A few types of partitions.

8·9   Partitions.   The materials to be used in partitions and the details of the construction will depend upon many things, among which are the following:

1. *Fireproofness.*   If partitions are not to be fireproof, then wooden framing may be used with lath and plaster, plywood or lumber, sheet rock, transite, or some special product made for such purposes. If fire-resistance is desired, bricks, tiles, gypsum blocks, precast-concrete sections, steel framing with metal lath and plaster, or steel and wire-glass panels may be used.

2. *Movability.*   In office buildings, living quarters, and some factories, expansion or contraction of personnel, changes of tenancy, and alterations of facilities may make it highly desirable to have strong, independent floors with lightweight partitions that may be removed, altered, and relocated easily. Steel and wire-glass panels, tile and gypsum blocks with plaster, and wooden construction come in this class.

3. *Soundproofness.*   Brick walls 8 in. thick and 6-in. tile or gypsum partitions with lath and plaster are usually quite soundproof. Special acoustical tiles or panels may be used. Any thin construction that can vibrate somewhat like a sounding board is to be avoided.

4. *Transparency or Translucency.*   Seldom is glass in partitions of great value in transmitting daylight into interior rooms. It may be beneficial in partitions

Fig. 8·19. This end view of the new Federal Telecommunications Laboratories, located at Nutley, New Jersey, shows to advantage the aluminum paneled exterior. Panels are insulated with a fiber-glass bat and reinforced with a structural metal backing, ensuring dry, weatherproof construction. Aluminum window frames, doors, coping, grillwork, and exterior lighting accentuate this Aluminum Living theme. Requiring only an occasional washing with a nonalkaline cleaner followed by a clear water rinse, this aluminum exterior will remain bright and nonrusting indefinitely. (*Courtesy of the Aluminum Co. of America.*)

Fig. 8·20. An illustration of attractive but simple brickwork utilizing the pattern, a few offsets, and a coping to produce a pleasing effect. (*Design and construction by the Austin Co.*)

that are perpendicular and close to the outer walls, for illuminating corridors, and when visibility from one room to another is desired.

5. *Load-carrying Ability.*   Wooden or steel framing, bricks, and concrete are generally suitable if partitions are to support floor loads.   The partitions, however, must be sufficiently strong, thick, and stiff, with adequate foundations or other supports under them.

6. *Space for Utilities.*   Sometimes the existence of piping, conduits, and ducts which it is desirable to conceal in partitions—or in chases with removable covers—will dictate the general details and construction that are best for the given case.

Fig. 8·21.   Erection of vacuum concrete wall panel with vacuum lifter. Notice the provisions for bonding the panels into the concrete frame.   (*Courtesy of Vacuum Concrete, Inc.*)

Various sketches of the construction of partitions are shown in Fig. 8·18.   These are in addition to ordinary bricks, glass blocks, and steel partitions.   The illustrations are merely for the purpose of giving the reader a few suggestions.   He should remember that ordinary nonload-bearing partitions should be steadied laterally, yet they should not be required to resist loads from overhead beams that deflect and press upon them.   Neither should the beams under them sag sufficiently to cause the floor to crack away from the bottom of the partition, or to cause shear cracking in the partition itself.

Chapter 9

STEEL MILL BUILDINGS

9·1 Adaptability of Steel for Industrial Buildings. Structural steel rightfully holds an important position among the materials that are adapted to use in the construction of industrial buildings. Its prime

FIG. 9·1. Erection of the structural steel frame of a modern industrial plant having high-low-bay roof construction. One of the girders of the bridge crane is being raised. Notice the longitudinal bracing of the crane runway.

function is that of constituting the skeleton framework which supports the roof and side coverings together with any other parts or equipment that must be attached to or supported by it. Steel is noncombustible, strong, yet relatively light in weight for its strength; it is ductile, reliable, and generally available; it can be fabricated in advance to form members of the desired strength and dimensions, which can be erected quickly in the field where strong connections are easily made. Thus, steel is well suited to use in large plants having long spans, heavy loads, and large clear heights like that pictured in Fig. 9·1. It is also adapted to use in small structures like the building shown in Fig. 9·2.

As a material for the framework of industrial buildings, steel has two very important advantages:

1. Almost any structure within reason may be built of structural steel. This is a tremendous asset because of the great variety of shapes and sizes needed to house various industries.

2. A steel-frame structure may often be remodeled or extended to suit changed conditions, new processes, and even completely new uses. Sometimes this is exceedingly advantageous. By the use of burning, welding, and riveting, extensive alterations may be made in the field without prohibitive expense.

Fig. 9·2.   The steel frame of the paint and cement shop of the Morenci Reduction Works of the Phelps Dodge Corp., Morenci, Arizona.

Another slight advantage, which may become important under special conditions, is the fact that the entire building may be dismantled and reerected elsewhere when circumstances require it.

How can one tell whether to make a building out of steel or some other material? There may be simple but important matters that give the answer; e.g., personal preference, available materials, effect of weight on foundations if the soil is weak, suitability for the purpose, fire hazards, similarity to other buildings previously used and found to be satisfactory, similarity to adjacent buildings to be constructed, and speed and ease of construction. However, the required strength of the material and the relative economy may overrule these other factors when spans are long and loads are heavy.

A designer should guard against slipping into the habit of thinking that all buildings should be made of steel or of any other one material. Each material has its assets and its liabilities; the advantages should be utilized, the disadvantages avoided. Surprisingly often—and properly so—it is not economy but the type of construction to be used for the large buildings in a plant that automatically dictates the construction to be used for the small structures in order to have uniformity of type and appearance. Just such a reason determined the use of steel framing for the building in Fig. 9·2. Nevertheless, the designer should make certain that his decisions regarding questions of material are wise.

The term "mill building" as used here denotes a single-story structure having one or more relatively wide aisles of considerable length and large clearance. The siding and roofing may be one or more of a wide variety of materials; generally, however, the whole construction is relatively light. Such a building generally houses large, heavy machinery supported directly on the ground; it may or may not have crane runways, trolley beams, or other overhead equipment for transporting materials. The manufacturing operations within it are usually those which require large areas on a single floor, and the handling of heavy or voluminous objects. Obviously, such buildings require long roof beams or trusses to span the aisles, slender but strong columns to carry heavy vertical loads, and substantial bracing to resist the wind forces against such large exposed wall areas. For all these, structural steel is admirably suited.

When planning the framework of a steel building, one should bear in mind the fact that commercial sections of steel are rolled in various sizes and shapes—but in these only. Unusual, complicated, and built-up members will naturally cost more per pound than will simple rolled sections without large fabrication costs. When special members are needed, however, they can be made up by riveting and welding, but they should be so planned that they can be composed of parts that in themselves are standard shapes.

The variety of shapes, sizes, and details of industrial structures is about as extensive as the needs for which each individual building is designed. The illustrations given here show general schemes of framing and the construction used in some special cases.

In this chapter many principles of the planning of structures are illustrated and described. These are generally applicable to many other structures that are built of steel, and to some that are made of other materials.

9·2   Mill-building Frames.   A few typical mill-building frames are shown diagrammatically in Fig. 9·3.   The combination of columns

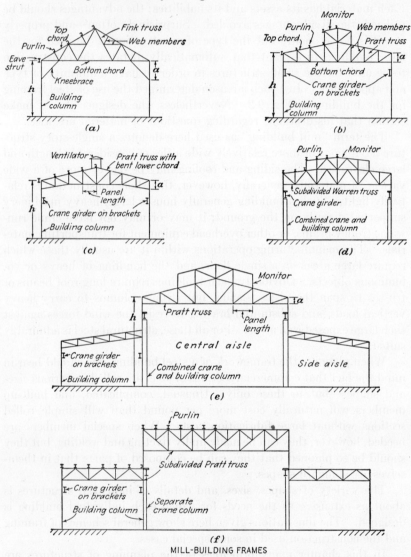

MILL-BUILDING FRAMES

Fig. 9·3.   Mill-building frames.

and trusses in one line across the aisles for the full width of the structure constitutes one "bent."   Sketch (*a*) pictures a Fink truss spanning a single aisle; it has knee braces to provide lateral stability and stiffness—a subject discussed more fully in Art. 9·10.   The other diagrams show various types of framing in which the top and bottom chords connect to the columns without knee braces but serve the same purpose in stiffening the structure.

The structural action of a typical bent is illustrated in Fig. 9·4 in which the crane beams are supported on brackets connected to the columns.   For simplicity, the truss is pictured as though it were

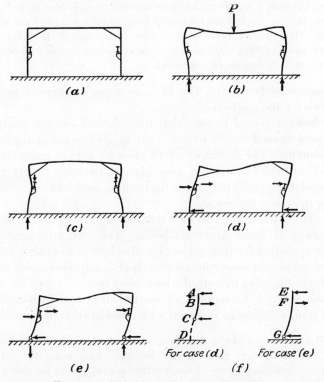

FIG. 9·4.   Action of steel bents under loads.

a beam—which, in effect, it really is—and the knee-braced type is assumed.   The bases of the columns are rigidly fixed to the foundation in all except Sketch (e).   The deformations are greatly exaggerated in order to picture the action more clearly.   An explanation of the sketches in Fig. 9·4 follows:

  a. A schematic sketch of the bent.
  b. The action of vertical loads on the truss, causing the columns to bow outward, this bending being small unless the trusses are very flimsy.

c. The vertical loads due to the crane cause, in this case, considerable bending in the columns along with the direct loads.

d. Lateral forces from the wind and crane make the columns bend somewhat as shown, unless there are special bracing systems to resist such loads.

e. The general shape of the bent due to lateral forces is shown for columns that are "hinged" (not restrained securely) at their bases.

f. It is easily seen that the bending moments in the columns in Sketch (*e*) will be greater than in (*d*) for the same loads because there is a point of inflection somewhere between *B* and *D* in the latter whereas there is none from *F* to *G* in the former, thereby causing the horizontal shear in Sketch (*e*) to have a greater lever arm. Obviously, if there were no knee braces and if the columns were hinged at *E* and *G* of Sketch (*f*), the structure would be unstable for lateral loads unless supported by bracing of some kind.

The action of bents with two or more aisles is generally similar to that shown for the single aisle.

The designer should be sure that the column bases are really fixed to the foundations if he relies upon restraining moments at the bottoms of the columns. The footings in turn must be able to resist the overturning effect before he can rely upon fixing of the bases. Any yielding of the foundations tends to increase the bending moments in the columns, and it is, therefore, dangerous.

Space is not available here for a detailed description of the design of the members of these structural bents. Texts on structural theory should be consulted for this. The objective here is to explain the basic structural action, to show various details of construction, and to assist the reader in planning industrial structures wisely.

Besides strength to support all vertical dead and live loads, mill-building frames should be designed with consideration of the following:

1. Stiffness is a desirable quality, regardless of allowable unit stresses, particularly in crane girders, columns, and bracing. Experience with structures under service conditions is one of the few trustworthy guides for sound professional judgment in this matter. As examples, the lintels above continuous or wide windows, and the eave struts supporting the sag rods, which in turn are to reduce the sagging of girts and window framing, may be strong enough, but the members may deflect sufficiently to break the windows or to interfere with their proper functioning. In one situation, a heavy, 9-in. beam with a span of 30 ft. was used, in order to provide clearance at a stairway. Of course, the beam sagged excessively under live loads on the floor.

2. Minimum sizes and thicknesses of material are desirable to prevent the use of flimsy members and to allow for corrosion if the steelwork is not properly maintained in the future. A practical *minimum* limit on this is ¼-in. material for truss web members and bracing angles, ⁵⁄₁₆-in. for truss chords and gusset

plates, ¼-in. for column and beam webs, and about ⅜-in. for column and beam flanges.   If corrosive gases are likely to be present, about $\frac{1}{16}$ in. should be added to these thicknesses, and care should be used to minimize spaces that cannot be painted (as between the legs of double-angle members with small air spaces between them).

3. Sturdy, simple construction is preferable to complicated work made out of many small members.

4. Clearances for cranes should be ample in all respects, and so should clearances over and around equipment because requirements for these things often have a tendency to increase.

5. Lateral and longitudinal strength of the structure must be provided by bending in the framework or by bracing systems.

6. Gib cranes, bracketed walkways, and other loads that cause local bending of columns will generally affect the sizes of these members.

7. The type of framing and shapes of members should be practicable and suitable for supporting the desired roofing and wall materials.

9·3 Planning the General Framing Scheme.   The general plan for the framing of an industrial structure is worthy of careful study.   It should be developed along with the layout of the equipment, planning of facilities for daylighting and ventilation, provisions for transportation and access, and the many other features that affect the size and shape of a building.

The following outline gives some of the procedure that may be followed in developing the framing scheme:

1. Locate the column rows so that the aisles (clear space between columns, in this sense) and crane runways accommodate the equipment and manufacturing processes.   These automatically determine the spans of the trusses.   If the building is high, it is generally economical to use moderately long trusses when planning the widths of the aisles, otherwise closely spaced rows of tall columns may use far more steel than would longer trusses.   For example, a building requiring four aisles 40 ft. wide with clearances of 35 ft. for cranes would seem to be poorly proportioned; two 80-ft. aisles appear to be more suitable.   Of course, there are very important reasons for using narrow aisles in some cases, as the illustrations given here amply show.   Try to equalize the widths of aisles or to have them reasonably proportioned in absolute dimensions and in relative size so that they will form the basis of a sensible layout and of a structure with a suitable architectural appearance.

2. Knowing what monitors or other provisions will be required in the roof for adequate daylighting and ventilation, make a diagrammatic cross section of the building and determine the general shape of the roof: sloping or flat; a series of peaks and valleys or a single ridge and long, side slopes; a flat main roof with rows of monitors or adjoining aisles of varying height like Figs. 9·3(e) and (f); or whatever other shape best suits the requirements of clear-

ances, lighting, etc. Subsequent study may change the first ideas about the basic shape, but that is not surprising. For instance, architectural appearance, drainage in wet climates, snow in northern districts, or the kind of roof sheathing and covering to be used may determine whether a series of valleys, a large flat roof, or a long sloping one is best. These matters may also control the question whether it is better to place monitors and sawteeth crosswise of the aisles so that the low bays will drain easily, or whether they may be parallel to these aisles, as in Fig. 9·6(*d*).

3. Locate end columns and any intermediate ones that are automatically required to be at specific points because of the mechanical layout. Also, place columns at outside and reentrant corners of offsets in the floor plan, *e.g.*, the junctions of any lean-to with the main building. Also, tentatively locate main doorways, tracks, conveyors, tunnels, and other parts through which a column must not pass.

4. Choose a tentative width of bay, the distance center to center of columns in each row. For steel construction, it is seldom economical to use less than 17 or 18 ft. for this spacing because it requires a relatively large number of columns, and the purlins in the roof and the girts or wall framing become so light that minimum practicable sizes of members should be used anyway. If the bays exceed 25 ft., the roof and wall members, if stiff enough, are likely to be so heavy that the total tonnage of steel used in them becomes uneconomical. An ordinarily assumed dimension for the bays may be 20 ft.

5. If continuous operating sashes are to be used in the side windows, ascertain what the width of the individual sash units will be so that the bay widths are multiples of this dimension, provided it is important or desirable to have it so. This may automatically change the spacing first selected. Such a change was actually made in planning the plant shown in Fig. 9·1.

6. On the general layout, with the column rows and any critical columns shown thereon, experiment with the selected width of bay to see if the spaces between critical points can be divided evenly to suit the desired dimensions. To do this, it is often advisable to work on a piece of thin tracing paper placed over the general layout so that the latter does not become marked excessively. Perhaps some of the end columns can be shifted slightly—preferably adding rather than reducing floor area—to make the spacing fit. Perhaps the width of bays must be corrected to divide given total spaces into equal parts; perhaps any excess or deficit can be placed in some one bay, such as an end or central one. It will probably be unwise to use bays of one size in part of a building with different sizes used elsewhere.

7. When a seemingly good, uniform spacing of columns has been found, but before locating the columns on the plan, make sure that the columns can be lined up to form complete bents for the full width of the structure. When such an arrangement is impossible, try to line up as many of the bents as practicable, then adjust the special ones to harmonize with them as best they can. For example, assume that 20-ft. bays are the typical ones but that they cannot be used in one portion of an inner aisle because two 30-ft. spaces are required

for equipment. It would be possible (perhaps) to use two 30-ft. bays clear across the building at this location. A better solution may be the scheme shown in Fig. 9·5 where the roof trusses are all at 20-ft. spacings but the ends of part of them are supported by jack trusses 30 ft. long placed between the columns, the central columns being tied in with bracing to the trusses and their lateral bracing system in order to steady the columns laterally. The interior row of columns at the right-hand side of Fig. 9·1 shows an opening more than 60 ft. wide over which a longitudinal double girder supports two intermediate roof trusses on stub columns. In the case illustrated in Fig. 1·1, the interior

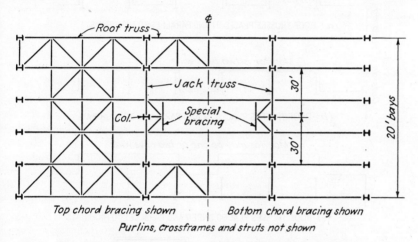

Fig. 9·5.   A framing scheme with unequal spacing of columns.

40-ft. spacing of columns was provided to minimize obstructions around the large equipment. There the use of jack trusses was typical.

8. Now check up provisions for the monitors, sawteeth, or other special features in the roof. If monitors run parallel to the trusses, the low bays may be carried by the bottom chords as in Figs. 9·6(a) or (b), which is an economical arrangement, the latter being used in Fig. 9·1; they may be on top of the main roof as in Fig. 9·6(c). In either case, it is almost necessary to have the monitor widths based upon the truss spacing so that the framing of the monitors can be supported directly by the trusses. An uneven truss spacing is undesirable because it might cause unequal monitor sizes and thus produce an unsatisfactory appearance. Furthermore, in Figs. 9·6 (a) and (b), the monitors must extend clear out to the side walls; no jack trusses can be used because they would project into the air unless they were placed under the bottom chords of the main trusses. Now see whether or not the number of bays will fit the monitor scheme so that there will be a low bay at each end because high end bays may cause unnecessarily high outer walls and provide extra windows where they do little good. A low bay at one end and a high bay at the other destroy the

symmetry of a building and may look as though someone made a mistake. Perhaps the column spacing may be adjusted so that the desired monitor plan can be used. If the monitors rest on top of the trusses, are parallel to them, and stop 30 or 40 ft. back from the side walls, the latter will probably look better because they are not serrated; however, this arrangement will generally require more steel than that of Fig. 9·1. If the monitors run lengthwise of

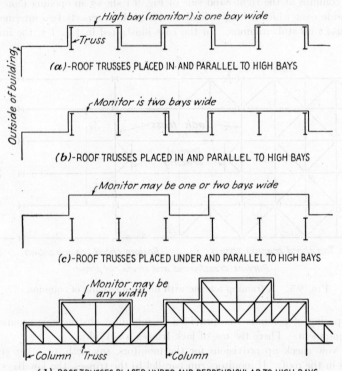

Fig. 9·6. Arrangements for high-low-bay roofs.

the building on top of the trusses, sketch them in the cross-sectional view already prepared, adjusting their sizes so as to make a pleasing appearance and to obtain sufficient light. It is preferable to have them—or one of them per aisle—centered along the mid-point between columns, a possible scheme being shown in Fig. 9·6 (d). Now sketch a plan of the columns and roof trusses that will fit all the applicable conditions.

9. Next, choose a spacing for the purlins which will be suitable for the strength of the roof sheathing and roofing—generally 5 to 7 or 8 ft.—and by which the truss length is divisible. This may result in different spacings over various aisles, but it is desirable to have a member at the column rows and at the

outer walls. This spacing may affect the width of the monitors running across the trusses, or the spacing may be determined by the dimensions of the monitors. Draw a series of these purlins on the plan to see that they fit properly.

10. Make diagrammatic vertical sections along all column rows and outside walls. On them locate the sills and lintels of all windows, the frames of doors, and members around other special openings; then add whatever extra girts or wall members seem to be needed to hold the siding. Locate also all crane girders, jack trusses, bin supports, platform beams, and other required members, and show them in the sectional views. Some such framing for a tall building with intermittent windows and corrugated siding is shown in Fig. 9·7. The channel girts fastened to the outsides of the columns were located to suit the windows, the pattern and elevations of which were determined only after making architectural sketches or side elevations of the walls.

11. Now look over the roof plan and the wall sections to find where bracing is needed. Add it in the pictures, planning the layout in accordance with the principles explained in Arts. 9·9 and 9·10.

In making these framing plans, avoid skewed and complicated construction unless there are important reasons why such things must be done. Work on the basis of providing a means for supporting all loads as directly as possible. Try to imagine in what ways the structure might fail, then see that something is provided to prevent it from failing that way. Later on, in the design calculations,

FIG. 9·7. Part of the secondary crushing plant of the Morenci Reduction Works. A 7-ft.-diameter Symons cone crusher is being lowered onto its reinforced-concrete foundation by the crane high up in the 70-ft. building. Notice the bracing, the girts, the frame, and part of the equipment for the tandem drive of a large conveyor. (*Courtesy of the Phelps Dodge Corp.*)

make sure that all members have adequate strength to serve their purposes.

The framework of one building is shown in Fig. 9·8. It consists of an aisle containing a suspended bin about 30 ft. deep, an adjacent aisle about 80 ft. wide with a 150-ton crane, and then three other crane-equipped aisles of varying widths and lengths arranged on a series of benches down the hillside.   The columns are lined up to form complete

Fig. 9·8.   Framing of suspended bin at the concentrator of the Morenci Reduction Works of the Phelps Dodge Corp.   All the steelwork in the near end is designed for future extension.

Fig. 9·9.   The high-low-bay sloping roof of the Morenci concentrator.   The building above the left side is the primary crushing plant on the hill in the background. The siding is galvanized corrugated steel; the roof, Robertson V-beam protected metal.

bents clear across the structure.   The short slope of the roof on the near side needs no monitors because the side windows are sufficient.

On the opposite slope, as shown in Fig. 9·9, every third bay of the roof
is depressed to the bottom chords of the trusses, thus forming monitors
to augment the light from the windows in the walls at the offsets of the
roof.   In this case, the near end of Fig. 9·8 and the far end of Fig. 9·9
show that the building starts with a high bay.   This was done to facilitate future extension.   Figure 9·10 shows some of the interior framing
of the aisle next below the monitored section.   Notice that special care
was taken to make the steelwork simple and neat, as well as strong.

Fig. 9·10.   The cleaner section of the Morenci concentrator below the high-low-
bay sections.   An expansion joint is located in the bay where the strut at the right
is discontinuous.   The heavy bases of the columns are to resist transverse wind and
crane forces.   (*Courtesy of the Phelps Dodge Corp.*)

This planning of the framing system of a structure requires good
foresight and judgment.   If well done, it will avoid much confusion and
many revisions.

9·4 Planning Trusses.   Trusses are really deep beams that are
made with many large holes in them—but holes in the right places—
thus saving considerable weight of steel.   Rolled beams or built-up plate
girders might be used for spans up to 40 or 50 ft. when shallowness is
necessary.   The shapes, types, and dimensions of trusses may be almost
anything within reason.   No fixed rules are feasible for determining
these things; however, certain principles and general data are given for
planning trusses.

The general shape of the roof, the slopes, the required vertical clearances, the monitors, the purlin locations, and the spans between the columns serve as starting points. These things have been or should be studied and determined as indicated in the preceding article. The planning of the trusses may then be worked out somewhat as described here.

First determine the slope of the roof. If it is to be covered with corrugated roofing such as galvanized steel, asbestos-protected metal, or transite, the minimum slope should be about 3 in. vertically to 12 in. horizontally in order to avoid leakage at the lapped joints of the roofing. In snowy areas, it may be advisable to use a steeper slope. If the covering is to be soldered sheet metal or built-up tar or asphalt roofing with a surfacing devoid of joints that can leak, the roof may be absolutely flat; it is often wiser to give it a slope of $\frac{1}{8}$ to $\frac{1}{4}$ in. per ft. to facilitate drainage.

When there are monitors or sawteeth on the roof, the drainage question should be settled at this stage of the planning. In the case of the plant shown in Fig. 9·1, the three aisles are 100, 75, and 50 ft. wide. The front of the building is at the left of the picture, and the entire roof is canted to slope at $\frac{1}{4}$ in. per ft. clear across to the eaves at the back, where large gutters and downspouts receive the water. The high bays can drain crosswise to the low ones which then serve as valleys to discharge the water to the gutters, as pictured in Figs. 9·11(a) and (b), or the high bays may also drain clear back to the gutters as indicated in (c) and (d). Of course, the lowest points of the trusses must be so located as to allow the proper crane clearances.

When the monitors or sawteeth are several hundred feet long, one continuous slope may cause too large a difference in height so that it may be better to have a series of low spots (at certain column lines) which can be drained by inlets through the roof and thence through downspouts to drainage pipes under the floor, or to other points of discharge, as shown in Fig. 9·11(d). These pipes may be a nuisance because of interference with foundations.

In cases where the monitors extend for long distances parallel to the aisles, it may be necessary to have downspouts along each row of columns as in Fig. 9·11(f).

Generally, place the top chords of the trusses parallel to the roof slopes so that the purlins can be supported directly on the top chords, thus avoiding fussy details and adjustments of purlin elevations. The bottom chords may be parallel to the top ones as in Figs. 9·1 and 9·10, level as in Figs. 9·3(a) and (b), kinked as in Figs. 9·3(c) and 9·35, or in any other desired position.

The depth of the truss may be any reasonable dimension. The deeper it is, the less the chord areas will become for any given condition

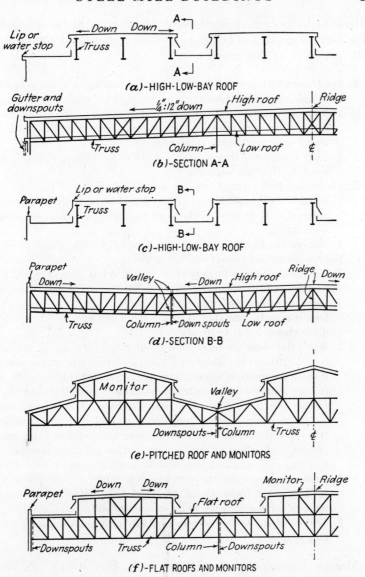

Fig. 9·11. Drainage schemes for roofs. (Saw-tooth roofs may be planned on same principles as high-low-bay construction.)

of span and loading, but the web members may become too long and slender. With ordinary roof loading, the following may be a guide in choosing the depths between the axes of the truss chords (between the centers of gravity or the gauge lines of the rivets in the chord members), using d as the depth and L the span—both in feet—and a total load of 75 lb. per sq. ft. of roof area:

> A. For trusses with parallel or nearly parallel chords up to spans of 120 ft.:
>   1. Simply supported trusses — $d = \frac{1}{10} L$ at the center.
>   2. Trusses continuous at one end — $d = L/12$ at the center, but the depth at the continuous end may have to be increased to $L/10$, or the chords may need heavy reinforcement.
>   3. Fully continuous trusses — $d = L/12$ at the center, with at least the same depth at the supports.
> B. For trusses with pitched roofs up to spans of 120 ft.:
>   1. Trusses of the type shown in Fig. 9·3 (a) will generally be deep enough automatically because of the slope but use $d = L/8$ at the center as a minimum.
>   2. Trusses like Fig. 9·3 (c) — $d = L/8$ to $L/10$ at the center.
> C. For trusses having spans from 120 to 200 ft.:
>   1. Use the same ratios for depths as given in A but remember that trusses over 11 or 12 ft. deep may have to be shipped knocked-down—individual members requiring field connections at all or most joints. Therefore, it may be desirable to reduce the depth to avoid this field work if the chords are not excessively heavy.
>   2. When the spans are more than about 130 ft., it may be advisable to consider trusses like those in Fig. 9·13, or to try to utilize continuity if there are multiple spans. For simply supported trusses 160 to 200 ft. long, double-gusset construction similar to bridgework may be best. In this case, it may also be advisable to have a system composed of a few heavy, deep trusses perhaps 40 ft. on centers, then to utilize deep transverse trusses about 20 ft. c.c. framing into them, supporting the purlins, and acting as cross frames. This is stated because of the fact that two such long trusses 20 ft. apart may weigh more than one stronger one carrying the same load, since there is considerable weight used for gusset plates, lacing, various details, and minor members that must be large if they are to be sufficiently stiff.
>   3. Trusses of the type shown in Fig. 9·3 (a) are not desirable for such long spans.

Monitor framing such as that shown in Figs. 9·3(b), (d), and (e) should not be relied upon as part of the truss itself unless the design is made especially for that purpose.

The depth a at the end of such simply supported trusses as shown in Figs. 9·3(a), (b), (c), and (e) should not be less than $h/7$ or a minimum of about 3 ft. (but it need not be over a maximum of about 6 ft.) if the bents are to act as a frame to resist lateral loads by bending, as pictured in Figs. 9·4(d) and (e). This is to enable the trusses to grip the tops of the columns satisfactorily.

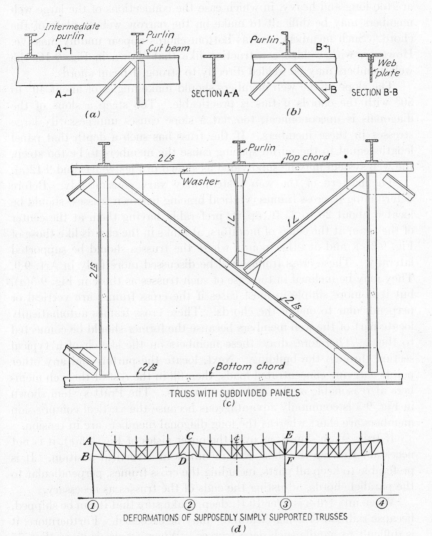

TRUSS WITH SUBDIVIDED PANELS
(c)

DEFORMATIONS OF SUPPOSEDLY SIMPLY SUPPORTED TRUSSES
(d)

FIG. 9·12. Deformations of supposedly simply supported trusses.

The web members should be arranged so that a panel point of the truss will be under each purlin, unless the chords are to be designed for combined bending and direct stresses, a procedure that may not be economical or desirable. However, chords made up like those in Figs. 9·12(a) and (b) are satisfactory for riveted construction unless the trusses are too long and heavy, in which case the connections of the large web members may be difficult to make on the narrow web or plate of the chord. Such members used as bottom chords appear unduly massive. However, with welded construction like that shown in Fig. 9·16, the web members may be welded directly to strong, I-beam chords.

The slope of the web members should make angles of about 40° to 50° with the chords if this is practicable. Too steep a slope of the diagonals is uneconomical; too flat a slope causes unnecessarily large stresses in these members. If the truss has such a depth that panel lengths equal to the purlin spacing cause the members to be too steep, the web system may be subdivided as shown in Figs. 9·3(f) and 9·12(c).

The pattern of the web system may vary considerably. Before determining it, cross frames (vertical bracing between trusses) should be located about 20 to 25 ft. apart, preferably having them at the center of the span, at the edges of monitors, at kinks in the chords like those of Fig. 9·3(c), and at other points where the trusses should be supported laterally. These cross frames will be discussed more fully in Art. 9·9. They may be inclined in the case of such trusses as those in Fig. 9·3(a), but it is more simple in most cases if the cross frames are vertical or perpendicular to one of the chords. These cross frames automatically locate part of the web members because the former should be connected to them. Therefore, draw these members on the sketch of a typical section through the building. Next, locate the purlins and any other points carrying concentrated loads, then fill in the rest of the web members at reasonable angles and panel lengths. The Pratt system shown in Fig. 9·3 is commonly advantageous because the vertical compression members are short whereas the long diagonal members are in tension.

If trusses are sloped, as over the outer aisles of Fig. 9·3(e), it is not necessary to keep the short web members in a vertical position. It is preferable to keep all parts, including the cross frames, perpendicular to the parallel chords, adjusting the ends of the trusses as necessary.

When any truss is over 10 ft. deep, make sure that it can be shipped, because railroad or other clearances may be exceeded. Furthermore, it is difficult to handle such deep trusses. When a truss is more than 75 or 80 ft. long, it may have to be spliced in the field. This generally is not very difficult to do.

Long, continuous roof trusses may be more economical than equivalent simply supported ones. This matter of relative economy is not important in the case of ordinary spans of less than 80 ft. For longer spans, continuity is worthy of consideration, but it is not an unmitigated blessing.   The following points should be thought about:

1. If the foundations are poor and any large differential settlements are likely, the stresses in the trusses may be seriously and detrimentally modified because of the settlements, although the effect is not so serious as one might

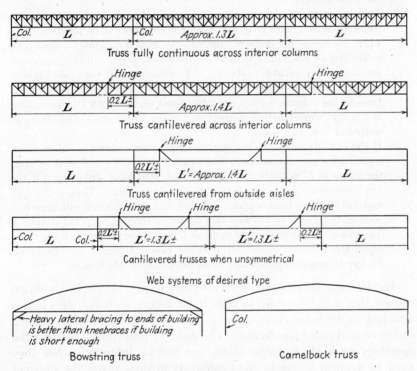

FIG. 9·13.   Suggestions for long trusses.

suppose unless the trusses are deep with respect to their spans, in which case the benefit of continuity is not great anyway.   Furthermore, such unreliable foundations should not be built in the first place.

2. A structure with continuous trusses may be much more difficult to remodel later because cutting or removing any part of one span will greatly alter the stresses in adjacent ones and, as simply supported members, they may be overloaded.

3. Continuous trusses may be stiffer than simply supported ones, but live-load deflections of roof trusses are seldom important.

4. Splicing trusses across columns and jack trusses may involve difficult details.   Such splices must be adequate if they are to be relied upon.

5. In the case of simply supported trusses, partial live loads will probably cause greater angular rotations of the ends than will occur when the trusses are continuous. The connections of trusses, or even of knee braces, to the columns cannot be tight at one time and loose at another. Figure 9·12 (d) illustrates how these angular rotations may affect truss connections:

a. The chord connections at A and B cause the column to bend slightly as the truss deflects.

b. The deflections of the trusses on opposite sides of column 2 cause the connections at C and D to act against each other. The junction at C, where the shears are delivered through the diagonal members, must hold or the trusses will fall. Meanwhile, the lower chords will be under compression if they are able to stand it. To relieve this, in the case of simply supported trusses, it may be preferable to fasten the bottom chord of one truss to the column, letting the latter bend slightly with the truss, then fasten the corresponding connection on the other truss with bolts in slotted or oversized holes.

c. If the end diagonals are in compression and slope down, as at F, these connections must be strong. The angular deflections will tend to open the joints at E, possibly cracking the roof or at least stretching it if the top connections cannot withstand the tension. Notice that, if the top- and bottom-chord connections are sufficient, the trusses will approach continuity in spite of the intended action as simply supported members. Therefore, the connections as made at C and D are preferable if the lower chord BD is rigidly connected at B but loosely bolted at D. However, be sure to steady each column by means of one of the trusses.

Incidentally, trusses should be designed to provide for the addition of loads that may be applied to them in the future, such as trolley beams attached to the lower chords, heavy pipes, equipment lifted by lashing chains around panel points, etc. The designer must remember that the operators are likely to forget about him and his intentions when they want to do such things in the future. If in their place, the designer would likely take a chance and do some of the same things if they were the most obvious procedures. To allow for such probable acts in heavy construction and for spans of 60 ft. or more, it may be wise to add an imaginary load of 5,000 lb. near the center of the lower chord, then the same load moved to either quarter point of the truss. For light construction and shorter spans, this load may be reduced to 2,000 lb.

Queer things can happen to structures, showing that a conservative safety factor used in designs may become most helpful. Two extreme cases that actually happened are the following:

1. A large duct was to be placed lengthwise of a building, shaped somewhat like the one in Fig. 9·3 (a). The desired location interfered with the bottom

chord of the truss at its center.   The chord was burned off, and the duct was erected.   The building still stood up owing to its action as a sort of three-hinged arch, hinged at the peak of the roof and near the bases of the columns.

2. Strong longitudinal bracing was provided in a 40-ton crane runway.   The operators decided to erect a machine in a different location from that originally intended.   Because the bracing was in their way, they cut it off, even neglecting to reerect it elsewhere.   Naturally, when this was discovered by the designers, new bracing was added in another bay.

9·5   Crane Girders.   Beams and girders supporting cranes are very important members of an industrial structure.   For convenience here, they will all be termed "crane girders."   Some important considerations and typical construction are described to assist the reader to plan crane runways wisely.

Cranes made by different manufacturers and for different service conditions may not cause the same wheel reactions.   It often happens that the contract for cranes has not been closed when a structure is planned, or even designed.   However, for preliminary planning and design work prior to receipt of information from the manufacturer giving design loads and wheel spacings, the data given in Table 9·1 may be sufficient.

The following specifications for the design of crane runways are given as a general guide:

1. Dead load—the weight of the member, as a uniformly distributed load.

2. Vertical live loads—the wheel loads (and their spacing) given by the manufacturer.

3. Vertical impact loads—25 per cent of the vertical live loads.   This allowance is partly for the effect of shock due to the sudden taking up of the slack in the hoisting cables and to the sudden application of the brakes on the hoist when lowering the loads; it is not to allow for speed alone.   This factor may be omitted entirely for hand-operated cranes; it may be reduced for slow-speed cranes of small capacity.   This reduction is not recommended because of the tendency of operators to lift anything they can get hold of regardless of the crane's rated capacity.

4. Lateral live loads—20 per cent of the rated lifting capacity of the crane applied by the wheels at the top of the rail on *either* side of the runway, each separately.   It is advisable to consider that this lateral force will act entirely on the girder adjacent to the trolley when the latter is hoisting a load near that end of the crane bridge.   For high-speed trolleys and hoists, increase this lateral force by 5 to 10 per cent of the crane's rated lifting capacity to allow for the weight of the trolley when braking, and for more severe shock effect. This lateral force is due largely to lateral pulling by the trolley and to swinging loads; it may be reduced to 10 per cent for hand-operated cranes.   Connections on the webs or the top flanges of the crane girders should be capable of delivering

Table 9·1 Dimensions and Clearances of Whiting Tiger Cranes

Dimensions of 4-wheel cranes, with and without auxiliary hoist. (Based on standard construction, employing notched girders with end trucks of M. C. B. or capsule type.)

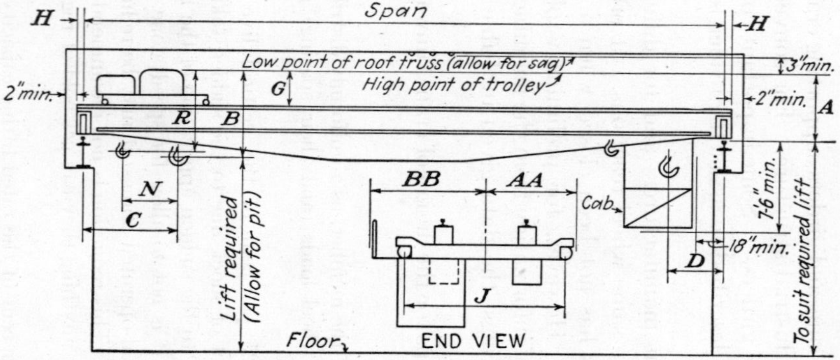

Capacity, tons	Span, ft.	A	B	C	D	G	H	J	N	R	AA	BB	Wheel load, lb.
5	25	4′6¼″	5′3½″	2′8″	3′2″	2′6½″	6″	8′6″			5′0″	7′6″	12,500
	40	5′3¼″	5′3½″	2′8″	3′2″	2′6½″	6″	8′6″			5′0″	7′6″	15,100
	60	4′6½″	5′3½″	2′4″	3′3″	2′6½″	7¼″	9′0″			5′6″	7′6″	18,300
	80	5′3″	5′3½″	2′5″	3′3″	2′6½″	8¼″	11′6″			6′9″	8′0″	22,500
	100	5′10″	5′3½″	2′5″	3′3″	2′6½″	8¼″	14′6″			8′3″	9′6″	28,000
10	25	5′2″	6′3″	2′9″	3′3″	2′11″	6″	9′6″			5′6″	8′0″	18,600
	40	5′5¼″	6′3″	2′9″	3′3″	2′11″	6″	9′6″			5′6″	8′0″	21,000
	60	5′4″	6′3″	2′4″	3′5″	2′11″	8¼″	9′6″			5′9″	8′0″	24,900
	80	5′6″	6′3″	2′4″	3′5″	2′11″	8¼″	11′6″			6′9″	8′0″	29,100
	100	6′5″	6′3″	2′4″	3′5″	2′11″	8½″	14′6″			8′6″	9′6″	36,000

Capacity, tons	Span, ft.	A	B	C	D	G	H	J	N	R	AA	BB	Wheel load, lb,
15	25	5′4¾″	7′0″	2′9″	3′3″	2′11″	7″	9′6″			5′9″	8′0″	23,400
	40	5′5¼″	7′0″	2′9″	3′3″	2′11″	7″	9′6″			5′9″	8′0″	26,800
	60	5′8″	7′0″	2′5″	3′5″	2′11″	8¼″	9′6″			5′9″	8′0″	30,200
	80	5′10″	7′0″	2′5″	3′5″	2′11″	8½″	11′6″			7′0″	8′0″	34,600
	100	6′5″	7′0″	2′5″	3′5″	2′11″	8½″	14′6″			8′6″	9′6″	41,300
20	25	6′1″	6′8″	2′8″	3′3″	3′3″	6¾″	10′6″			6′3″	8′6″	28,700
	40	6′1″	6′8″	2′8″	3′3″	3′3″	7¼″	10′6″			6′4″	8′6″	32,700
	62	5′10½″	6′8″	2′8″	3′4″	3′3″	8½″	10′6″			6′5″	8′6″	37,000
	82	6′5″	6′8″	2′8″	3′4″	3′3″	9″	12′0″			7′2″	8′6″	41,000
	100	6′8″	6′8″	2′8″	3′4″	3′3″	9½″	14′6″			8′6″	8′6″	49,000
20 and 5-ton aux.	25	5′10½″	6′7½″	6′10½″	3′7″	3′3½″	6¾″	10′6″	4′5″	5′11″	6′3″	9′6″	31,300
	40	6′1″	6′7½″	6′10½″	3′7″	3′3½″	7¼″	10′6″	4′5″	5′11″	6′4″	9′6″	35,200
	62	5′10½″	6′7½″	7′4″	3′11″	3′3½″	8½″	10′6″	4′5″	5′11″	6′4″	9′6″	39,600
	82	6′5″	6′7½″	7′4″	4′0″	3′3½″	9″	12′0″	4′5″	5′11″	7′2″	9′6″	43,600
	100	6′8″	6′7½″	7′4″	4′2″	3′3½″	9½″	14′6″	4′5″	5′11″	8′4″	9′6″	51,600
25	25	5′10″	7′4″	2′8″	3′2″	3′3″	7¼″	11′0″			6′7″	8′8″	33,900
	40	6′1″	7′4″	2′8″	3′2″	3′3″	8½″	11′0″			6′7″	8′8″	38,200
	62	6′1½″	7′4″	2′8″	3′2″	3′3½″	9″	12′0″			6′7″	8′8″	42,500
	80	6′3″	7′4″	2′8″	3′3″	3′3½″	9″	12′0″			7′1″	8′10″	47,000
	100	6′8″	7′4″	2′8″	3′3″	3′3½″	9½″	14′6″			8′6″	8′10″	55,000
30	25	5′10½″	6′8″	2′10″	3′3″	3′3″	7¼″	12′0″			7′1″	9′3″	39,700
	40	6′4½″	6′8″	2′10″	3′3″	3′3″	8½″	12′0″			7′1″	9′3″	44,000
	62	6′1½″	6′8″	2′10″	3′4″	3′3″	9″	12′0″			7′1″	9′3″	48,000
	80	6′5½″	6′8″	2′11″	3′4″	3′3″	9½″	12′0″			7′4″	9′3″	53,000
	100	6′9½″	6′8″	2′11″	3′4″	3′3″	9½″	14′6″			8′6″	9′3″	60,500
30 and 5-ton aux.	25	5′10½″	6′8½″	6′11″	3′7½″	3′3½″	7¼″	12′0″	4′6″	6′0″	7′1″	10′2″	42,400
	40	6′4½″	6′8½″	6′11″	3′7½″	3′3½″	7¾″	12′0″	4′6″	6′0″	7′1″	10′2″	46,400
	62	6′2½″	6′8½″	6′10″	3′9″	3′3½″	9″	12′0″	4′6″	6′0″	7′1″	10′2″	50,900
	82	6′6½″	6′8½″	6′10″	3′11″	3′3½″	9½″	12′0″	4′6″	6′0″	7′0″	10′2″	55,900
	100	6′9½″	6′8½″	6′10″	3′11″	3′3½″	9½″	14′6″	4′6″	6′0″	8′6″	10′2″	63,400

the reactions from these lateral loads to the columns. No reliance is to be placed upon the connection of the bottom flange of the girder for this purpose because of the tipping tendency of the girder itself. For some of these details, see Figs. 9·15 and 9·19.

5. Longitudinal live loads for each line of girders—20 per cent of the vertical wheel loads without impact. This force is due to tractive or braking forces and to longitudinal pull on lifted loads. The seats or other connections of the girders should be able to deliver these forces to the vertical longitudinal bracing of the runway.

6. All these loads are to be applied through the wheels and at the locations causing maximum stresses.

7. The laterally unsupported length of simply supported girders should be the distance center to center of lateral connections to the columns or other lateral supports. When the girders are continuous for vertical and horizontal action, the unsupported length of the top flange, when there are no lateral connections except at the columns, may be called $0.8L$ for fully continuous girders and $0.9L$ for those having continuity at one end only, L being the span center to center of supports.

8. When more than one crane is on a given runway and the nearest wheels of adjacent cranes are not over 15 ft. apart, the vertical impact loads may be considered as applicable to one crane only, but the lateral and longitudinal forces should be included for both cranes because they may pull laterally or longitudinally at the same time.

9. For vertical loads the stresses in the extreme top and bottom fibers of crane girders should be found on the basis of a composite section, omitting the rail; the lateral loads should be considered as resisted by the entire effective top flange as a composite member; and the resultant maximum fiber stresses should be computed. The critical stresses may be assumed as those obtained by algebraically adding the stresses caused by both of the preceding calculations. If the girder is a double (box) member, centrally loaded, and if proper provision is made for the transfer of longitudinal shears and torsional forces between the two main parts of the double girder, it may be considered as a composite unit. The longitudinal loads generally have little effect upon a crane girder as a whole, but they must be provided for in the longitudinal bracing and the connections at the supports of the member. The allowable stresses in the girders may depend very largely upon their lateral stiffness and the provisions made to guard against twisting of the flanges and buckling of the "wing" stiffening parts. [See the brackets in Figs. 9·14(d) and (e).]

Some typical sections of crane girders are shown in Fig. 9·14. Comments about the various sketches follow:

(a) This is a wide-flange rolled beam. It is for light loads and short spans. The rail is held by pairs of hooked bolts placed about 2 ft. apart, permitting lateral adjustment. They are used when the girder flanges are narrow, but they should not be used for heavy, speedy cranes.   A cover plate may be added on the top flange when greater lateral strength is needed.

(b) This is a modification of (a), having a channel connected to the web for lateral stiffness.   It is advisable in this case to design the beam alone to carry

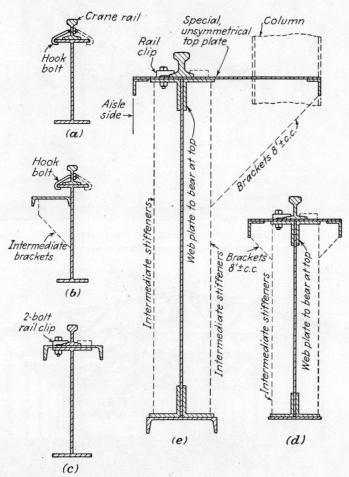

FIG. 9·14.   Some typical crane girders.

all vertical loads, and the channel to support all the lateral ones.   Hook bolts or clips may be used to hold the rail.

(c) Here is a customary type for medium loads and moderate spans.   The rail is attached by bolted clips which permit a small adjustment.   For very heavy loads (about 50 tons and over) and high speeds, these clips should have two bolts each to prevent twisting.   They should be placed alternately because,

Fig. 9·15. Steel framing and reinforced-concrete foundations for the upper crushers, secondary crushing plant of Morenci Reduction Works, Phelps Dodge Corp.

Fig. 9·16. Time-saving construction and low-cost erection were the results of a recently completed building of welded design to be used as a brass foundry by the Hays Manufacturing Co., Albion, Pennsylvania. Constructed of prefabricated trusses and columns, the building has a floor space of 11,645 sq. ft. and is 209 ft. in length and 52½ ft. in width. The height from the floor to the bottom member of the truss is 17 ft.; and to the ridge of the roof, 34 ft. 7 in. (*Courtesy of the Lincoln Electric Co., Cleveland, Ohio.*)

if opposite each other, so many holes at one location may weaken the member. The spacing of the clips may be 2 ft. c.c. along each side for heavy loads and high speeds, 2 to 3 ft. in other cases. These attachments are very important.

(*d*) These girders are for heavy loads and long spans. If the top corner angles have a clear distance of more than 2 or 3 in. from the inner angles and if the former are larger than 4 by 4 by ½, one should consider using brackets about 5 to 10 ft. c.c. to support them.

(*e*) This type was used for the 50-ft. crane girders shown in Fig. 9·17 to carry two 60-ton high-speed cranes. The unsymmetrical top was due to keeping the aisle side lined up with the flanges of the 20-ft. adjacent girders; the wide side was to provide the necessary width of flange for lateral stiffness and to permit satisfactory connections for lateral forces at the columns.

One trouble to be guarded against in all cases where rail clips are used is interference between rivets and rails, also proper edge distances for the bolt holes in the beam flanges. Wide flanges and flange angles, or welded construction, generally eliminate this difficulty. Of course, care must be taken to see that the omission of rivets at the clips does not cause a weak spot for resistance to longitudinal shear, or permit buckling

FIG. 9·17. Framing along one side of the converter aisle of the smelter at the Morenci Reduction Works. Notice the heavy framing and bracing, the 50-ft. girders for two 60-ton cranes, and the 300-ton bin behind the girder at the left.

of the cover plates; hence the possible advantage of staggering the clips. The rivets or welds attaching the flanges to the web must take care of longitudinal shear plus the wheel concentrations; planing the web plate of a built-up girder like Fig. 9·14(*d*) and setting it flush with the tops of the upper angles will permit the wheel loads to be delivered directly to the web. For computing stresses in rivets and welds, the load from a wheel may be considered to be spread over a length of girder top flange equal to about 2 or 2½ times the combined vertical depth of rail and flange angles. Welding of the rails to the girders may cause the former to crack, the rails cannot be adjusted for alignment later, and replacement of the rails will be difficult.

The connections of crane girders to their supporting columns are sometimes sources of weakness and trouble.   One of the inherent difficulties is shown in very exaggerated scale in Fig. 9·18, which assumes light, simply supported crane girders seated on the flange of a column, as in Fig. 9·19(b).   When the member on the left is loaded, the girder deflects, causing it to "ride" the edge of its support If the neutral axis remains in the same position as before loading, the bottom flange elongates and tends to slide along a distance d at each end, deforming the bolt as shown unless one of the girders has slotted holes to permit

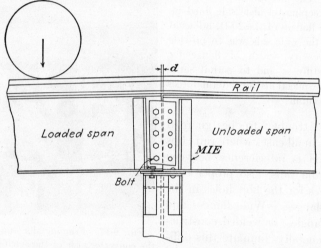

Fig. 9·18.   Action of simply supported crane girders under concentrated loading.

this motion, or unless the column moves with the bottom flange.   The top flange correspondingly opens a space that tends to produce tension in the rail or to slide the rail along the girder.   The end of the loaded girder tends to lift up so that, if the flange of the column is wide, the former tries to lift the other girder slightly.   The angular rotation also tends to kink the rail at the junction of the beams.   The closer the rail clips are to the joint, the more violent is the stress condition in the rail and the tension in the clip bolts due to the rail's trying to lift itself off the top of the unloaded girder.   When the truck wheels are on both sides of the joint, the opening and curvature conditions affecting the rail and the girder connections may be even worse.   Cutting the rail at the joint relieves the stress but is objectionable from the standpoint of operation, because of the presence of so many splices.

These details of movements and rotations may be even more serious

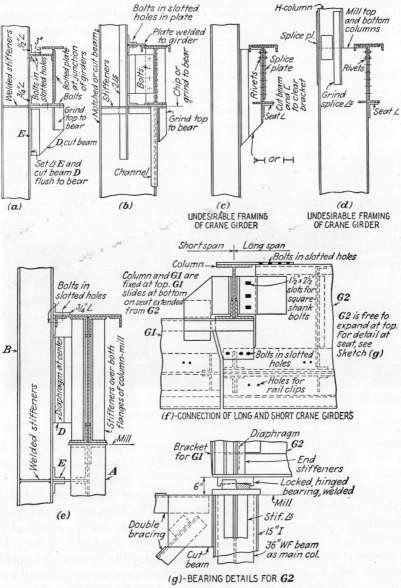

Fig. 9·19. Some details of supports for crane girders.

when so-called "simply supported" crane girders are riveted or welded directly to column flanges or brackets, as shown in Figs. 9·19(c) and (d). When the cranes are heavy, the angular rotations are likely to overstress the end connections because they are not designed to resist these rotations; as a result, the joint is likely to be worked back and forth until it fails. The column or bracket cannot bend sidewise with the loaded girder because the connection of the other girder resists this motion. Such connections should not be made for simply supported crane girders; it would be better to seat the girders as in the other cases shown in Fig. 9·19. In these pictures, notice the lateral supports of the girders, which permit angular movement in a vertical plane without allowing

FIG. 9·20.   The silica bins, converter uptakes, and continuous 20- and 40-ft. crane girders in the Morenci smelter of the Phelps Dodge Corp.

tipping. The vertical diaphragms must warp as necessary; the slotted holes in the top clips should be so located that the bolts are in shear when lateral forces are applied.

The preceding discussion shows that stiffness of crane girders is desirable in order to minimize these motions. The deflection at mid-span should also be small enough so that the crane operator does not feel a yielding and sagging effect with a corresponding hard spot at the columns; in other words, the crane motion should not be bumpy. The permissible deflection at mid-span is not a definite, specifiable quantity for all cases. As a guide, it may be limited to $L/1,000$ for ordinary conditions, or even less if the cranes are heavy, high-speed ones.

When foundations permit it (no likelihood of serious differential settlement), continuous crane girders are ideal to minimize vertical deflection of the members and harmful motions at the supports. The splices of these continuous girders should be made near the quarter point of a span, using as long sections as shipment and erection make desirable.   The splices should develop the necessary bending strength.   These continuous girders may be bolted tightly at the bottom, whereas play is permitted in the lateral connections near their tops to allow angular motion of the girder but not transverse tipping.   The lateral connections may be somewhat the same as in Fig. 9·19, but they need not be double. Some similar details for continuous girders can be seen in Fig. 9·15. However, continuous girders should not be used if adjacent spans vary by more than about a ratio of 2:1 because of uplift at the far end of the short span when the long one is loaded.   Such a continuous construction with alternate 20- and 40-ft. spans is shown in Fig. 9·20.   It is obvious that such girders eliminate much of the detail troubles that are inherent in the simply supported ones pictured in Fig. 9·17.   The important details of the bearing of the 50-ft. girder are shown in Fig. 9·19(g).

The use of continuous crane girders seems to have a great many advantages because of the reduction of the rotations and movements that would occur at the supports of simply supported members, and because of the better transfer of lateral and longitudinal forces.   This is regardless of any possible saving in the material composing the girder. The argument that unequal settlement of foundations may upset the assumptions on which the design was based is not a good one.   An engineer ought not to build such poor foundations.

One interesting but unusual case of the advantage of continuity is this: the bracket forming an intermediate support of a continuous, seated crane girder suddenly gave way under the passage of the crane. The failure was seemingly caused by fatigue of the material.   Although the girder sagged badly, it held the crane.   The member was jacked up, and the support was repaired.   Fortunately, this girder was designed for stiffness as well as for unit stress.   The fact that it held the crane not only saved the thousands of dollars that a new crane would cost but it probably saved human life and avoided the great loss that would have occurred because of the suspension of plant operations.   Both the owner and the designer were grateful.

Many are the problems that arise when lateral supports for long-span crane girders are planned, for which the buckling tendency of the top flange would be serious.[1]   These problems should be solved when one is planning the general framing scheme of a structure.   The following examples may illustrate some of the principles to bear in mind:

[1] The permissible unit stress in bending is generally limited by the L/b requirement of the design specifications.

1. Behind the 40-ft. spans shown in Fig. 9·20 are two struts and the other members pictured in Fig. 9·21(*a*). The inclined beams holding the converter hood rails are supported by a sliding joint on these struts; hence the deflections and vibrations caused by the crane girders are not completely transmitted to the hood framing. The platforms shown near the bottom of Fig. 9·20 could

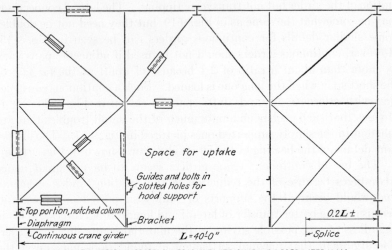

Space for uptake

*Guides and bolts in
slotted holes for
hood support*

Top portion, notched column *Bracket* $0.2L\pm$
Diaphragm
Continuous crane girder   *L = 40ᴸ0"*   *Splice*

(***a***)-PLAN OF PLATFORM SUPPORTS AND BRACING TO STEADY CRANE GIRDER LATERALLY

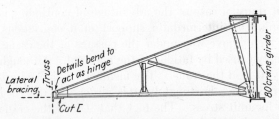

*Details bend to
act as hinge*

*Lateral
bracing*   *Truss*

80'crane girder

Cut L

(***b***)-BRACES 20'± C.C. TO PREVENT TIPPING AND PROVIDE LATERAL SUPPORT

FIG. 9·21. Illustrations of lateral supports for long crane girders.

have been hung conveniently from these struts, but they were carried on supports from below rather than to have the vibrations transmitted into them.

2. An 80-ft., simply supported, crane girder was steadied as shown in Fig. 9·21(*b*). The lateral struts were made triangular in shape so as to hold the girder against tipping; the struts were partially hinged at one end to allow rotation. The hinged connections were supported by the lateral bracing of the adjoining roof.

3. Behind the 50-ft. crane girder shown in Fig. 9·17 are two 300-ton charge bins for a reverberatory furnace. The bin framing could have connected to

the center of the girder and thereby steadied the latter, but the deflections of
the girder under load would have caused detrimental warping and vibration of
the bins.   Therefore, the top flange of the crane girder was made as shown in
Fig. 9·14(e), thereby being able to span the full 50 ft.; the bottom flange was
stiffened with a channel as a cover plate, automatically improving its appearance and making it look stiff, strong, and more in harmony with the massive
top flange.

In mill buildings with several parallel and adjacent crane aisles, there
are likely to be crane girders on both sides of interior columns.   These
girders may be the same size or may differ, and they may or may not
be at the same level.   Figures 9·25 and 9·26 illustrate some possible
cases.   Even when the girders are the same size and their tops are at
the same elevation, the girders should be made entirely self-supporting
vertically and laterally.   At first glance, one would think it an excellent
idea to lace the two tops together so as to form a horizontal truss which
would automatically stiffen both girders laterally.   However, since either
girder can be loaded alone, it will deflect with respect to the unloaded
one.   This action would warp the lacing back and forth and result in overstressing or at least fatigue failure.   The addition of vertical diaphragms
between the girders in order to prevent differential vertical deflections will cause twisting of the combined member and lateral as well as
vertical movement of the top flanges.   Furthermore, the shortening (or
any longitudinal deformation) of the top flange of the loaded girder will
produce stressing or an accordionlike action of the lacing, which might
bring about its disintegration.
Various tricks might be resorted to in order to support adjacent
crane girders laterally.   For instance, one might argue that a pinned
strut between the top flanges at the center of the span would brace one
girder against the other, canceling adjacent lateral forces or at least
utilizing both girders to support the side thrust acting on the loaded
one.   This is unwise.   The crane girders are likely to have the buckling
tendencies of both, and the lateral forces on both, acting together in the
same direction; then, of course, each must take care of itself.   The
designer should remember that a structure does not need to fall down
more than once.   This once is what he wishes to avoid.
The possibility of future alteration of the structure is another reason
why each one of the crane girders should be self-sufficient.   If they are
so, one girder may be removed, relocated, and replaced by a heavier one
without disturbing its neighbor.
Among other details to plan in connection with crane runways are
the following:

1. Determine the locations and attachments of the conductors as shown in Fig. 9·17.

2. The bumpers must be located so as to avoid collision between the crane and the end of the structure.

3. Access to the cab of a crane from the floor may be by ladder up a column, but a stairway is preferable.

4. A trolley hoist—or beams for the attachment of one—should be installed in the roof over the runway so that crane motors and other parts may be removed quickly for repairs.   Access to this hoist must also be provided.

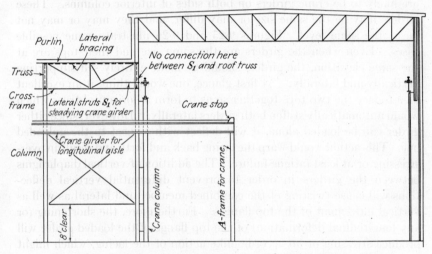

Fig. 9·22.   Transverse crane across series of longitudinal crane aisles.

5. When more than one crane is working on a given runway, it may be advisable to make the runway long enough so that a disabled crane can be pushed to either end where it can be repaired without interfering with the operation of the other crane.   In such a case, a hoist and a repair platform alongside the crane with access by a stairway may be desirable at each end of the runway.

6. When there are a series of parallel crane runways, a small crane running crosswise of and above the main ones may be desirable for repair purposes.

7. If a transverse crane is to be used in the handling of materials from one crane aisle to another, it may be planned as shown in Fig. 9·22.   If so, the lateral bracing to steady its supports over the main crane aisles may need special attention.

8. When a crane runway extends outside of a building to a storage yard, as shown in Fig. 9·23, special end doors may be required.

Additional matters affecting the planning of crane girders and runways will be given in Arts. 9·6 and 9·11.

9·6   Building and Crane Columns.   The columns of steel mill buildings are generally tall, slender, and subjected to bending in addition to compression.   The height results from the proportions of most such buildings; the slenderness is because steel is a high-strength material. Some of the bending may be caused by wind blowing against the side of the building and curving the columns inward between the trusses and foundations; some may be produced by the tendency of the wind to shove the building sidewise and cause the frame action pictured in

Fig. 9·23.   A-frames and crane doors for the crane runways at the west end of the furnace refinery extension of the Phelps Dodge Refining Corp., El Paso, Texas.

Figs. 9·4(*d*) and (*e*).   It is therefore natural and logical to use H- or I-beams as columns.   Of course, columns can also be built up by using plates and angles, but the cost of fabrication is usually sufficient to render them uneconomical except for unusual conditions; they may be used, too, for duplicating existing members that were made that way.

The webs of columns should be perpendicular to the exposed side of a building so that the maximum strength and stiffness of each member can be utilized in both column and beam action because the large unsupported height about the axis of the member parallel to the wall is the critical one.   Bracing in the plane of the wall should be used to reduce the unsupported lengths affecting the L/r for the weaker axis parallel to the webs.

Ordinarily, corner columns should be placed with their webs in the same direction as the main roof trusses even though no truss connects to them. These columns are then capable of receiving trusses in case of future extensions, and the typical wall framing will fit these corner columns.

Simple mill-building columns should be designed for the maximum conditions of direct loads and the bending caused by wind. It is also very important for the designer to provide for any gib cranes or other equipment that may bend them. Columns are very important members.

Fig. 9·24. Erection of welded rigid-frame construction for the new research laboratory of the Air Reduction Co. near Providence, New Jersey. The central span is 60 ft.; the side aisles, 40 ft. A machine shop will be at the right, and laboratories at the left. (*Courtesy of the Air Reduction Co.*)

A truss, beam, or girder may give way without completely wrecking the building whereas, when a column fails, everything attached to it will come down, too.

The columns supporting cranes may be separate members, or they may be the same ones that hold up the building. Generally, crane columns are rather long because of the large clearances required. The lateral forces caused by the crane operations produce overturning and bending tendencies which must generally be resisted by the building columns, or by them and the crane columns combined. As it is important to provide lateral strength and sturdiness for any crane runway, the columns must be both strong and stiff.

Crane columns can be made in a variety of styles if they are properly designed. It is easy to see that crane brackets on the sides of the building columns, as shown in Figs. 9·10 and 9·19(a), constitute one simple arrangement, but they cause severe bending moments in the columns if the crane loads are large. The use of separate columns under the cranes, as shown in Fig. 9·19(e), is advisable for very heavy loads because it eliminates this bending, but it is uneconomical for small loads. A notched beam such as that pictured in Fig. 9·19(b) is a satisfactory column when the cranes are not too heavy. Table 9·2 gives suggestions regarding the crane loads for which these three general types of column are suitable. However, framing conditions and the preference of the designer may govern the choice of the type to be used in a given case.

Table 9·2

Type of crane column	Capacity of crane, tons	Span of crane bridge, ft.	Span of crane girders, ft.
Brackets on building column . . .	Up to 7½	Up to 60	Up to 25
Notched column. See Fig. 9·19(b).	7½ to 75	Up to 100	Up to 50
Double column. See Fig. 9·19(e).	Over 75	Any reasonable limit	Any reasonable limit

In the case of the notched column like those in Fig. 9·15, the crane girder is supported on one flange. Below the notch, the deep beam resists the bending tendencies; above the notch, the extension that carries the roof and wall framing must resist the bending moments. It is easily seen, therefore, that the junction of the extension with the heavy beam must be strongly spliced. In many cases such as Figs. 9·17 and 9·19(b), the flange that supports the crane may be reinforced with a cover plate, channel, or I-beam. This stiffener or reinforcement is very useful for the following reasons:

1. Area is added where the compression caused by the vertical crane and building loads is the greatest because the crane loads are generally larger than those produced by the roof and walls. The moment of inertia of the column is also increased.

2. The unbalancing of flanges causes the neutral axis of the column below the notch in Fig. 9·19(b) to move toward the right. This decreases the lever arm to the edge that is under the crane, thereby reducing the bending stresses that must be added to the direct compressive ones at this point.

3. The radius of gyration of the column about an axis parallel to the web of the main I-beam is increased, making the column less slender in a direction parallel to the wall.   Because of the emphatic lack of symmetry of the column shaft, there is doubt as to how this radius of gyration should be computed.   As

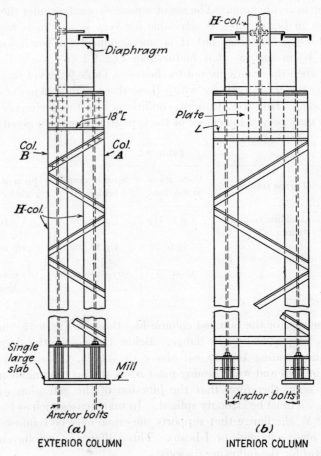

FIG. 9·25.   Laced double crane columns.

a free-standing member, it is difficult to see how the reinforcement of one flange of a 24-in. beam with a 12-in. channel will help the other flange 2 ft. away if the latter "decides" to buckle sidewise.   It seems to be more sensible to compute $r = \sqrt{I/A}$ for the reinforced portion as though it were composed of the channel and the adjacent half of the I-beam whereas r for the unreinforced flange is that of the half-beam alone.   The wall bracing should then be designed to provide safe unsupported lengths of each part of the column.

4. The reinforced flange along the crane aisle is less likely to be kinked if hit during operations—and this frequently happens. The column may also be used more effectively as a support for gib cranes and other auxiliary equipment.

The double column of Fig. 9·19(e) has some important advantages for very heavy loads. The following points should be noted:

1. All the crane loads can be applied centrally on column A, which can be made almost any size.

2. The crane column has its web parallel to the girders, and the end stiffeners of the crane girders are placed over the flanges of the column. This is a great advantage if the girders are simply supported.

3. In the illustration, the building column B is placed with its strong axis to resist wind and crane lateral forces. In many cases it should be designed to support these by itself.

4. The diaphragms E connecting columns A and B should be strong in a horizontal plane in order to support A against buckling sidewise and to hold A and B in the proper relationship. The diaphragms may be about 4 or 5 ft. c.c.; they may also be backed up by stiffeners on the web of B if there is insufficient lateral bracing to hold the columns properly. In this case, the diaphragms E are purposely made flexible vertically so that they will not "drag" stresses caused by crane loads across from column A to column B—called "participation stresses."

5. Another method of connecting the two columns is shown in Fig. 9·25. In this case, the two shafts and the lacing constitute a built-up member which will be able to resist lateral forces as a vertical beam cantilevered up from the foundation. However, the secondary and participation stresses in the columns and the lacing caused by unequal loading should be investigated and provided for. Having the two columns the same depth and facing the same way makes simple details and a strong member, but lateral forces will bend the top extension of the building column about the weak axis. The Warren-type lacing shown in Fig. 9·25(a) is preferable to a system having diagonal and horizontal members because it produces less participation of column B in the vertical action of column A under crane loads because there can be an accordionlike action.

The construction shown in Fig. 9·26 appears to be rather complicated. It illustrates one method of supporting two crane girders at different levels, using riveted construction. As the cranes are of unequal capacity, two different girders are shown. The roof trusses are carried by an extension of the main column. This problem is met frequently in large mill buildings having several parallel crane aisles. Figure 9·25(b) pictures another arrangement that can be used when conditions permit it.

9·7 Column Bases. The bases of mill-building columns generally must resist lateral forces and bending moments as well as vertical loads. The last can be provided for by means of steel billets or built-up bases which have sufficient area and strength to spread the loads over a suitable area of the concrete foundation. The bending moments, however, can be troublesome. If the restraint at the base is relied upon in the design, means must be provided to develop it.

The tilting of a column, as shown in Fig. 9·27(a), automatically causes a resisting moment if the resultant of the vertical loads is somewhat as indicated in the picture. The vertical load P is assumed to act at or near the center of the column. When the latter tilts so as to ride the compression flange, the resultant righting moment caused by the vertical load alone is PL. Unless the column is very deep and the dead load is very heavy, this moment PL should not be relied upon. One is wiser if he makes the connection between the column and the foundation strong enough so that the moment Td, Fig. 9·27(a), is sufficient to resist the overturning moment. The bending of the base angles is likely to be severe, or even excessive.

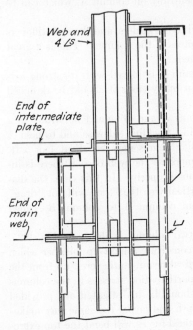

Web and 4 ∠s →

End of intermediate plate

End of main web

FIG. 9·26. Details at an interior crane column.

One simple type of column base, shown in Fig. 9·27(b), is a satisfactory arrangement for small overturning moments. As previously stated, any severe uplift will bend the angles and cause such large angular motions that the assumed restraint probably never materializes. The angles A should be about ¾ in. thick if they are to be reasonably stiff. This connection will, however, resist horizontal shearing forces by means of bearing of the angles upon the anchor bolts if friction alone is not enough to transmit the shearing forces, and if the column slides a little.

The "boots" composed of angles A and stiffeners B, pictured in Fig. 9·27(c), constitute one arrangement for developing large tensile forces in the anchor bolts without producing harmful yielding and rotation of the base. Not only must the tensile side be stiff, but the compressive side must have sufficient area and stiffness to avoid overstressing and buckling; therefore, riding the tips of flanges or plates may be dangerous. Figure 9·27(g) shows an arrangement that may be useful when projecting angles are undesirable.

When the double-shaft type of crane-and-building column is used, the crane column generally has a much larger vertical load than does the building column. If one large billet is used under both columns, as shown in Fig. 9·25(a), this will probably provide excessive steel under the building column; if two separate billets are used, as in Fig. 9·27(d), and if they have different thicknesses, errors in setting the plates or in fabricating the steelwork are likely to occur.

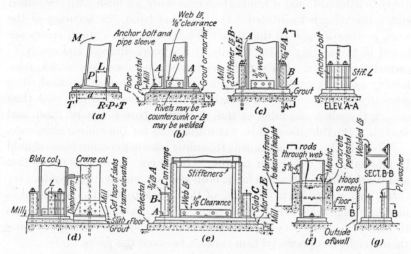

FIG. 9·27.   Some details of column bases.

The details adopted for any column bases should be selected with proper consideration of the erection of the steelwork. For a heavy, long column, the billet should be placed and carefully grouted first, then the column should be erected and connected to the billet and anchor bolts. It is both difficult and dangerous to erect a long column with an attached billet by hoisting the column, setting its base on wedges or shims, plumbing it, and steadying it until the base is grouted and the grout has thoroughly set. Furthermore, provision should be made for erecting heavy billets by a crane. In Figs. 9·27(b), (c), and (e), notice especially the "web" angles attached to the billets so that the rivet or bolt holes permit the use of pins around which a sling or hook can be placed when the slabs are lifted. The rivets attaching the web angles to the billets have button heads on the bottom. These rivets might be countersunk, or the angles could be welded on, but the rivet heads will serve as lugs to resist shearing forces if necessary, and they seldom cause any interference. Further discussion of the setting and grouting of column bases is given in Arts. 14·3 and 14·4.

The number and size of anchor bolts should be determined upon the basis of the tensions and shears to be withstood. Because of corrosion, the computed unit stress in the anchor bolts should not exceed about 60 to 75 per cent of that ordinarily allowable in structural steel.

The milling of column bases is a subject that often causes considerable argument. If the shaft only is milled square and the base details are then attached, and if the bottom angles are set flush with the milled end, fabrication is facilitated. On the other hand, the accuracy of the work is always open to question. When, after fabrication, errors are found in the setting of the details, it is always difficult and costly to correct the trouble. For very heavy important bases with angles, reinforcing plates, gussets, etc., which are to help spread the load, it is generally worth the cost of attaching all base material first and then milling the whole assembly so that the entire base is square, flush, and smooth. Provide about $\frac{1}{8}$ in. extra thickness for the milling allowance.

There is also much argument regarding whether column bases should be fabricated by welding or riveting. If the column shaft is milled first and the details are attached later, both welding and riveting require very careful placing and firm clamping of the details to avoid slight displacements during the welding or riveting. Tack welding of column bases to billets is satisfactory if performed after the columns are erected and their weight has produced firm contact between the parts.

The bases of columns are too often allowed to become dirty, thereby collecting and holding moisture. This aggravates the corrosion of the steelwork. It is desirable in many cases to place the bases on concrete pedestals 3 to 6 in. above the floor as indicated in Fig. 9·27(e). If thick enough, the grout or mortar serves to elevate the column somewhat, as indicated in Fig. 9·27(c).

Inasmuch as the column bases project beyond the shafts, some engineers bury the bases in concrete below the floor. This presents a neat appearance but is likely to cause serious corrosion of the steel where the latter enters the concrete; and the construction is more difficult. When encasement of the bottom of a column is necessary or desirable, it should be properly made if cracking of the concrete is to be avoided. Some suggested details are shown in Fig. 9·27(f).

9·8 Bracing in General. The function and importance of bracing in mill buildings should not be overlooked or neglected. Such buildings are generally flexible; they may be harmfully so. One of the best ways to consider the problem of bracing is to ask one's self "What may happen to my structure? How may it fail?" Then make sure that it will not fail that way. Besides providing strength alone, the bracing should produce sufficient rigidity. The latter is a statement that generally means different things to different people.

In many cases the use of bracing in a steel mill building is not dependent upon actual determinable forces. In other cases the known forces are so light that the bracing is not designed upon the basis of permissible unit stresses. It is often advisable to use bracing very largely from the standpoint of common sense, placing it where it is most advantageous and making it of such a size that it is stiff enough to avoid undue vibrations and movement of the structure.

It is customary and also advisable to brace many members that theoretically need no bracing. An instance of this is the bottom chords of trusses. Even though these members will never receive compressive forces, it is advisable to steady them laterally—perhaps every 20 to 25 ft.—so that some unforeseen action—hooking tackle to them, or otherwise causing them to distort—will probably not result in harm to the structure.

When bracing is double, as in the sides of mill buildings, where one set is in the line of the building column and the other in the line of the crane girders, it is advisable to tie the members together. Batten plates, as shown in the lower part of Fig. 9·17, are satisfactory for tension members, but lacing bars with batten plates at the ends, as pictured in the struts of Fig. 9·15, are far more satisfactory when members may take tension or compression, and when they may be subjected to lateral bending. It is often advisable to introduce small secondary members to break up the unsupported length of horizontal struts and long diagonals, to reduce the bending stresses caused in members by their own weight, and, if they carry compression, to minimize the eccentricity that such bending deflections will introduce into their action as compression members.

When studying the choice of tie-plated or laced members as bracing, one should consider the use of ¼-in. or other thin plates as a substitute for latticing when the members are not too wide. This arrangement provides built-up channels of whatever width is needed to connect to the column flanges, and the metal in the plates is useful as load-supporting material. Such plates may also be easier to paint and clean than lacing would be. Channels and beams are also useful as bracing.

When planning the bracing system of a structure, the designer should think of the building as a whole, because the horizontal and vertical bracing are so intimately related.   The entire system should be as simple, direct, positive, and effective as it is practicable to make it.   Each member should be sketched on the framing plans after the latter are drawn to scale, otherwise the designer may overlook the fact that the members are too long or too short, the intersections do not connect

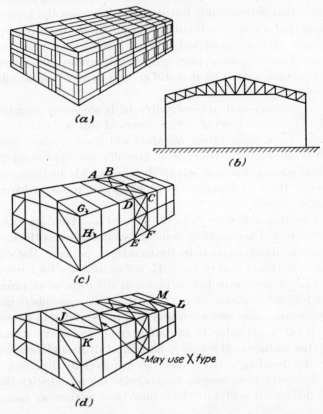

Fig. 9·28.   Bracing a building.

properly with other members, there may be missing links in the system, and the members may pass through openings or equipment which necessitate revision of the bracing.

In order to illustrate the method of approach, assume a small, simple building with framing as pictured in Fig. 9·28(a), a cross section of which is shown in Sketch (b).   The building may fail by flattening down vertically, tilting or bending over sidewise, or collapsing lengthwise like a series of cards.   When the trusses are stiff enough laterally and the columns cannot buckle, there is no need of bracing as far as the static condition for vertical loads is concerned because each bent will carry its own load without dependence upon any other part of the building. However, such a condition should not be trusted in practical structures.

The first need, even in the case of vertical loads, is the addition of struts and bracing such as $ABCD$ in Fig. 9·28(c) to keep the trusses from buckling laterally.   The second step is the addition of bracing $CDEF$ to avoid buckling of the columns and to resist any forces tending to tip

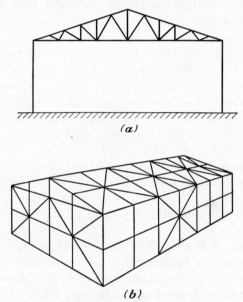

(a)

(b)

Fig. 9·29.   Bracing a building.

the bents lengthwise of the building.   The roof and wall bracing thus form a complete truss or tower system.   The purlins, the eave struts G, and the wall struts H connect the other trusses and columns·to this braced tower.   In this building, transverse loads must be resisted, and the structure must be steadied laterally by the frame action of the trusses and columns so that bracing is needed only in the gable end, as pictured in Fig. 9·28(c).   It is advisable, however, to install at least a light bracing system in the roof for the full length of the structure as pictured by $JKLM$ in Fig. 9·28(d), unless the roof sheathing and the roof covering have considerable stiffness.   The purpose of this bracing is to line up the building and to prevent any concentrated lateral loads from deforming the structure locally; this bracing is very important if there are cranes in the building.

Another basic method of bracing a mill building is pictured in Fig. 9·29. Sketch (a) is a cross section of the building. No knee braces are used between the trusses and columns, but the roof is strongly braced for its full length, as illustrated in Sketch (b). Thus the columns are steadied at the top, and the bracing of the roof delivers all lateral loads to strong vertical braces in the ends of the building. This method is often desirable for small, single-aisle buildings; it provides greater stiffness than generally is obtained through sidewise bending of tall, slender columns. However, when the building is longer than approximately 200 ft., the advantages of this system decline because of the length of the lateral trusses.

It is ordinarily preferable to have one definite, predetermined, and adequate means of resisting any given loads. The provision of more than one bracing system to serve a given purpose is uneconomical and leads to uncertainty of action; however, multiple systems may be used for military or special purposes when the damaging of a specific truss, column, or other member must not cause complete failure. For example, the plant shown in Fig. 9·1, which was built in 1942, has complete cross frames in the high bays so that, if one truss should be injured, these braces would probably pick up its load sufficiently to prevent complete collapse.

Further and more detailed discussion of bracing will be given in subsequent articles.

9·9 Bracing of Roofs. The roofs of mill buildings are generally covered with relatively lightweight materials, and the truss spans are long. Pitched roofs are commonly used on narrow structures whereas some type of monitored, saw-tooth, or flat roof is best for wide buildings containing several parallel aisles. Although the bracing of these roofs seldom needs to be heavy, it serves a very useful function and its proper design is important.

Roof bracing may be in the plane of the top chords of the trusses, or it may be in the plane of the bottom chords. In the former case, the bracing can be bolted to the purlins so as to reduce the sagging of the members caused by their own weight. This also decreases the unsupported length of the diagonals. When the bracing must span open spaces in the plane of the bottom chords, the length of the diagonals is likely to be 25 to 30 ft.; hence the members must be heavier and stiffer, unless one frankly resorts to the use of adjustable tie rods placed under initial tension.

When approximately horizontal bracing members are composed of one or two angles, and when these members have a long span, it is best from the standpoint of bending and longitudinal loads to have the out-standing leg of each angle at the top, as shown in Fig. 9·30(a). This arrangement provides some lateral stiffness for the top flange of the member and, because of the eccentricity of the neutral axis, the compressive stresses are smaller than the tensile ones. On the other hand, the

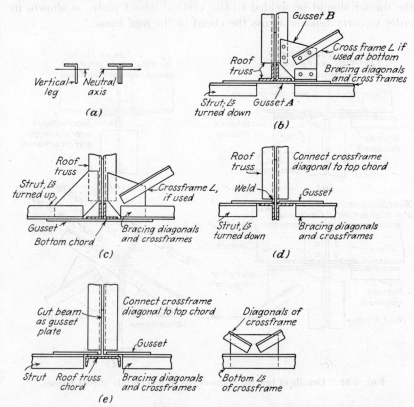

FIG. 9·30.   Details of bracing connections at bottom chords of roof trusses.

bracing projects below the truss chords so that it is conspicuous. This system is pictured in Fig. 9·30(b). If the bracing system is raised above the bottom chords, the details become needlessly complicated; the diagonal's components that act parallel to the truss will be eccentric with respect to the chord areas, causing a moment at the joint; and the tensile forces have to be carried across the roof truss by the bending of angle legs, or by tension in rivets or welds. Furthermore, the bracing will not steady the bottom chords of the main trusses unless special brackets are added. It is therefore common practice to place lateral bracing angles with the outstanding legs at the bottom as shown in Fig. 9·30(c). However, when the angles are long and subjected to large stresses, the arrangement of Fig. 9·30(b) should be considered if the bracing must be in the plane of the bottom chords. Other possible arrangements are given in Figs. 9·30(d) and (e). The chord angles of the former should be welded to the vertical gusset plate, as shown, in order to carry tension across the chord of the roof truss.

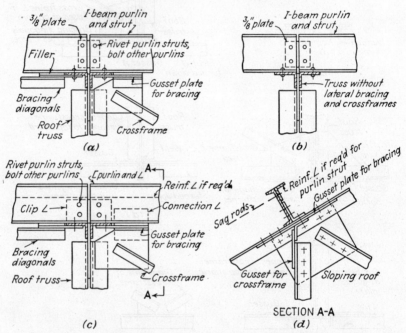

Fig. 9·31.   Details of bracing connections at top chords of roof trusses.

When the roof bracing is in the plane of the top chords of the truss, the details are simpler and the troubles that have been pointed out previously will generally vanish. Figure 9·31 shows some connections for such bracing. One of the greatest advantages is the fact that the slender diagonals, when connected to the purlins at all intersections, have such short unsupported lengths that these members have appreciable value in resisting compression even though they may be designed as tensile members only.

Seldom is it necessary or desirable in mill buildings to brace both top and bottom chords of roof trusses with separate lateral systems. On the other hand, both chords should be braced thoroughly—even the tensile chord should be steadied every 20 or 25 ft. so that its maximum L/r does not exceed 150 to 200, depending upon the importance and size of the trusses.   When the ends of bottom chords resist compression, the L/r in the compression zone should be limited to 120.   Such cases exist when there is frame action as shown in Fig. 9·4, and when the trusses are continuous.

In order to illustrate a method of supporting the trusses against buckling laterally, assume the simple case pictured in Fig. 9·32.   Sketch (a) shows the plan of the trusses and purlins; the lateral bracing is to be in the plane of the top chords.

As a first case, assume that single-angle tension members are to be used as diagonals, whereas certain purlins and the eave struts are to serve as compression members, thus forming a lateral truss with the roof trusses themselves acting as its chords.   The central bay is to contain the lateral bracing.   Referring to Fig. 9·32(b), notice the following points:

1. The diagonals are conveniently laid out at approximately 45°, thereby making the most desirable intersections with purlins and trusses.

2. The centers of the diagonals intersect at purlins B, D, and F, which are connected to the bracing, thus making the lateral unsupported length of the top chords of the roof trusses equal to 10 ft. instead of 20 ft.

3. Point A is a junction between the truss, column, eave strut, and bracing. This detail is likely to be complicated, and it is illustrated in Fig. 9·55(a).

4. When the roof has a steep slope, the intersection of the diagonals at the center of purlin F causes a downward component at the center of the purlin. This may be of little consequence unless this purlin (it may be two channels) at the ridge is long and flimsy; if so, the diagonals should be reversed as shown by the dotted lines intersecting at the center of purlin E, in which case the diagonals must be designed to resist compression as well as tension.

5. The purlins at C and E and the eave strut A are compression members in the bracing system.   If these purlins are channels and if they have reasonably large direct compressive loads as bracing members, they should be reinforced with an angle, as shown in Figs. 9·31(c) and (d), or an I-beam may be used for these particular purlins.

Another system for this roof bracing is shown in Fig. 9·32(c), in which the following should be noticed:

1. The K system of bracing is used throughout, so that the diagonals must carry either compression or tension.   This may be called a slight disadvantage.

2. The roof trusses are still supported laterally every 10 ft.

3. Complicated details at the ends of eave strut A are avoided—an advantage.

4. The bracing connects to eave strut A at its mid-point.   This may be of some value in steadying the strut if the connection is high enough.

5. Purlins *B, C, D,* and *E* are all struts, possibly requiring more steel as reinforcement. Since the diagonals connect to the bottoms of these purlins, they are not very reliable braces for supporting the purlins laterally.

A third system, shown in Fig. 9·32(*d*), combines most of the good features of both the systems pictured in Sketches (*b*) and (*c*). Notice the following:

1. The bracing connects at the center of eave strut *A* and avoids complicated details at the columns.
2. Only purlins *B, D,* and *F* are struts.
3. All except the end panel have tension diagonals only.
4. The diagonals connect at the ends of purlin *F* and at the peak of the roof truss—an advantage.
5. By itself, this trussing seems to be satisfactory. It is advisable, however, to investigate its relation to the other trusses and to the columns in the ends of the building. This last relationship will be explained in connection with Fig. 9·33.

With some other framing arrangement, almost any special bracing system may be worked out to secure desired results. For instance, Fig. 9·32(*e*) shows a suggested system for nine panels in the half truss. Purlins *K* and *L* are held partly by the bracing, but, technically, the unsupported length of the top chords of the roof trusses is *JM* unless the dotted members *QR* and *ST* are added. However, since this requires more members, the arrangement in Fig. 9·32(*f*) may be even better.

In order to brace the other roof trusses shown in Fig. 9·32(*a*), all the purlins in the lines of the struts of the lateral bracing should be sufficiently well connected in series and to the respective roof trusses so that each truss is tied to the braced bay. Figure 9·31 shows some such connections. These purlins are usually stiff enough to resist any buckling of the truss chords. If, however, heavy thrusts from the end walls must be transmitted through the roof to this central lateral system, the entire row of purlins corresponding to the struts of the lateral system should be designed as members subjected to compression and bending. In such a case, it may be desirable to use a lateral system near each end of the building rather than to have one truss system near its center.

When a building is very long, these transverse lateral systems to steady the roof trusses should not be located with more than five unbraced bays between them, as illustrated in Fig. 9·33(*a*). Then truss T_1 can be considered as braced to T_2; T_4 and T_5, to T_3; and T_6 and T_7, to T_8. A similar limit of two trusses between the end of the building and T_2 is desirable.

None of these top-chord bracing systems previously discussed will prevent the trusses from tipping over lengthwise of the building like a series of cards. To illustrate how to prevent such action, assume the framing system shown in Fig. 9·33(a). Sketch (b) shows how the bot-

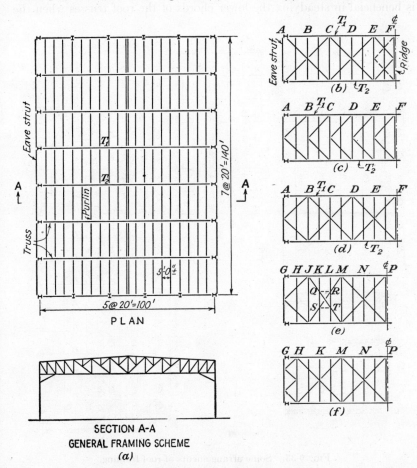

FIG. 9·32. Lateral bracing between roof trusses.

toms of the trusses now are unbraced. If bottom-chord struts are added as in (c), all trusses may still tip the same way; therefore, cross frames are installed to stop this, as pictured in Sketch (d). Preferably, these frames should be vertical, and they should be in the bays containing the transverse lateral bracing, but this is not essential. The purlin struts and bottom-chord struts must be strong.

Thus far, this roof bracing has been planned with consideration for itself alone.   What else should be considered?   Referring again to Fig. 9·33, Sketch (e) shows the cross frames with respect to the trusses of Sketch (a).   The presence of the outer lines of frames and struts at B is beneficial in steadying the lower chords of the roof trusses when the

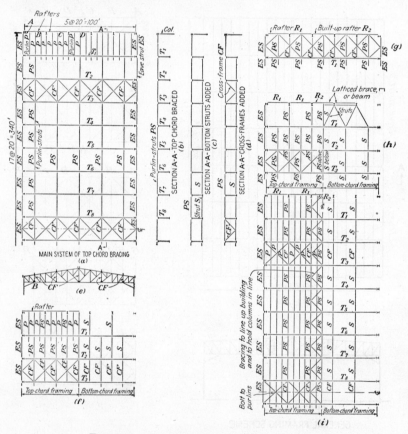

FIG. 9·33.   Some arrangements of roof framing.

knee braces carry compressive loads.   On the other hand, what holds the tops of the columns in the gable ends of the building?   These end columns are placed as shown in order to permit the use of large doorways at the ends of the central part of the main aisle.   Sketch (a) pictures their relationship to the framing as it now is.

The following schemes might be used to steady these gable columns, especially for resisting wind loads:

1. Design the purlins that are in line with the end columns as struts to deliver the wind loads to the lateral system. For wind loads, this causes these columns to act in bending as though their tops were hinged. The addition of knee braces from the columns to these purlins will cause some stiffening of the former but the latter are not generally very stiff. They would have to be reinforced to withstand both compression in the knee braces caused by pressure and tension in the braces resulting from suction.

2. Install bottom-chord struts, strengthen the purlins in line with the columns, and add cross frames as pictured in Sketch (f). This adds several members.

3. Move the lateral bracing to the end bays of the structure as shown in Sketch (g), add one more braced bay, and relocate all the bracing. Not only is this costly but the vertical cross frames, if located in these end bays, have certain disadvantages, which will be explained subsequently.

4. Strengthen the purlins in line with the end columns, and add diagonal struts from the columns to the bottom-chord struts as indicated in Sketch (h). If the columns are long and carry a heavy wind load, a double, latticed strut should be added between the columns to keep them from twisting.

5. Because each of the preceding arrangements is only a remedy for the situation that develops when the roof laterals are planned with no initial regard for the locations of the end columns, it is desirable to replan the entire bracing with proper consideration for this important item. This means that the purlin struts and bottom-chord struts should be in line with these columns; therefore, the arrangement shown in Sketch (i), which is the same as that of Fig. 9·32(b) with the central panel modified, is probably the best after all, provided the eave struts are adequate, the bottom chords of the trusses near the knee braces are stiff, and the details at the junctions of bracing and side columns are made properly.

This roundabout way of arriving at the final plan for the roof bracing is followed purposely so as to emphasize to the reader the fact that he should study the entire structure in order to find the important features which will affect the planning of the bracing before he decides what he is going to do about it. He can then take care of the important features first and overcome whatever detail troubles may be involved later. Furthermore, the preceding discussion describes various framing arrangements that can be used when they are desirable.

As a matter of detail, should a cross frame be made with its diagonals as shown in Fig. 9·34(a), (b), (c), or (d)? In general, the author prefers the first for the following reasons:

1. The bottom chord CD of the frame is supported at E.
2. When the diagonals intersect at F, the cross frame will support purlin

loads if possible; hence it should be designed to resist these forces. The strength of the typical purlin is sufficient without the help of the frame, unless it is to carry large compressive or tensile loads.

3. When the roof is sloping and the diagonals meet at F, there is a twisting or buckling action, as shown in Fig. 9·34(e). However, this does not exist in the case of flat roofs.

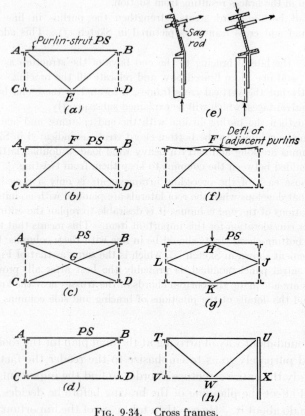

Fig. 9·34. Cross frames.

4. The purlins that are supported at F will deflect differently from the typical ones, as pictured in Fig. 9·34(f). This may produce "hard spots" in the roof and be undesirable.

5. Ordinarily, the proportions of bay widths and truss depths are such that frames like Figs. 9·34(c) and (d) are not practicable because the diagonals are too flat for proper details. The member CB in Sketch (d) is so long that it must be heavy in order to resist compressive forces. In the case of closely spaced, relatively deep trusses or girders, these systems may be satisfactory. Each case should be so designed that the members and the details of their

connections are as simple and economical as conditions permit. However, the entire frame must be strong enough to serve the purpose for which it is built.

Be careful to make each cross frame so that its members form proper truss triangles rather than parallelograms that act merely as "accordions" when subjected to forces. For example, a framework like that of Fig. 9·34(*g*) will try to carry a purlin reaction, but the frame will tend to spread points *L* and *J* apart whereas *H* and *K* draw together. This may be particularly harmful in bending the web members of the trusses. When such a frame is subjected to shears, it tends to twist the trusses.

FIG. 9·35. A runway for a 150-ton crane, showing auxiliary columns under continuous crane girders. Notice the framing at the end of the building and the laced struts between columns at the lower chords of the roof trusses. (*Courtesy of the Phelps Dodge Corp.*)

Furthermore, if member *AE* of Sketch (*a*) is omitted, the system is incomplete and its strength depends mostly upon the resistance of *CD* to bending.

When a cross frame, as pictured in Sketch (*h*), Fig. 9·34, connects truss *TV*, which deflects appreciably, with column *UX*, which has negligible deflection, the frame may be heavily stressed, or the truss and column may be bent. In such a situation, it is advisable to use the purlin strut *TU* and add the bottom-chord strut *VX*, letting them rotate or spring slightly if necessary and then connecting them to cross frames on the left side of truss *TV*. This use of two struts greatly stiffens column *UX* because, when subjected to bending under wind loads, the top portion of the member is strongly restrained.

When either chord of a roof truss is kinked, it is desirable to have the cross frames in line with the bend. This is illustrated in Fig. 9·35, where the trusses are similar to Fig. 9·3(c). Here the bend points of the

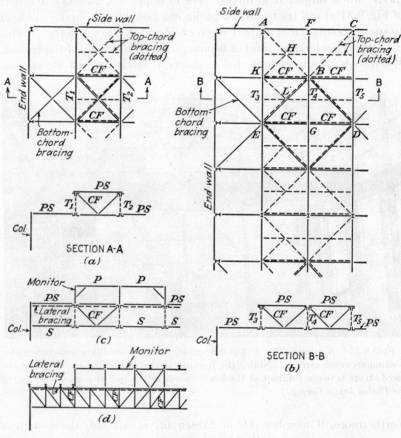

Fig. 9·36. Bracing for high-low-bay roofs.

trusses were purposely put in line with the gable-end columns. Since the latter are very high, cross frames are used in all the bays near the end of the building in order to brace the columns as well as possible; furthermore, the roof trusses are stiff enough so that the end cross frames can be used safely.

The bracing of monitors and high-low-bay roofs may be arranged in several different manners. For example, the sketches of Fig. 9·36 show the following:

(a) Each high bay has cross frames in the lines of the end columns, and there is lateral bracing between the top chords of trusses T_1 and T_2. Thus each pair of trusses is braced for its full length, but there is no bracing to hold various bays in line. Therefore, a truss system is installed across the trusses and in the plane of the bottom chords. It is best to have this last system in one plane and complete in itself because a system that steps from the low bay to the top of the next high bay and down again to the adjacent low one, etc., probably will not be rigid enough.

(b) These monitors are two bays wide. Cross frames between T_3 and T_4 are technically sufficient if T_5 is properly tied in to them. It is best, however, to add the other frame shown in B-B. The top-chord lateral system between T_3 and T_5 is shown in the form of a large X-type and is two bays wide. This scheme illustrates an important principle in planning bracing; i.e., the chords of this lateral system are trusses T_3 and T_5, thereby giving twice the truss depth that exists between T_1 and T_2 of Sketch (a), whereas it uses the same number of diagonal members. This increased depth is important when the bracing trusses are long and when the greater strength and stiffness are needed. On the other hand, the diagonals AD and CE do not brace the top chords of the roof trusses except at such points as F, B, and G. This makes the slenderness of these chords such that it is probably advisable to add the subdiagonals like HK, KL, etc., or even full-length diagonals FK and KG, in order to attach to intermediate purlins which in turn steady the chords. Longitudinal bracing is also used in the plane of the bottom chords of the roof trusses. This system can be in the bay next to the side-wall columns, but interior bays seem to be more desirable here. The greater depth of this bottom-chord bracing system is used as an illustration for the case of a very long building with heavy lateral crane loads; the diagonals are, however, so slender that they are probably worthless in resisting compression.

(c) With this arrangement having the monitors above the roof trusses, the bracing system of the roof can be planned in whatever way seems to be best. If the monitor posts are knee-braced, or steadied as pictured in Figs. 9·6(d) and 9·11(e) and (f), they are generally held sufficiently.

(d) Lengthwise of the trusses, a few knee braces or diagonals should be used in each row of posts. It is possible to use lateral bracing in the tops of the monitors, but this is seldom necessary when the main roof is braced adequately.

Saw-tooth roofs may be built in various ways. Figure 9·37 shows two possible framing schemes for vertical windows. In connection with these sketches, notice the following points:

(a) In this case, the roof trusses are set behind the windows in the sawteeth and frame directly into the columns. The purlins, trusses, and bottom-chord struts form a triangle. This steadies the trusses laterally, provided sufficient bracing is installed in the plane of the bottom chords. In this case, one system extends the full length of the trusses in every fourth or fifth bay; the other system across the trusses is for lining up the structure.

(*b*) Here is a roof in which the sawteeth are on top of and across the trusses. The lateral bracing in the portion *ABCD* is in the plane of the top chords; it is used in alternate bays in order to steady each pair of trusses. If the bottoms of the vertical portions of the sawteeth are connected properly, if the necessary bottom-chord struts are used, and if intermediate top-chord struts are added or the truss chords are designed for long unsupported lengths, this bracing could be used in every fifth or sixth bay only. The bracing in the portion *EFHG* is shown to be double-bay width and to extend clear across the building.

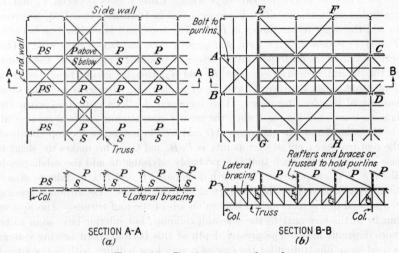

SECTION A-A
(*a*)

SECTION B-B
(*b*)

Fig. 9·37.   Bracing saw-tooth roofs.

9·10 Vertical Bracing of Ordinary Buildings. The type and details of vertical bracing to be used in a building depend upon many of the special features of the structure itself. The function of the bracing, however, is that of resisting forces that tend to tip the building in a direction parallel to the plane of that bracing. Also, the system is generally used to reduce the L/r of the columns in a direction parallel to the wall containing them.

Preferably, the vertical bracing in side walls should be in the form of local towers which are really continuations of the braced bays in the roof, as pictured in Figs. 9·28(*c*) and (*d*). Before deciding upon the positions of these towers and the members composing them, the designer should make certain just where every door, window, passageway, obstruction, and other possible controlling feature is located, doing this for both sides of the building and for all interior, parallel column rows. When any features make it inadvisable to have bracing in any particular bay in any column line, mark these bays on a plan of the building so that one can see at a glance which bays across the structure are available for bracing.   Where are these bays with regard to the roof bracing?   This will show the designer that he would be unwise to draw and design the latter before learning what the wall bracing might have to be.

It is desirable to have all the wall bracing lined up in the same bays across the building.   When this is not practicable, the wall framing should then be designed to carry the reactions from the roof bracing to wherever the towers are located.

What is the best position for the braced bays?   Figure 9·38(a) shows the side elevation of a long building, with the wall framing arranged for continuous windows and corrugated siding.   Suppose that bracing is placed as shown in Fig. 9·38.   The horizontal struts are located so that they line up with the girts, window sills, lintels, or whatever members give satisfactory proportions to the bracing panels.   For clarity, the side framing has been omitted from the sketches.   Referring to these pictures in Fig. 9·38 by sketch number, the following comments may be helpful:

(b) Bracing in the end bays seems to be logical.   However, this bracing cannot hold tightly for one purpose and simultaneously be loose or yielding for another.   The bracing must be tight and act immediately if it is to resist wind and other longitudinal forces without objectionable swaying of the structure.   On the other hand, changes in temperature are likely to be large in a building like this.   Assume that the maximum annual variation in temperature is 100°F.   Since the bracing is symmetrical, the building can be assumed to deform horizontally with respect to a fixed point at the center of the wall.   The total movement of the end columns will be approximately

$$\Delta = 0.0000065 \times 100 \times 150 \times 12 = 1.17 \text{ in.}$$

Assume that the building is erected at a mean or average temperature so that the movement of the end columns will be 0.58 in. either side of the normal position. The bracing tries to stop this motion, but, generally, the area of the wall framing is so large that the bracing will have to distort an amount nearly equal to this 0.58 in.   Perhaps the upper portion of the tower can deflect this amount without serious harm, but the bottom panel is very likely to be stressed beyond the yield point.   This is harmful because the bracing will then be permanently loosened or lengthened (the compression members will probably bow sidewise).   For example, if the top of a bracing panel 20 ft. square is displaced 0.58 in., the tension diagonal will have a stress of about $f = 30,000,000 \times (0.58 \cos 45°)/(240 \sec 45°) = 36,000$ psi.   If the bracing is made stronger it "fights" the thermal deformation even harder and may overstress the wall

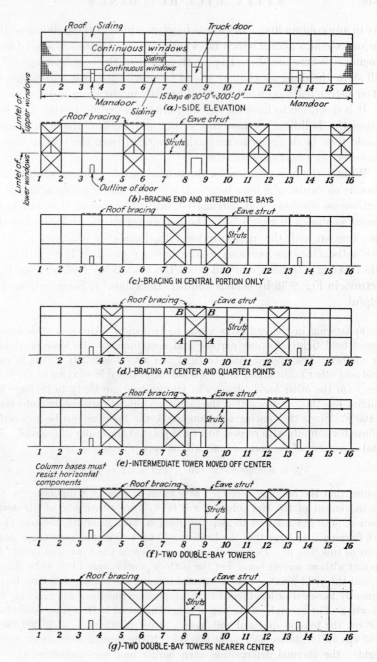

FIG. 9·38.   Some arrangements of wall bracing.

framing because, if a piece of steel is rigidly held and is subjected to a temperature change of 50° F., the resultant unit stress is

$$f = E\delta = 30{,}000{,}000 \times 0.0000065 \times 50 = 9{,}750 \text{ psi.}$$

This stress must be combined with whatever stresses already exist in the wall members. Although the actual condition probably lies between these two extremes, nevertheless the bracing should be located so as to minimize thermal stresses.

(c) This picture shows the obvious reaction to the difficulties of Sketch (b). Since the truck door is in the central bay, two bracing towers are placed alongside it. The eave struts and wall framing are then made strong enough to deliver any necessary loads to these towers. This arrangement eliminates overstressing of the bracing caused by temperature, but it also means that the columns near the ends of the building will bend somewhat because their bases cannot move. This bending, however, will not be severe if the lower line of struts is sufficiently high. The longitudinal forces must travel a long way from the ends of the building before they reach a reaction point. This arrangement is too extreme for this case even though the principle is correct.

(d) This sketch pictures a sort of compromise between Sketches (b) and (c). It shows the towers in the same bays as the roof bracing. The lower part of the central tower must act as a portal frame because of the doorway. The stiffness of this frame is so much less than that of the other towers (because of the sidewise bending of the columns) that it will be largely ineffective.

(e) Here the central tower is moved one bay to the left. This can be done because there is little harm due to the lack of symmetry.

(f) This sketch shows another arrangement, using two towers, each two bays wide. This greater width causes less stress in the columns and less pressure or uplift on the foundations for a given longitudinal load. These are important features to bear in mind when narrow towers are used.

(g) This arrangement is a slight modification of that of Sketch (f). The towers are one bay closer to the center of the wall, and the roof bracing is located closer to the ends of the building.

When bracing members are short, it is often more economical to use a single diagonal instead of an X because such a short member may act readily in either tension or compression, and because the details of the connections are relatively costly so that the number of connections should be minimized. Furthermore, practicable minimum sections are likely to be used anyway so that one member is sufficient. Even in the case of long members, a single, strong diagonal with a light subdiagonal to support its center may be advisable in order to minimize the interference of bracing with clearances and useful space near the floor.

In the case of small structures such as that pictured in Fig. 9·2, knee braces to form a portal system may be sufficient. This idea can be utilized for a large building, too, if all the bracing towers are made somewhat like the central one in Fig. 9·38(d) so that they will act similarly, provided the columns are designed accordingly and the structure is sufficiently stiff.   In such a case, it is best to make the struts at the level of A–A and B–B strong enough to cause all the columns to share in resisting the longitudinal bending.

The vertical bracing in the ends of buildings should be planned upon the same principles as those described for the side towers.   When this bracing is depended upon for carrying the reactions from long lateral systems in the roof, the designer should take advantage of the greatest practicable width for the bracing towers.   The sizes of the end columns are often determined largely by the bending produced by wind because

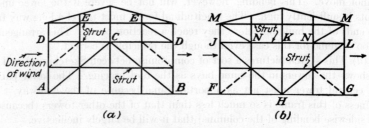

FIG. 9·39.   Bracing in end of a building.

the vertical loads are small; also, narrow towers are likely to cause excessive uplift on column foundations.   Figure 9·35 shows one case where the end bracing was designed with tension or compression members.   Unfortunately, the presence of a doorway at the right prevented the use of a simple main system consisting of two diagonals from the central column to the corner columns.   Figure 9·8 pictures the use of two double-bay X-systems.

Which way should the diagonals slope in the end bracing?   Figures 9·39(a) and (b) show opposite cases.   If the diagonals are tension members, AC will cause downward pressure on the central column and uplift at A; HL causes just the opposite.   The former is preferable because the foundations and dead load of the corner columns are generally larger anyway.   If the diagonals can withstand tension and compression, the vertical components at C and H tend to neutralize each other and the uplifts on A and F are minimized.

If the end columns shown in Fig. 9·39 are to be steadied by the lower strut, additional diagonals, such as those shown dotted, may be added to complete a secondary system to serve this purpose more fully.

There are many details to consider when bracing is planned. One of these is the proper holding of the columns so that they cannot twist. For example, Fig. 9·40(a) shows the diagonals connected to gussets along the inside flange of a column. If the struts are narrow and connected only to these same gussets, there is no reliable connection between this bracing system and the other flange of the column. If the struts, however, are beams or channels connected to both flanges of the column,

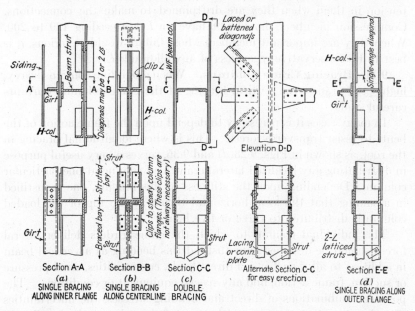

FIG. 9·40. Some systems of bracing for building columns. (Diagonals are assumed to be on near side only.)

they will square up the columns. The beams catch dirt, and channels are rather flimsy unless supported at their middle. A modification of this single-plane bracing is shown in Sketch (b). It is not so simple as that of (a) but the bracing does not project beyond the column flanges when double-angle members are used. This type of strut is not so stiff laterally as are beams or channels.

When the columns are 14 in. or more deep, and when large forces are to be carried by them, it is best to use double bracing attached as shown in Fig. 9·40(c). This arrangement may weigh more but it holds the columns firmly. It is generally better to use a few such sturdy members than it is to have more but flimsy ones.

The amount of steel to use in bracing is largely a matter of judgment.

Sometimes small rods might be strong enough, but the structure would move and vibrate excessively. In general, the diagonals in important roof bracing should not be less than one angle $3 \times 3 \times \frac{1}{4}$; single diagonals in vertical bracing, one angle $3\frac{1}{2} \times 3\frac{1}{2} \times \frac{5}{16}$. It is also wise to keep the computed unit tensile stresses under 16,000 to 18,000 psi for the sake of stiffness, and the diagonals should be given a "draw" of $\frac{1}{16}$ in. plus an additional $\frac{1}{16}$ in. for each 10 ft. of length in order to produce initial tension in them when they are driftpinned to make the connections. Compression members should not have an L/r exceeding 120 to 200. When they are important members whose failure would be serious, it is best to be conservative regardless of any allowable L/r.

9·11   Bracing Crane Columns.   When a building contains heavy, high-speed cranes, the vertical bracing of the crane columns warrants careful study.

In many cases it is necessary to depend upon the frame action of the bents to resist transverse forces. This is where longitudinal bracing in the roof, as shown in Figs. 9·28(d) and 9·36, serves a very useful purpose in distributing any localized lateral crane load coming at one particular column. Depending upon the stiffness of this bracing, one is justified in assuming that the local horizontal thrust at the top of the loaded column is distributed to three or five bents.

The individual column to which the crane girders deliver lateral forces should be designed to withstand this bending as a vertical beam in addition to all the effects of direct loads, eccentricities, wind pressure or suction, frame action, and any special equipment or conditions. The possible combinations of direct and bending stresses, the uncertainties of end restraint at the top and bottom of the column, the bending in the column caused by varying deflections of the trusses—such things as these complicate the design of combined crane and building columns. The designer may make careful, theoretical analyses of the stresses in such columns, but the answers are no better than the assumptions regarding loading upon which the computations are based. Since stiffness of such columns is important, since crane operators are so likely to pick up any load that they can get away with, and since the inclination of cables and yanking of loads are so uncertain, it is wise to design such columns conservatively. The effect upon the total cost of the plant, if this is done, is very small, but the effect upon its safety and the satisfactoriness of its service can be great.

The effect of lateral loads upon the top portion of a notched crane column, such as shown in Fig. 9·41(b), is especially important because this extension is so flimsy compared to the main column. When the extension is made by cutting the top of the main section and making the inner flange by means of two angles, or when the top is an H-column with a milled bearing and a splice, the length of the splice over the web of the lower column should be at least equal to the depth of the lower section in order to ease the localized stresses brought into this web by the bending of the extension. The first of these two arrangements is the better from the standpoint of stress action, but the second is often the easier to fabricate. It is sometimes desirable to stiffen the lower part of the extension by adding a cover plate on the outer flange and a slotted cover plate or two narrow ones joining the inner flange and the web of the main column. It is also important to make sure that the junction of the two parts cannot twist or buckle locally. The sketches in Fig. 9·19 illustrate some of these details.

Sometimes there are narrow aisles alongside or interspersed among the wider ones containing the cranes. Then it may be possible to use vertical bracing at certain points in the narrow aisles to resist lateral forces, as was done in the building shown in Figs. 9·17 and 9·20. In this case, the roof bracing was designed to deliver the lateral forces to these braced towers in the narrow aisles. In general, a system of bracing with substantial diagonals is far stiffer and more efficient than one that depends upon the bending of columns in frame action; hence it should be utilized when practicable.

Longitudinal loads delivered to crane columns should generally be carried directly from the girders to the foundations. For example, consider the sketches in Fig. 9·41:

(a) This shows a bracketed crane girder. If there is double bracing connecting to the column flanges, the latter are restrained, but the crane forces tend to twist the brackets sidewise. This may be satisfactory for hand-operated cranes, but it is inadvisable for heavy-duty ones. If batten plates A are extended at one end of the struts to connect to the crane girder or if a diaphragm is used for the same purpose, a latticed strut may be strong enough to resist the bending effect and to prevent twisting of the brackets, but this arrangement is not very satisfactory. It is obvious that, if the inner set of vertical bracing is placed in the plane of the bracketed crane girders, the downward component of stress in the diagonals will add to the load on the brackets and the bending in the columns. In most cases this is inadvisable.

(b) In this case, the crane girder is supported upon a notched column so that double bracing can be used conveniently, and connected to both flanges of the main column. The crane girder itself thus becomes a strut in the bracing system connecting to the inner flange of the column. A separate strut B should then be used in the plane of the other vertical bracing. This strut should be opposite the bottom flange of the crane girder so that the two sets of diagonal bracing line up and the parallel members can be laced or battened together.   Above strut B, the outer bracing can be carried up as a single system fastened to one flange of the column, or double bracing can be used to connect to both flanges of the upper column if it seems to be advisable.   In the latter case, connections at the batten plates between strut B and the crane girder will take care of the offset in the inner bracing.   An even better system is the use of a double-member strut at the bottom of this upper system (at the level of the strut B).

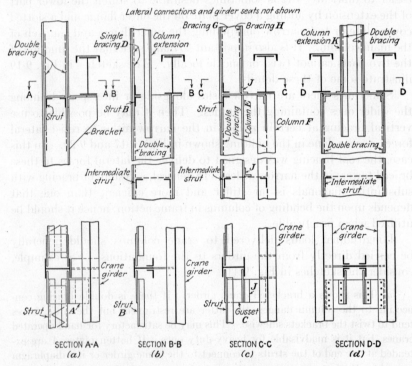

Lateral connections and girder seats not shown

FIG. 9·41.   Some systems of bracing for combined crane and building columns.
(Diagonals are assumed to be on near side only.)

(*c*) Here one set of bracing is used below the crane girder whereas another is connected to the outer flange of the building column E.   Above the crane girder, the latter column may be held by single bracing G or by double bracing G and H.   Ordinarily, single bracing B is sufficient, but the inner flange of column E should be steadied.   One way of doing this rather poorly is by the use of angles J.   The connection of gusset C to the crane girder should be bolted in order to allow slight adjustment and motion of the girder.

(*d*) Intermediate columns with heavy crane girders on both sides should be held by double bracing under the girders.   Then the extension K should be held by single or double bracing, the latter being preferable but not always necessary. If the girders are at different levels, as in Fig. 9·26, it may not be possible to make the two bracing systems line up. It will then be best to make both systems alike up to the horizontal strut that is next below the crane girders, and to make the upper portions of the bracing separate and of whatever shape may be needed, as pictured in Fig. 9·42(*f*). When the crane girders are at

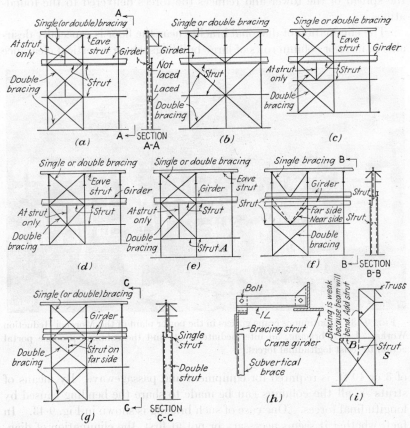

FIG. 9·42. Wall bracing for crane and building columns.

levels that differ by less than 4 or 5 ft., it may be sufficient and also better to terminate both systems of bracing at the bottom of the lower girder, let the longitudinal forces from the higher girder be carried to the top strut opposite the other girder by bending in the columns, and then extend the bracing of the building column or extension from this level, as shown in Fig. 9·42(*g*).

Various systems of bracing crane columns are pictured in Fig. 9·42. Sketch (*a*) shows a simple tower; (*b*), a double-bay tower; (*c*), a single tower with a height to the girder of about 1½ bays; (*d*), a single low tower with an intermediate strut; and (*e*), a partial tower without diagonals in the lowest panel.   Notice that the single-bay towers make it easy to support the horizontal struts by single-angle subverticals, thus reducing their *L/r* and bending, whereas the double-bay system increases the spread of the tower and reduces the forces delivered to the foundations.

The elimination of diagonal bracing near the floor is especially desirable in interior column rows of large buildings where a vertical clearance

FIG. 9·43.   Continuous crane girders in the power plant of the Morenci Reduction Works.   Laced bracing, an intermediate strut, and the columns produce portal action to resist logitudinal forces.

of 8 or 10 ft. is required for equipment and passageway.   By means of struts *A*, all the columns can be made to share the bending caused by longitudinal forces.   One case of such bracing is shown in Fig. 9·43.   In fact, whether it seems necessary or not at first, the elimination of diagonals close to the bottoms of interior columns is likely to become desirable at some future date; obviously it is best to design the structure this way in the first place when it is possible to have large areas of open floor space.

Figure 9·42(*i*) illustrates another principle of bracing that should not be overlooked.   Horizontal forces applied at the top of the structure will be resisted by the narrow, upper bracing only insofar as beam *B* can resist the resultant bending, and as the bracing stiffens the upper part of the column somewhat in the fashion of an outrigger knee brace. Furthermore, a deflection of beam B caused by other loads tries to drag down the bracing, thus shifting vertical forces into the latter. The addition of strut S will improve the bracing system if the members are designed to support the resultant vertical forces.

Thus far, nothing has been said about the question of whether or not it makes any difference to the bracing if the crane girders are simply supported or continuous. This is really an important matter.

When the girders are continuous, the bracing systems previously described can be used advantageously, and the crane girders themselves will readily deliver longitudinal forces to the braced towers. However, when there is a bracing strut opposite the bottom of the crane girder, as in Figs. 9·41(b) and (c), it is unwise to lace the strut and girder together because elongation and deflection of the girder will be harmful to the strut. On the other hand, when the strut is too flimsy laterally, it may be steadied by means of a bolted angle link, as pictured in Fig. 9·42(h). Any longitudinal movement at the column caused by passage of a crane over the continuous girders is generally so small that the column can warp a little without harm.

When the crane girders are simply supported, the longitudinal bracing presents some problems to the designer when he considers the angular motions and the linear movements that should be permitted at one end, as previously described in connection with Fig. 9·18. The linear motion particularly may cause trouble because the bracing cannot be connected strongly to a column and girder so as to prevent motion at one time but be loose so as to permit movement at another time. Obviously, too, the crane girders cannot have bolts in slotted holes to allow movement at their ends and still transmit the longitudinal forces in series from one girder to the next to reach the localized bracing towers unless there is enough slippage to take up the slack, and this slipping will cause undesirable wabbling of the structure. Sometimes these matters are overlooked and yet the structures do not fall down; nevertheless, the buildings would be better if this looseness and play did not exist.

The following are suggestions to be considered in the planning of crane runways in which simply supported girders are desired:

1. Be careful not to bring two expansion ends together because neither one will be firmly connected to the column. Figure 9·44(a) shows one arrangement for such a runway. Notice that both ends of the girder between columns 6 and 7 are fastened in order to hold the end column, even though the girder may cause some slight horizontal distortion of this column. An alternate

scheme is shown in Fig. 9·44(*b*) in which the girder between columns 3 and 4 has two "fixed" ends.

2. How can the runway in Fig. 9·44(*a*) be braced? It is obviously uneconomical to brace every bay, or even alternate bays. If bay 6–7 is to contain the longitudinal bracing, the crane forces must be brought through a long series of girders when the crane is in bay 1–2; and the deformations caused by tem-

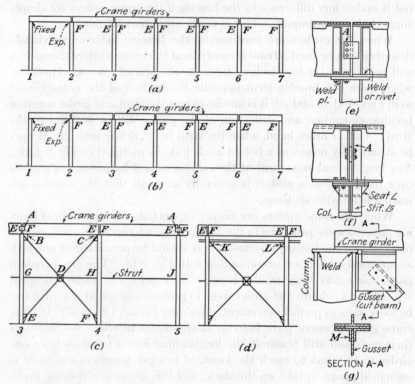

FIG. 9·44. Some details for bracing simply supported crane girders.

perature changes will bend the far columns unduly, especially column 1. It is wiser to place the bracing in a more central position.

3. Assume that the bracing of Fig. 9·44(*a*) is to be placed in bay 3–4. As pictured in Sketch (*c*), the gusset plate at *B* is connected to both the girder and column whereas that at *C* is fastened to the column only. Diagonals *BF* and *CE* should be able to withstand compressive as well as tensile stresses. If the frictional forces at the bottom of the girder are sufficient to compel the column at *C* to move with the girder flange, this deformation is generally small enough to keep the bracing from being overstressed, and all parts will recover their normal positions after the load has passed. These principles can be used

with a variety of diagonal systems, whether an X as shown, two X's, a series of K's, or a K and an X.

4. If the bracing is placed in bay 3–4 of Fig. 9·44(b), then the gussets at B and C can be connected to the girder as well as to the columns.

5. The girders in the other bays should be connected in series to the braced bay. It is generally satisfactory to make this junction at the neutral axis of the girders, using some such arrangements as those pictured in Figs. 9·44(e) and (f).

6. When struts are needed to reduce the L/r of the columns, they can be used somewhat as shown in Fig. 9·44(c), but they should not be too close to the tops of the columns because some length is desirable to permit the top portions of the columns to spring longitudinally. In some cases where the spans are long, where the girders are deep, and where the movement of the bottom flange is too great, the bracing may terminate in a top strut, as shown in Fig. 9·44(d). The bracing and struts, however, must be sufficient to compel the girder to slide on its bearing.

7. If the gusset plates at B of Fig. 9·44(c) are too long, vertical deflection of the girder may overstress the plates or the connections. In this case and at other times when the same principle is useful, the connection may be made as shown in Fig.

Fig. 9·45. Simply supported girders for a 75-ton crane. Notice the tie-plated diagonals, the laced strut, and the double columns with vertically flexible diaphragms.

9·44(g) where narrow fillers are used under long-legged angles M so that the latter can take the settlement in bending. Even though the angles are overstressed by this action, fatigue failure will seldom occur because they are not overstressed sufficiently often.

In Fig. 9·45 is shown some bracing for simply supported girders carrying a 75-ton crane. The intermediate struts are used to steady adjacent building columns, but they are not needed for the crane columns.

When crane runways extend out of doors, as in Fig. 9·23, it is customary to use A-frames to support each line of girders separately. These frames can provide the necessary transverse strength if the details and foundations are suitable. The longitudinal bracing can be designed in accordance with the principles previously described, and it is generally sufficient if this bracing is in the plane of the vertical columns only.

When the side walls of a building are brick or tile, their thickness may interfere with the longitudinal bracing. It is undesirable to have the diagonals rake through the walls; neither is it satisfactory to depend upon these walls alone for longitudinal stiffness unless they are heavy

FIG. 9·46.   Eagle Creek Pumping Station, showing the character of some of the equipment.   (*Courtesy of the Phelps Dodge Corp.*)

and in broad units.   With continuous windows, such walls are obviously ineffective.

One illustration of a small steel-framed building with brick walls is shown in Fig. 9·46.   The hand-operated crane runs on bracketed crane girders.   The brackets are sufficient to transfer longitudinal forces to the columns, the inner flanges of which are connected to a single plane of bracing just inside the brickwork.   The latter encases the remainder of each column and steadies them sufficiently.   Incidentally, there are no knee braces, but the roof is braced longitudinally to two partial or portal systems just inside each end wall.   These walls, being nearly solid brickwork, would be satisfactory alone but the diagonals assist them and were especially useful during the erection before the walls were built.

Some suggested arrangements of columns, bracing, and brickwork are shown in Fig. 9·47. The basic scheme to be used in any building should be determined before the framing is designed.

9·12 Bracing of Tall, Narrow Structures. In many instances, one has to build light but tall and narrow structures such as that shown in Fig. 9·48. Small though the lateral forces may be, the structure still must be braced. The wind load alone, even when the siding is erected,

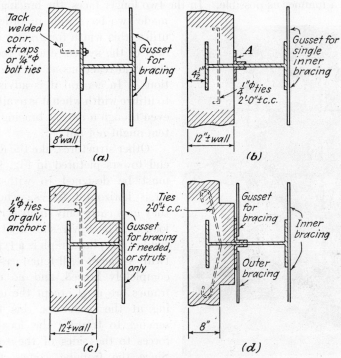

FIG. 9·47. Details of brick walls at columns.

requires very little strength in the diagonal bracing. The design of the bracing, therefore, should be done largely upon the basis of stiffness and practical construction.

In this example (Fig. 9·48), the elevating equipment makes lateral rigidity desirable. Hence all four faces of the building contain individual bracing systems. The two upper platforms serve as partial cross frames, but a full horizontal X is used at the roof line. Such cross frames may seem to be superfluous, but they should be used to hold the building in proper rectangular shape because the four vertical bracing systems alone may not be satisfactory in preventing the distortion of the structure into an oblique parallelogram.

Just how much bracing to use, what the type of system should be, how large to make the members—these are questions to settle individually for each case.   When the bracing in Fig. 9·48 was planned, the doorway at the bottom, the launder near the top, and the passageway from the launder bridge to the platforms were first sketched on elevation views of the building, then the bracing was fitted around them in as simple a manner as possible.   In the two longer faces, the bracing was made two bays wide in order to utilize this width for greater stiffness of the system and to reduce the wind reactions at the foundations.   In general it is advisable to utilize width when it is available even though a narrow bracing system might not fail.

FIG. 9·48. Framing for the support of a large bucket elevator at the Morenci Reduction Works. The 100-ft. diameter concentrate dewatering tanks are at the left.

Other structures, like the dead-end towers pictured in Fig. 9·49, must be designed to withstand large horizontal forces, whereas they may carry only slight vertical loads.   The tower shown at the right of the photograph is a typical twin A-frame. All four faces are completely braced, and no cross frames are used except the trussing at the insulators, this truss serving to transfer the localized forces to the sides of the tower. Since the framing comes to a single top strut, cross frames are not essential because the structure cannot distort out of a rectangular cross section; nevertheless, when such towers are exceptionally tall, an intermediate horizontal cross frame may be of some value from a practical standpoint.

In the rectangular tower shown at the left of Fig. 9·49, the large pull is perpendicular to the wide side of the structure; each pair of columns is completely and strongly braced to resist this force.   A heavy, full-length cross frame is also placed across the entire top of the main structure near the cable connections.   Thus, in case of greatly unbalanced forces caused by the cables or by failure of any of them, each set of four columns can act as a tower by itself, but the top truss will bring all bents into action. On the other hand, since the horizontal forces parallel to the wide sides of the tower are relatively small, only one bay on each of these sides is fully braced; the other columns are strutted to this braced portion.

When planning such towers, be sure to ascertain the exact positions and magnitudes of all forces, the positions and sizes of openings for erecting and replacing transformers or other equipment, and the locations of stairways and all other features that may affect the system.   Be

Fig. 9·49.   Framing at Substation "B," Morenci Reduction Works, showing two different towers to withstand the unbalanced pull of cables.

very careful to determine the foundations, too, before proceeding with the design of the towers themselves.

It is possible to use portal or frame action in the bracing of tall, narrow structures, but their flexibility is likely to be too great unless the members are heavy and very stiff.   It is advisable to rely upon the resistance caused by bending of the members only when a trussed system cannot possibly be used.

9·13 Expansion Joints.   When a steel mill building is more than 250 to 300 ft. long or wide, it is advisable to consider the use of expansion joints that will cut it into units of about 200 to 250 ft. each.   There is no absolutely fixed limit to the size of such units; the joints will prevent the accumulation of excessively large deformations and the resultant stresses caused by temperature changes.   This is the same principle previously discussed.   The foundations and the bottoms of the columns cannot slide back and forth; therefore the changes in size of the main superstructure will wrack a building.

When the walls are made of bricks or other masonry materials, it is advisable to use even shorter units because the movement—or the forces trying to produce movement—of the steelwork will, if the columns are embedded in the walls, tend to crack and disintegrate the brittle masonry construction.

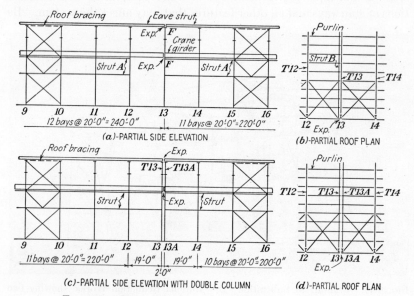

FIG. 9·50.   Expansion joints perpendicular to column rows.

First, consider expansion joints crosswise of the column rows.   Let Fig. 9·50(a) represent part of the framing of a 460-ft. building which is to have an expansion joint in bay 12–13.   The windows are assumed to be continuous, and the siding is corrugated transite; however, girts and minor members are omitted from the picture.   When the loads on the members are light or when they are moderate and temporary as in the case of the crane girder, it is generally satisfactory to seat all purlins in bay 12–13 on roof truss 13, to seat the crane girder on one side of column 13 or on a double bracket, and to support all the wall members on seats at one side of this column.   These members should be attached to their seats by bolts in slotted holes.   It is extremely inadvisable to use such bolts for the transfer of end reactions, except in the case of the bolts that steady the crane girder laterally.

The designer must be careful to provide a straight, clean cut through the framing and the siding at the line where the movement takes place, using lapped flashing or other details to seal the joint. If the line of movement is offset by having part of it occur at column 13 whereas the rest takes place at column 12, the resultant shearing action will probably tear the siding to pieces.

In Fig. 9·50(a), notice that the two portions of the structure are braced as individual units. The struts A are purposely stopped at columns 12 and 13. Ordinarily, the longitudinal roof bracing is omitted from bay 12–13; therefore, lateral crane forces coming at columns 12 and 13 are not distributed over as many bents as they would be otherwise. When the cranes are heavy, high-speed ones, it may be desirable to extend this bracing as shown in Fig. 9·50(b). The lateral system is terminated by the double-angle strut B, and the transverse shear is carried by the purlins across to their seats on truss $T13$; thus the bracing on both sides can act somewhat as cantilevered trusses picking up shears at $T13$.

When the bays are long and when the loads to be carried by the members are large, it is frequently advisable to use a double column and two trusses at the expansion joint, as shown in Fig. 9·50(c). In this case, purlins, girders, etc., are cantilevered across to a clean cut between columns 13 and 13A, and between trusses $T13$ and $T13A$. Each portion of the structure is then framed completely as an independent unit. However, it is preferable to have some device for transmitting shearing forces so that the columns, and particularly the crane girders, cannot get slightly out of line. A horizontal gusset between trusses $T13$ and $T13A$ with bolts and slotted holes at one side may be sufficient. Sliding, shear connections may also be provided between girts, purlins, or even the crane girders themselves.

Now consider expansion joints that must be parallel to column rows. If the structure is very light, the roof trusses on one side may be seated on top of one side of the columns, or upon brackets along the sides of the columns. In most cases, however, it is wise to use the double-column principle at such joints. One can readily imagine the difficulties that would occur if one girder of a crane runway moved with one portion of the structure whereas the other girder was carried in the opposite direction by the remainder of the building.

Figure 9·51 shows some details that might be used at a double-column expansion joint with cranes in both aisles. The two columns are purposely made different in order to illustrate a variety of possible details. In connection therewith, notice the following features:

1. Column at left:

a. This arrangement is to illustrate possible details of welded construction with heavy cranes.

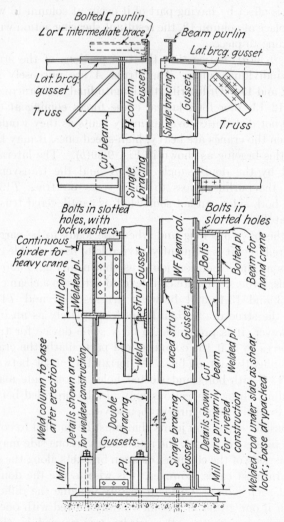

Fig. 9·51.   Double column at expansion joint parallel to column rows.

b. The base is fixed. This tends to resist expansion action and forces the deformation to cause bending stresses in the column; these may be especially severe in the extension. Such a deep column should not be forced to tilt so that it rides either flange.

c. The extension is an H-section spliced to the lower portion.

d. The lower, double bracing is carried up the right-hand flange of the extension to avoid offsetting at the strut. The top bracing angles should be turned toward the left.

e. The bottom of the double bracing terminates above the base slab. This causes some bending and shear in the bottom of the column, but the flanges of the latter are tack-welded to the slab after erection.

f. The edge purlins at the joint are channels placed so as to complete the bracing, to avoid a wide joint in the roof, and to eliminate cantilevering the roofing across them.

g. The lateral bracing in the plane of the top chords of the roof trusses should have large gussets connecting across from the chord angles to the edge purlins.

2. Column at right:

a. This arrangement is to illustrate mostly riveted construction with light, bracketed crane girders.

b. The base is "hinged," thus easing resistance to thermal deformations. With light loads, any tendency to ride the flanges of the column will not be serious.

c: The vertical bracing is single, with double, laced struts, and is placed on the right-hand flange in order to be close to the crane girder and the truss connection. The diagonal angles should preferably be turned in toward the left.

d. The beam purlin is placed close to the joint to reduce the opening and the cantilevering of the roofing. Since the purlin is too far away to constitute a satisfactory top strut for the vertical bracing, the top chord of the truss is carried over to stiffen the top, to carry some shear across to the purlin, and to serve as a seat for the purlin itself.

e. The lateral system in the plane of the top chord of the roof trusses can connect easily to the purlin and the chord angles.

Double columns are not always desired at expansion joints. It is then necessary to devise some satisfactory arrangement for seating the roof trusses on one side. As in other structural work, the number of possible details for this purpose is legion. A few suggestions are pictured in Fig. 9·52, and the following comments are given regarding each sketch:

(a) One truss has a seated connection as part of the top-chord gusset plate. This is supported upon a seat on the column flange, and the bottom chord is merely steadied by a clip angle. One serious trouble with this scheme is the fact that frictional resistances cause a twisting action which tends to bend the truss members as shown in the small line diagram.

(b) In this truss, the end diagonal is a compression member, and the column bracket is under the bottom chord. The frictional resistances are therefore resisted directly by the bottom chord. The end angles A complete the truss, support the end purlin, and serve as bearing stiffeners. If the top chord is properly braced, an occasional cross frame, plus the purlins, will steady the ends of the movable trusses. This general arrangement can be used also if the end diagonal is a tension member and angles *A* are a compression end post, as shown in the line diagram.

(*c*) In this case both trusses are seated on the column. The top of the latter is steadied by double bracing and a top strut; the trusses are braced by end cross frames of which the purlins form the top. This is a feasible plan for heavy trusses whose reactions are too large to be carried on brackets.

The locations of expansion joints in a large structure will depend upon many considerations: dimensions, locations of columns, general

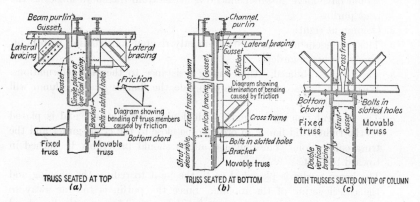

FIG. 9·52.   Seated trusses at expansion joints.

shape, column spacings, and details of the construction. In Fig. 9·53(*a*), the expansion joints are placed so as to cut the structure into reasonable rectangular units; *e.g.*, part *BCDE* is first isolated by using double columns along *BE;* part *EFGH* is also cut on the projection of *ED* so that no expansion joint is offset or jagged in plan because it is best to have all relative motion at the joints an opening or a closing action. Similarly, the building in Sketch (*b*) has the two wings isolated from the main structure; then the latter is cut in the middle to make symmetrical portions.

If the aisles in parts *KLMN* and *PQRS* of Fig. 9·53(*b*) open into the main building, long-span end or jack trusses may be needed along *KOS* to carry the trusses in the right-hand aisles of *JKOU* and *UOST*. Here the use of double columns is especially advantageous because it is inadvisable to have trusses move transversely on sliding bearings.

9·14 Provision for Extensions. When there is the probability— or even the possibility—of future extensions of a building, it is advisable to plan the structure and its details so that these additions can be made without serious difficulty and expense. One possible solution for this is to design the main frame and the foundations with provision for an expansion joint between the old and the new parts. This joint may be

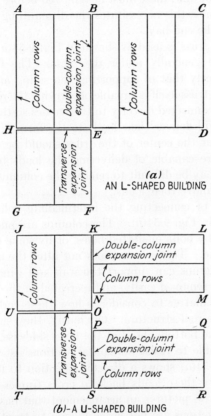

(a)
AN L-SHAPED BUILDING

(b)-A U-SHAPED BUILDING

FIG. 9·53. Examples of planning locations of expansion joints.

planned for future seating of new members on the old columns, or it may be the double-column type in which the new columns are to support all the additional loads. The latter gives greater flexibility for future changes in the details of the framing.

To be considered in planning future extensions is the minimizing of interference with operations. This applies to the planning of the structure as well as to that of the mechanical layout because a plant should be so designed that manufacturing can continue most of the time in spite of alterations and additions.

If an aisle of a building may be increased in length, it is desirable to install a roof truss at the extendible end, then to fit the initial wall framing accordingly, preferably having the members connected by means of ordinary or turned bolts. If rafters, end columns, and other gable framing are used at first, these must be removed before the new truss can be erected; of course this necessitates the dismantling and replacement of the roof over the end bay.

When an end truss is used as shown in Fig. 9·54(a), the columns in the end wall are generally under the truss. The function of these columns is primarily that of supporting the siding and resisting wind pressure since the truss itself is capable of carrying the roof loads. These columns may be connected directly to the trusses so that the latter cannot deflect but will deliver their loads to the former; in this case, the web members near the center of the truss should be checked to make sure that they are capable of delivering the loads to these columns. Furthermore, it may be difficult to remove the columns without jacking up the truss to remove their loads.

Another way of connecting the intermediate columns to the end truss is pictured in Fig. 9·54(b). The columns are purposely cut short and are steadied by bolts in slotted holes, or by some other device that serves the purpose. This scheme does not alter the action of the end truss, yet the columns can support the wall and wind loads and they can be tilted out, removed easily, and reerected in the future.

An important matter to consider is how these end columns deliver wind loads to the roof structure. Obviously, they should not be permitted to bend the bottom chord of the truss sidewise, and the connections should be able to resist horizontal suctions as well as pressures. Of course, Fig. 9·54(a) shows a direct connection to the bottom-chord struts which carry these loads back to cross frames and to the roof bracing. Sketch (b) pictures an arrangement that has been used when the horizontal reactions are not large enough to twist the truss chord. When the forces require it, gusset A may be added with a cross frame in the end bay to stiffen strut B by supporting its middle; or vertical web member C may be crimped (or placed on fillers), extended over the chord angles, and welded to the outstanding legs of the latter.

The intermediate end columns in a tall building generally need to be braced about their weak axis. Figure 9·54(c) pictures a case in which the main building resists lateral forces by frame action; hence end bracing is really needed only to steady the three temporary end columns. If the tops of the latter are held as in Fig. 9·54(a) and if there is a door as shown, the diagonals F and struts G will be sufficient; if, however, the more advisable arrangement in Sketch (*b*) is used, it may be desirable to add diagonals *H* and struts *J*.

A possible arrangement for the extension of the purlins to form the gable end of a roof is shown in Figs. 9·54(*a*) and (*b*). This is for some

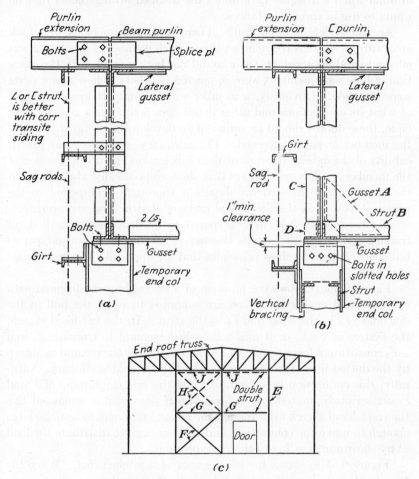

FIG. 9·54.   End columns and trusses.

form of light siding. If a temporary brick wall is built in the end of the structure, the slip joint shown in Sketch (*b*) should not be used because it is difficult to make the brickwork and steel framing act similarly. It is then better to support the truss rigidly and to build the wall just clear and outside of the truss.

9·15 Miscellaneous Details. The variety of construction used in steel mill buildings is too vast to illustrate completely in this book; the variety of details encountered in such buildings is still more extensive. Nevertheless, there are certain principles that should be borne in mind when a designer determines the detailed arrangements that he wants to use in specific instances.

Are these details important? There have been persons who took great care to see that the main section of each member of a building was adequate and appropriate, yet who did not bother much with the question of how such members were connected to others or how minor parts were attached. Obviously, a member will not support loads in excess of what its connections and other details can hold. As a general principle, these details should be sufficient to develop the useful strength of the member or part concerned. The adequacy, economy, and practicability of the details, the ease of their fabrication and of the erection of the members—these are matters that show emphatically whether or not the engineer who devised the details is thoroughly competent in the practical as well as the theoretical matters of structural engineering.

Figures 9·55 to 9·57 were prepared to illustrate some methods of framing steelwork; the details themselves are not so important per se but some of them do show principles that are applicable to a wide range of details.

Figure 9·55(a) shows the junction of a lateral bracing diagonal with the truss and eave strut which are supposed to resist the pull in the diagonal—F_1 in the truss and F_2 in the strut. In the left-hand sketch, the system is weak, or it might be called incomplete trussing; F_2 and $-F_2$ constitute a force couple which tries to distort the column as shown by the dotted lines A, assuming the strut to be held stationary. Naturally, this connection is undesirable, and the safe magnitudes of P and F_2 are seriously limited. It is far better if the detail is somewhat like the right-hand sketch even though the gusset plate may have to be large enough to make the connection, and thick enough to distribute the load P by shear and bending to those connections.

Figure 9·55(b) shows the ridge gusset of a pitched roof. When the top-chord angles are separated and unspliced, their thrust tends to overload the top edge of the plate. A simple remedy is to weld the ends of the angles together. The welding of the outstanding legs is especially desirable to prevent lateral jackknifing of the truss during shipment and erection; it also increases the ability of the truss to transfer horizontal shears across the space between the two channel purlins. The transfer of compressive stresses through the outstanding legs of the chord angles

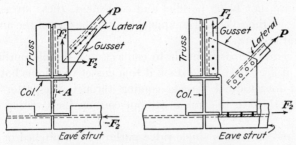

Weak detail   Stronger detail
(a)-CONNECTIONS OF LATERAL BRACING IN A ROOF

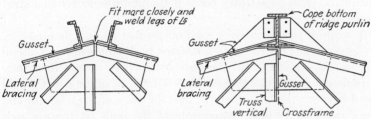

(b)-SPLICE OF CHORD ∠s AT PEAK OF ROOF   (d)-PITCHED ROOF WITH SINGLE RIDGE PURLIN

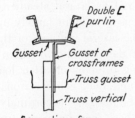

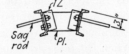

(e)-DIAPHRAGM AT DOUBLE RIDGE PURLIN
(A bent rod as a central link can be
used for light loads)

Connections for a
vertical crossframe
(c)-CONNECTION OF VERTICAL CROSSFRAME
TO DOUBLE PURLIN

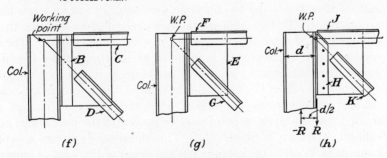

(f)   (g)   (h)

FIG. 9·55. Miscellaneous details.

is poor because, not being parallel and coincident, these stresses have nothing to resist their vertical components, and the legs of the angles are likely to bend upward.

When a central cross frame is to connect to a double purlin, as in Fig. 9·55(c), it is advisable to attach it to a gusset that joins both channels so that longitudinal thrusts coming through the latter can be delivered directly into the frame without causing the twisting of light members.

One method of using a single ridge purlin with a pitched or peaked roof is pictured in Fig. 9·55(d). Unless the purlin is so located that the bracing gussets and cross frame can be connected to it, detrimental bending of the truss gusset may occur if the purlin is to act as a strut in the system.

With many types of covering used on pitched roofs, it is necessary to have intermediate sag rods 5 to 8 ft. apart to eliminate harmful lateral bending in and sagging of the purlins. When these rods deliver their pulls to a double purlin like that of Fig. 9·55(e), a tie of some sort should be placed between the two channels. In the cases of Sketches (d) and (e), the downward vertical components of the pulls on the sag rods should be considered in the design of the members. Whether or not the sag rods themselves can be considered as lateral steadiers of the ridge purlins is a question whose answer is dependent largely upon the shearing resistance of the roofing and the lateral stiffness of the other purlins. When the pulls are equal, the rods may tend to stiffen a ridge purlin but, when they are unequal owing to snow or other loads, the rods tend to pull the purlins sidewise and may cause serious lateral bending; hence the ridge purlins should be designed accordingly.

When columns are relatively deep, there may be a question as to where the working point for the end diagonal of the truss should be. As pictured in Fig. 9·55(f), the end gusset may become unduly large, and member D may be too far from top chord C to make a practicable arrangement. Perhaps this can be partly remedied by lowering the top of angles B and extending top-chord C nearer to the column. The connection might be improved even more by omitting angles B and the gusset, then substituting a piece of cut beam as shown by E in Sketch (g); when the end of F is nearer to the column, this improves the bracing details. In many cases, especially when the truss reactions are relatively light, the working point may be moved to the near flange of the column, as shown in Sketch (h). This theoretically causes a bending moment of $\frac{1}{2} dR$ in the column, but the detail of the joint is improved.

Occasionally, mitering of angles H and J, and welding of their junction, may be used, but this is seldom necessary.

Some details for tied or battened members are shown in Fig. 9·56(a), and Fig. 9·45 pictures their use in some actual members. These plates are primarily spacers in the case of members that are supposed to carry nothing except tension. In practical construction, however, the members should also be able to resist some compression. The diagram at the left of the sketch shows the action of the tie plates in a member that is

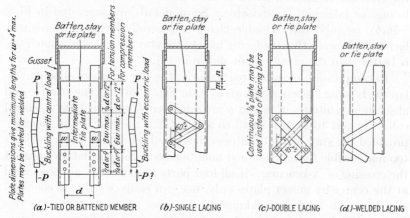

FIG. 9·56.   Details of laced (or latticed) and tied members.

buckled in the plane of the plates. Of course they are ineffective in preventing buckling in the plane normal to themselves. If the ends of the member do not rotate, both angles can buckle the same amount and with the same curvature, carrying the intermediate tie plates with them. Only when tie plates in such a member as this are relatively long and close together do they assist appreciably in stiffening the member; therefore, the designer should not assume that ordinary tied members are worth much more in compression than the sum of the strengths of the two component parts alone. The data labeled in the sketch as applicable to compression members are primarily for the purposes of detailing.

When the force at one end of a tension or a compression member is applied at one side and that end can rotate, whereas the other is fixed as shown in the deformed-structure diagram at the right of Fig. 9·56(a), the tie plates will not greatly assist in the distribution of the load to both parts of the member. This action is uncertain; the force will try to go directly through the initial side to its reaction point unless the deformation is enough to enable the tie plates to compel the other half of the member to participate in resisting the force.   One can also see that the transfer of shearing stresses through a tie plate from one side to the other will tend to twist the plate and to cause bending stresses in the main angles.   Similar action will take place when a tie-plated member is subjected to lateral loads that cause it to bend sidewise, because it then acts as a relatively weak Vierendeel truss.

When lateral buckling is to be prevented or when unequal loads on the ends are to be distributed to both parts of the member, the use of lacing (or latticing) is advisable.   Some details are suggested in Figs. 9·56(b), (c), and (d).   Double lacing is generally stronger than single lacing, and connecting the lacing bars to the stay plates, as in Sketch (b), is better than the arrangement shown in (d).

In compression members particularly, the end tie plates should overlap the bracing gussets as shown by m in Fig. 9·56(b).   The relative and absolute magnitudes of m and n are a matter of judgment; as a general rule it is best to keep n small so as to stiffen the end of the member, provided the stay plates of intersecting members do not make the joint too inaccessible for erection and maintenance.   Similar details occur at the crossing of X-bracing.   If all four parts of such an X are connected at the center by gusset plates only, one can easily see that a compressive load will tend to jackknife the member at the center.   On this account it is best to have one-half of the X composed of one completely laced member, then connect the other half as two separate, short members with stay plates at both ends.

In Fig. 9·56 there are shown three arrangements of end gussets connecting bracing members with the columns.   In Sketch (a), the plates fit onto the insides of the column flanges.   This avoids interference with the connections for girts, roof trusses, and other parts attached to the outside faces of the flanges.   In Sketch (b), the plates are outside the flanges.   This arrangement may be desirable if the inner flanges are beveled, if the column is very shallow, and if large forces are to be delivered through the gussets from one brace to another without passing through the column flange.   The advantage of the compromise arrangement shown in Sketch (c) is that the gussets of long lines of struts may be shop-connected to the bracing, which can then be erected by swinging it against the column instead of having to slide the member down between closely fitting gusset plates.

Some minor weaknesses of details are shown in Fig. 9·57.   The following explanation of each sketch should emphasize the principle involved:

(*a*) Purlins should not rest on the edges of truss chords because the canti-lever moments and bending in the angles may be severe. The distance x should be only about ¼ in., and a bolted web plate or angle should join abutting purlins, especially if the latter are also struts.

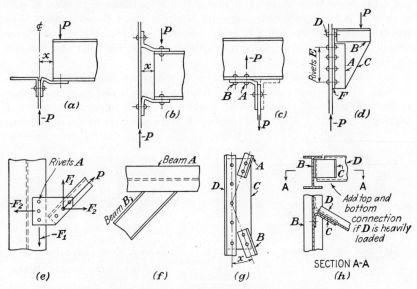

Fig. 9·57. Illustrations of inadvisable framing.

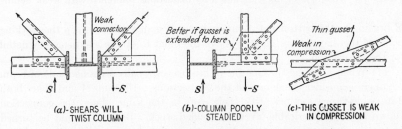

Fig. 9·58. A few examples of weak bracing connections.

(*b*) Seated beams, even when held by top and bottom angles, will bend the angles when x is large; x should be approximately ¼ in. but stiffeners under the seat angle, or web connections, should be used when the end reactions exceed 5 or 10 kips.

(*c*) Angles as hanger connections are too flimsy for heavy loads. Rivets B add nothing to the strength of the connection because they cannot act until the other rivets fail. Thick angles, cut beams, and double angles as shown by the dotted lines are about the best that can be used. One must remember that the bottom flange of the supporting beam may also bend seriously.

(d) If the connection angles A of this bracket are cut so that the outstanding legs (against the column) extend up to include rivets D, the latter are of little value in helping rivets E to resist the bending caused by load P, because the extension is too weak. It is better to use fillers under A or B so as to lap one set of angles over the other, to crimp A or B for the same purpose, to stop B short of A, or to substitute a piece of beam for gusset C and angles A. In the last case, or when gusset C bears against the column, the effective lever arm of rivets E can be measured from close to point F, the point of attempted rotation.

(e) When the loads are heavy or the members are flimsy, eccentric connections like this may cause harmful bending moments and twisting because of forces F_1 and $-F_1$. The force P should more closely intersect the center of gravity of rivets A. A detail of this type is often necessary at the connections

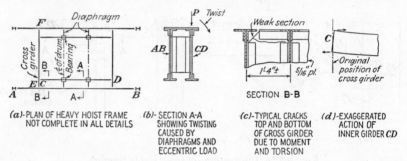

(a)-PLAN OF HEAVY HOIST FRAME   (b)-SECTION A-A   (c)-TYPICAL CRACKS   (d)-EXAGGERATED
NOT COMPLETE IN ALL DETAILS   SHOWING TWISTING   TOP AND BOTTOM   ACTION OF
                               CAUSED BY   OF CROSS GIRDER   INNER GIRDER CD
                               DIAPHRAGMS AND   DUE TO MOMENT
                               ECCENTRIC LOAD   AND TORSION

FIG. 9·59. Example of failures caused by distortions combined with weak details

of bracing to the bottoms of columns, hence it is desirable to keep the working point of the diagonal far enough above the billet to obtain a satisfactory detail for the connection.

(f) When planning the framing of beams—especially trussing made of beam members—consider the details of the connections. If beams A and B are both 8-in. wide-flange sections with their axes in the same plane, the connection shown is very undesirable, even for welded work. Beam B should be turned so that its flanges can be connected to those of A by gusset plates or welding.

(g) When angle x is too acute, the interference of A and B with D makes gusset C impracticably long and narrow.

(h) Assume that channel D is connected to beam B by a bent plate C. This connection can twist easily. It would be better to put C on the other side of D and to bend the plate as shown by the dotted lines or to weld the web of D directly to that of B.

Many other illustrations of detailing might be shown, but these should suffice to emphasize the importance of careful consideration of such matters in the planning of a structure.

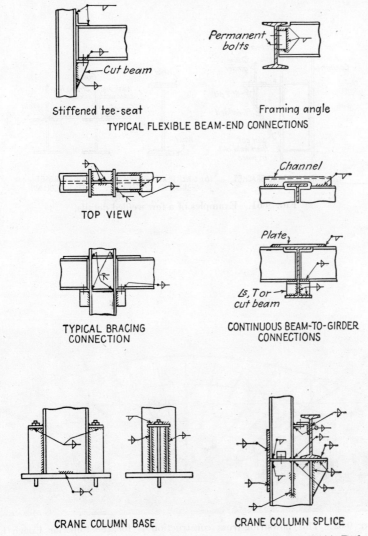

Stiffened tee-seat

Permanent bolts

Framing angle

TYPICAL FLEXIBLE BEAM-END CONNECTIONS

TOP VIEW

Channel

TYPICAL BRACING CONNECTION

CONTINUOUS BEAM-TO-GIRDER CONNECTIONS

Plate

∠s, T or cut beam

CRANE COLUMN BASE

CRANE COLUMN SPLICE

Fig. 9·60.   Some details of welded construction recommended by Air Reduction Co.   (See "Manual of Design for Arc Welded Steel Structures," by Air Reduction Co., for additional data.)

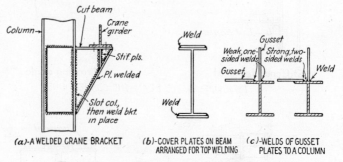

(a)-A WELDED CRANE BRACKET   (b)-COVER PLATES ON BEAM   (c)-WELDS OF GUSSET
                               ARRANGED FOR TOP WELDING   PLATES TO A COLUMN

FIG. 9·61.   Examples of a few welded details.

FIG. 9·62.   This bowstring-truss construction is for the Superior Coach Co., Lima, Ohio.   The spacing of trusses is 20 ft.   A 1½-in., 20-gauge steel roof deck is to be welded to the purlins.   (*Courtesy of Geo. L. Mesker Steel Corp., Evansville, Indiana.*)

FIG. 9·63.   Neat, welded steel construction of the parts warehouse of Plant No. 3, Cleveland Diesel Engine Division of the General Motors Corp., Cleveland, Ohio. (*Design and construction by the Austin Co.*)

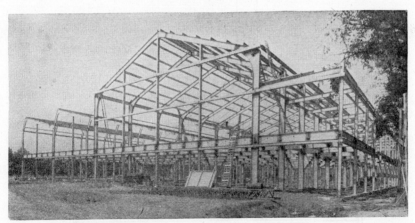

FIG. 9·64.   Welded rigid-frame construction of a 200,000-sq.-ft. addition to the Cleveland, Ohio, plant of the Lincoln Electric Co.   (*Photo courtesy of the Lincoln Electric Co., Cleveland, Ohio.*)

Fig. 9·65.   An illustration of welded Vierendeel-truss construction at the plant of International Agriculture, Chicago, Illinois. (*Design and construction by the Austin Co.*)

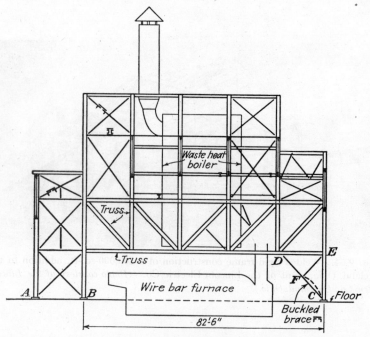

Fig. 9·66.   Example of result of thermal expansion and vertical deflection when both ends of framing are fixed.

Fig. 9·67.   An illustration of the effect of connecting one side of a heavy diagonal brace to the web of a column near the column's base.   The punching action of the diagonal is shown by the bowed web and the crimped flange beyond the lower rail.

Chapter 10

MULTISTORY STEEL BUILDINGS

10·1 Introduction. Multistory buildings with structural-steel "skeleton" frameworks are widely used for office buildings, public edifices, apartments, schools, hotels, warehouses, and many industrial purposes. This chapter is confined to those of the last-mentioned group, but the general principles discussed are applicable for the planning of multistory buildings of almost any type. In the industrial field, multistory structures are generally within the range of two to six stories in height—a range in which reinforced concrete can be a strong competitor of structural steel.

Any owner likes to have an attractive plant as well as a productive one. In the case of public edifices, office buildings, and large apartments, an architect may turn to the engineers for help in making his structure stand up; in the case of industrial work, however, the engineers and operators generally determine what the building must house and what general shape it is to have, then they should turn to the architect for his assistance in developing an attractive structure to serve these purposes.

There are several reasons why structural steel has been and probably will continue to be favored for many such industrial buildings. One of these is its great strength; another is its adaptability to many uses. Even though a multistory structure may be designed primarily to serve one specific purpose and to accommodate one given layout of equipment, storage, or offices, the exigencies of industrial life will almost inevitably bring about the desire—or even the necessity—on the part of the owner to change the nature of its occupancy, to install more modern equipment, or to revise the layout of machinery and the details of manufacturing. By the proper exercise of ingenuity, engineers can usually make surprisingly varied alterations of steel-framed structures. The torch, welding equipment, drill, and riveter make it possible to remove almost any member, to reinforce members, to add new ones, and to alter or move parts. Even an occasional column may be removed and the framing bridged across to new or other reinforced columns. In other words, the framing is made of a strong material that can be "worked" readily.   The structural action of the framework is usually rather simple and reasonably definite.   However, the details of the connections of members in an industrial structure should be made especially sturdy because this is where the greatest difficulties of alteration frequently occur.

One should not assume, however, that the difficulties of altering and strengthening a reinforced-concrete structure should automatically elim-

Fig. 10·1.   The Steel Point Station of the United Illuminating Co. at Bridgeport, Connecticut.   The exposed steel framing is for an extension.   (*Westcott & Mapes, New Haven, Connecticut, Architects and Engineers.*)

inate it from consideration.   It is the engineer's duty to study each case carefully and to use his best judgment when recommending the type of construction to be used.

Another advantage of structural steel for multistory industrial buildings is the fact that the framing can be made to suit almost any conditions, and generally without undue difficulties of design or uncertainties of structural action.   The erection of the framework, moreover, is relatively easy.   Once it is in place, the floors, walls, partitions, and roof can be added quickly to "the bones of the skeleton."   With steelwork, relatively long-span construction can be used without great difficulty and expense.

10·2 Developing a Framing Scheme. Multistory industrial buildings with steel framework are composed primarily of steel beams and girders, which constitute the main supporting members of the floors and roofs. These in turn are supported completely upon a system of steel columns; and the walls and partitions are merely "fillers of open spaces," each story being carried by the floor system under it. As in other industrial buildings, the requirements of the equipment, operations, and general use should take precedence over the details of structural framing. If the steelwork is protected against corrosion and fire by encasing the beams in concrete and the columns in brickwork, concrete, or hollow tiles, the structure may be really fireproof, but it is often desirable to leave the steelwork bare in order to save weight and money, and to use it as supports for trolley systems, piping, and miscellaneous appurtenances. Many of the principles of planning the framework are the same as those described in the preceding chapter.

The number of stories that a building is to have will be determined almost always by such matters as use, land values, area of land available, floor space desired, economy, relation to other buildings, foundations, desired widths of building for daylighting and ventilation, the magnitudes of the loads to be carried, and someone's judgment as to what is best for the particular case. The most important of these is generally that of the kind of occupancy—what the building is to be used for.

Seldom does one construct a multistory industrial building without having definite—or reasonably definite—ideas regarding its purpose and function. This may not be completely the case, however, when a warehouse or structure for light manufacturing is built in a port or congested city with the hope that, once the facilities are available, tenants will be found. The usual procedure is to ascertain first what is desired, then to see if it can be built.

When planning the layout of a multistory structure, give early attention to those features which affect more than one story: elevator shafts, stairways, chimneys, chutes, ramps, conveyors, shaftways, light courts, setbacks, and even duct systems. These facilities should be coordinated in all floor plans as soon as possible. In all probability they will indicate certain desired positions for some of the columns. Next, determine the typical construction to be used for floors, walls, partitions, and roof, and decide whether or not the steelwork is to be fireproofed; then make the general mechanical and architectural layouts so that they will conform reasonably well to the intended type of construction. After the general shape, size, positions of equipment, clearance requirements, positions of corridors and aisles, and locations of partitions are tentatively determined, try to work out on the plans a simple rectangular pattern for the columns so that each can extend vertically from its foundation to the top of the structure. Naturally, a regular, checkerboard pattern is the most advantageous. The ordinary width of bays is 20 to 25 ft.; sometimes, greater spans may be desired in at least one direction.

The presence of so many columns in a multistory building, together with stairways and elevator shafts, may result in considerable loss of usable space. When an industrial plant is to house large and heavy equipment, it may be found that lightweight, single-story construction

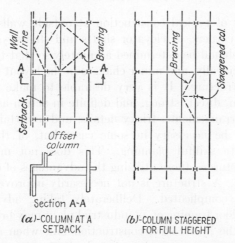

Section A-A

(a)-COLUMN AT A   *(b)*-COLUMN STAGGERED
SETBACK   FOR FULL HEIGHT

Fig. 10·2. Two irregular arrangements of columns.

is cheaper than a multistory structure. However, as stated before, available property and its cost, also a desire to avoid spreading over large areas, may influence one to build a multistory structure in preference to the other.

If a uniform spacing pattern for column locations is found, then see if the architectural features of the exterior walls can be adapted to it. Can the windows, doors, pilasters, jogs, recesses, and other irregularities used for architectural effect be made to fit properly? It is obvious that a column should be at all major corners unless cantilevering and other special features are desired.

When a uniform spacing pattern for column locations will not fit the necessary mechanical and architectural features, one should then try to modify the spacing, keep the columns in straight rows both ways, and minimize the variety of bay lengths used. Because of the strength and adaptability of structural steel, columns can be offset perpendicularly to the walls and carried by heavy beams or girders even though it may be expensive to do so. They can be offset parallel to the walls and the intermediate framing can be made accordingly, although this may not be conducive to lateral stiffness. Some such arrangements are shown in Fig. 10·2. If the floor at such an offset. is to be poured concrete, and especially if the beams are to be encased also, the floor may provide sufficient stiffness to steady laterally the member that supports the offset column, as in Sketch (a), or the staggered column shown in (b). Otherwise, steel lateral-bracing members may be desirable to steady such critical points.

The details of typical construction at outside walls, at projecting and reentrant corners, at elevator shafts and stairways, and at other special points should be determined accurately so that the columns can be located specifically, and minor changes in the layout can be made to simplify the structure. It is very desirable to make the framing as simple, uniform, direct, strong, and definite in action as is practicable. Complicated arrangements, tricky details, and uncertain action of the structure may be necessary in some cases but, of themselves, they do not indicate skillful planning. This does not mean that indeterminate structures—those utilizing the advantages of continuity—are to be avoided. A structure is not necessarily improved as its design becomes more complicated. Deliberately taking advantage of continuity in the floor framing of an industrial plant may bring about slight economies in the initial steel construction but, when revisions of the steelwork become necessary, that continuity may cause considerable inconvenience.

In all of his detailed planning, the structural designer should think about the deformation of the individual members. When should a member be designed upon the basis of stiffness rather than upon that of permissible unit stress alone? Some such cases may arise in connection with supports for high-speed or vibrating equipment on upper floors, for long beams carrying light loads, and for long columns carrying lateral or eccentric loads or bending imposed by long connecting members. These matters involve the use of good judgment as well as calculation. General rules for all such cases cannot be set up.

Considerable money may be saved, particularly in the cost of formwork for floors and concrete encasement of steel members, if close study is given to the planning of successive floors so as to secure the maximum practicable duplication of parts and dimensions.

10·3 Resistance to Lateral Forces. Substantial lateral stiffness should be provided in any multistory structure. The relatively low height of those used for industrial purposes generally results in buildings that are not severely stressed by wind loads. Resistance to vibration and to earthquakes is another matter.

In the consideration of lateral stiffness, it is appropriate to remember these two statements: (1) "A structure will not fall down if there is any possible manner in which it can act and still stand up." (2) "If there is one path provided whereby the loads can be supported safely, they will be supported that way before the structure will fail." In other words, there should be provided a system of supports that is capable of holding the loads safely. Nevertheless, as illustrated in Chap. 16, this philosophy should not be allowed to lead one astray when he is dealing with unusual structures.

It is the author's belief that the shear due to wind loads acting upon most multistory steel-frame buildings of moderate height and without diagonal bracing is carried largely by the exterior walls and interior partitions, because of their relatively great stiffness compared to that of the steelwork. The greatest part of the forces will go down the stiffest available path of resistance if it can do so without failure of the parts concerned. Nevertheless, this is not sufficient justification for disregarding these lateral forces when the framing of a structure is planned. Although the walls and partitions may resist considerable lateral force in any direction, complete dependence upon them for this purpose in industrial structures is inadvisable unless these parts are specifically designed to act safely in such a manner.

The rigid-frame action of the steelwork of a building—its resistance as a frame with bending at the joints—generally results in so much sidesway that, for industrial structures particularly, it seems to be desirable to look for and to provide a stiffer, stronger path of resistance.

One of the most obvious and effective means of resisting lateral forces is the use of diagonal bracing in vertical planes. Since exposed bracing may not present the most pleasing appearance in a large, multistory building, places should be sought in which it may be concealed, or at least where it will be inconspicuous. Frequently, stair wells and elevator shafts can be used as towers of resistance with diagonal bracing between their supporting columns and so located as to be encased in the walls or visible only from the inside of the enclosure. When planning such towers, however, the designer should endeavor to locate them as symmetrically as possible with respect to the resultant of the lateral forces in order to avoid torsional action upon the framing of the structure. When a building has a large horizontal cross section the requirements of the building codes, as well as those of common sense, generally result in a floor layout that accommodates this arrangement.   The floors themselves are ordinarily stiff enough as horizontal diaphragms to transfer the lateral loads through each floor to the towers.   Of course, when a building is long, towers near the quarter or third points of its length are preferable to those located at the extreme ends, because of the resultant reduction of stresses in the towers caused by changes of temperature.

Knee braces may be used between floor beams and columns when regular diagonal bracing cannot be installed.   Of course, this arrangement is not so· effective as regular trussing.   Moreover, the designer should not overlook the fact that knee braces under beams try to relieve the beams of bending caused by vertical loads, and they produce lateral bending in the columns unless the bending and horizontal thrusts of knee braces on opposite sides of a column annul each other.   It is therefore obvious that knee braces should be placed where live-load effects are not great if the bending resistance of the column is to be reserved for withstanding the intended lateral forces.

When the architectural design permits it, diagonal bracing may be used in at least one bay or wide strip in each exterior wall where it can be concealed, or it may be placed in certain interior partitions.   In other cases, one may frankly place such bracing in certain wall panels, and leave it exposed, provided it is not an obstruction.   The author suspects that the occupants of the building will soon accept such bracing as a natural part of the structure, just as they do in the case of columns; visitors may even get the impression that the structure certainly is strongly built.

Another feasible method of making these towers is through the use of reinforced concrete, or solid brickwork, for the walls of stairways, elevator shafts, certain corridor partitions, corner panels, or other places that fit into the architectural scheme.   Naturally, the resistance provided by such towers is likely to be limited by the shearing strength of the walls, hence concrete is much better than brickwork.

If no stiffer system can be employed, the steelwork of the building may be designed to resist lateral forces as a rigid-frame structure.   It is probable, however, that the building will be considerably more pliable, more indeterminate in action, and even more expensive than it would be if diagonal bracing were used.

In the designing of joints for a multistory structure to resist bending moments, the following questions are worthy of consideration:

1. In riveted construction, will angle legs and column flanges that are subjected to bending yield sufficiently to reduce seriously the actual restraint offered by the connection?   This action is illustrated in Figs. 10·3(a) and (b).

2. In welded construction, will the welds be able to transmit the necessary forces, especially tension, required to prevent relative angular rotation of the connected members?

3. In any case, will the reversal of stresses produced by lateral loads cause eventual slippage of rivets or permanent deformation of the welds or of the main material?

4. Can a joint provide restraint against lateral loads and not do likewise in case of vertical loads? For example, assume the case pictured in Fig. 10·3(c).

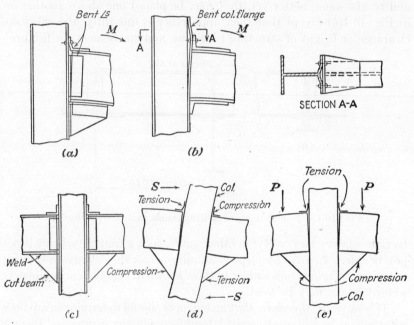

FIG. 10·3. Some illustrations of possible yielding of and action at junctions of columns and beams.

When lateral loads are applied, the connection is assumed to act somewhat as shown in (d). If it is sufficiently stiff and strong, it will resist the required bending moment. On the other hand, when vertical loads act upon the beams, as in Sketch (e), the joint will try to restrain the ends of the beams. If the connection once yields in the latter case, will it be able to offer the necessary resistance when the action in Sketch (d) tries to recur? It seems that, if a connection is to resist the bending moments caused by lateral loads, it should be able to do likewise when vertical loads are applied. Any halfway measures may result in such permanent deformation under the latter case that the beneficial action of the joint in the former is chiefly psychological. As Hardy Cross has often said (substantially), "Has the beam learned when and how it is supposed to act?"

5. When the ends of beams are assumed to be strongly restrained and when the central sections of these beams have been designed for the theoretically reduced positive bending moments, will unanticipated yielding of the joints cause overloading of the central portions of the beams?

True continuity in the floor framing of multistory steel buildings is generally more difficult to secure than the novice suspects. Beams may be spliced across beams as shown in Fig. 10·4(a), although this is costly and troublesome; better yet, they may be placed one above another as in Fig. 10·4(b) except that their appearance is unsightly, the effect on clearance or height of structure is serious, and encasement for fire pro-

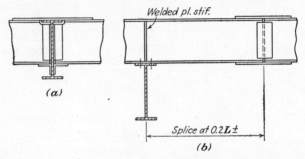

FIG. 10·4. Two methods of splicing beams to secure continuity.

tection is heavy and costly; in other words, such a framing scheme is not practicable. In any case, true continuity across the columns is difficult to secure. Connections similar to those shown in Fig. 10·3, or completely welded joints, may be used.

It is obvious, therefore, that an engineer should determine in advance what means he will use to resist lateral forces in any given case; then he should frame the structure accordingly. Too often, this matter of lateral strength is treated as something to be investigated after most of the designing is completed.

10·4 Expansion Joints. Multistory buildings that are properly heated in cold weather are not generally subjected to such large deformations caused by variations in temperature as are thin-shelled mill buildings. Obviously, this is beneficial as far as the minimizing of stresses and cracking is concerned. Nevertheless, the framing of the roof and the exterior walls is affected by changes of weather much more violently than is the interior framing. In addition to this, the walls are generally made of bricks, concrete, tiles, concrete blocks, or even stucco, and these materials are likely to crack if the upper portion of a building expands or contracts considerably with respect to the practically immovable foundation and the less violently affected central portion of the structure. The structure may therefore try to act somewhat as shown to exaggerated scale in Fig. 10·5.

When the walls and partitions of the first story of a building are composed largely of windows, these may be installed so that distortions in the planes of the windows can occur without harmful results. In such a case the upper stories may expand or contract as a unit and cause relative deformations in the first story only. Narrow brick or concrete piers at columns and corners may be able to deform sufficiently without visible cracking if stress-relieving joints are provided. The columns, of course, should be able to withstand the bending produced by the horizontal deformations.

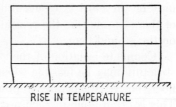

RISE IN TEMPERATURE

It seems to be advisable, however, to cut a large multistory structure into units of reasonable size by means of expansion joints in the same general manner as described for steel mill buildings. When the length (or width) of a building exceeds 200 to 250 ft., it appears to be desirable to study this question seriously.

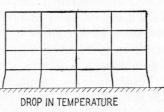

DROP IN TEMPERATURE

FIG. 10·5.   Illustration of deformation of columns of first story because of changes in temperature.

10·5 Vibrations. Reciprocating and high-speed equipment in a multistory structure may cause vibrations of the building as a whole, or of a portion of it. The objectionable feature may be the sound or the physical movement; and an effective remedy may be difficult to secure once the structure is built. It is therefore almost essential to anticipate such troubles and to overcome them in advance during the planning and design of the structure.

Objectionable vibrations may come from a movement of a part of the structure as a sounding board that actually causes vibration of the air and amplification of the original impulses to the extent that the sound is definitely noticeable. On the other hand, the vibrations may be "telegraphed" elastically through the structure so that the occupants are annoyed by the movement.

Four general methods of minimizing such vibrations are the following:

1. Eliminate the equipment that causes the trouble.
2. Isolate the supports of the vibrating equipment from the rest of the structure.

3. Cushion the vibration by supporting the equipment on some pliable material.

4. Damp the vibration of the supporting structure.

The first of these—elimination of the source of the vibrations—is not quite so facetious as it sounds. There are likely to be many cases in which one type of machine runs much more quietly and smoothly than another. Purchase of the better equipment at somewhat larger cost may be the most economical and practical procedure. A modification of this idea may be the relocation of the equipment, such as placing it on the ground floor.

Complete isolation of the supports of the equipment from the main structure may be feasible when the machinery is on the first or second floor, but it is generally impractical when the equipment is higher up. This is often done in such a case as turbogenerators in a power plant. A separate foundation must be sufficiently strong all by itself, and it must be actually cut away from the adjoining structure. If it depends upon the latter for horizontal steadiness or support, the purpose of the construction will probably be defeated by the transmission of horizontal forces through the points of contact.

Cushioning the vibrations may be effective in reducing them below the nuisance level. The details of such a solution, however, depend upon the individual conditions. The machinery may be placed upon cork or special mastic pads somewhat as shown in Fig. 14·10, provided the pressures are low and the amplitude of the vibration is small. Twists and overturning tendencies that necessitate the use of anchor bolts will require that the bolts themselves be held, yet isolated—sometimes a difficult combination to secure. The use of coil springs as supports may be suitable for absorbing occasional and irregular shocks but, when the impulses have a constant period, the repeated increase and decrease of the reactions delivered to the supporting structure may set the latter into sympathetic vibration unless there is suitable mass in the spring-supported foundation of the machine.

Damping of vibrations is assumed to denote a decreasing of amplitude because of the mass or weight of the vibrating portion of the structure. This principle is used frequently in the case of high-speed equipment attached to massive foundations or to heavy concrete floors. Of course, there is always the question of whether or not a small impulse that is repeated long enough and at the right frequency will eventually set a large mass into similar vibration. This seldom will occur when the anchoring mass is relatively very large, unless the impressed impulses have a low frequency. It is obvious, therefore, that machinery foundations supported directly upon bedrock or undisturbed granular soil will generally engage so great a mass that the vibrations will not be transmitted to the surrounding structure to any objectionable extent, provided the base (or footing) of the equipment is also isolated from the remainder of the structure.

In most cases where vibrating machinery must be carried on upper floors, more than one of the previously mentioned principles can and should be employed to ensure that the vibration will not be objectionable. It is generally advisable to design all the supporting beams of the equipment on the basis of stiffness; it is desirable to brace the affected columns firmly so that lateral forces are carried down to the ground instead of permitting them to set the structure vibrating like a tuning fork; it is best to be very generous in the use of concrete in the floor and the foundations under the machine; and it is desirable to connect the supporting structure to other masses and systems of resistance which have widely different characteristics and which will not vibrate in the same manner. This last arrangement may reduce vibrations because of the interference of connected parts that cannot vibrate with the same periods. Heavy brick walls are very helpful in resisting horizontal impulses parallel to their length.

Problems of the vibrations of structures are difficult to solve quantitatively. Much helpful qualitative information may be obtained from past experience and from practices that have been found to be satisfactory. The engineer should look for what, to him, may be the unexpected, and should be careful how he permits someone to do things that destroy the effectiveness of his plans. One case is the following:

An ore-crushing plant was built of reinforced concrete as shown in simplified form in Fig. 11·21. Because of the low bearing value of the soil, a heavy mat foundation was used. The two crushers at the first floor were founded upon heavy piers resting upon this mat, and steadied by the massive construction of the first floor and outer walls. The crusher on the third floor was also supported upon concrete piers but these rested in part upon heavy reinforced-concrete beams and partly upon two heavy concrete walls. The massive construction of the second and third floors tied these piers and beams ·into the outer walls Above the third floor extended the cantilevered concrete crane columns and the concrete structure housing the stairway and supporting the screen and conveyor. In order to permit the passage of a large dust-collecting duct, a hole was cut in one crusher pier; furthermore, an access doorway was cut in the other wall. The final result was that, when the top crusher was running empty, the slight vibration of the crusher foundation caused a similar vibration of the upper portion of the main concrete structure to build up in about 10 min. This vibration was then magnified through the cantilevered columns and the stair well until it became sufficiently severe at their tops to be a distinct annoyance. Did or did not the weakening of the piers produce the objectionable results, or did it merely aggravate them? Would a structural-steel building have behaved better or worse? At least, this case shows that such problems should be studied most carefully. A similar installation of equipment in the building pictured in Fig. 9·7 was tied into a heavy retaining wall holding back the hillside at the rear of the structure. This installation proved to be satisfactory.

10·6 Details That May Cause Trouble. A few major sources of possible trouble with the structural parts of multistory steel buildings are given for the illustration of the general principles involved. Many others probably will be encountered, but all cannot be described here.

Small offsets, or setbacks, of exterior walls are used frequently in office and public buildings for architectural effect, for the admission of light, or because of building code requirements; they are seldom used in industrial structures. Nevertheless, they are discussed in order to illustrate some important principles, such as the following:

1. Assume the condition shown in Fig. 10·6(a). A partial plan of the columns is pictured in Sketch (b). Columns E and F above the third floor are carried on beams CG and DH, respectively, whereas all the other columns extend to the foundations. These beams are therefore relatively "soft spots" in the supporting system because they may deflect appreciably. This local sagging as the load comes on is likely to crack the walls above and alongside the offset.

2. If column A of Fig. 10·6(b) is also supported on beam BJ, the deflection may cause local cracking and crushing of the exterior walls below and adjacent to point A, as well as cracking of the wall above it.

3. Using beam CG of Fig. 10·6(b) as a particular case, what type of end connections should be used in attaching it to its columns? The shear at end C may be very large so that a framed connection may look somewhat as shown in (c). This may cause a bending of column C as pictured in Sketch (d) because the column must rotate along with the beam; it must also support a heavy eccentrically applied load. A seated connection, as in Sketch (e), may seem to remedy a large portion of this trouble, but downward curvature of the beam will still tend to make the load concentrate upon the inner flange of the column. At the light end, G of Sketch (b), it may be preferable to simulate a hinged connection somewhat as shown in (f) rather than to bend the column excessively. It is obvious that stiffness should be considered for such members as CG in

order to prevent large deflections, harmful curvature, and the opening of cracks in the floor.

4. When heavy beams or girders are seated, as in Fig. 10·6(e), they should be steadied by bracing in the plane of the outer wall so that, in case of shock, they cannot jackknife, as shown in Sketch (g).

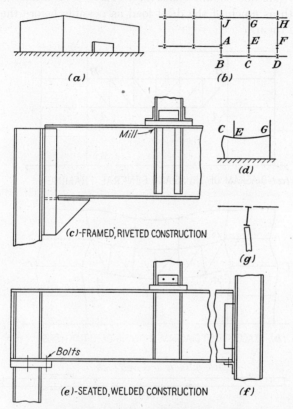

Fig. 10·6.   Supports for offset columns.

There may be situations in which a column in an outer wall must be omitted in the first story to allow for a wide opening.   This column may have to be supported by a beam or girder that is in and parallel to the exterior wall itself.   The deflection of this beam is likely to crush any masonry under it and crack the walls above and near its ends, as illustrated by the action pictured at C in Fig. 10·6(d).

When a wall, or a stiff partition resting upon a beam, is built before the beam is heavily loaded from other sources, the beam may sag underneath the wall sufficiently to make the latter crack horizontally at the bottom, if the wall is able to arch across to the supports. If the wall cannot span the opening or distort in accordance with the deflection of the beam, the wall will undoubtedly crack in shear. It is obvious, therefore, that one should endeavor to have long beams and girders loaded with as much of the dead load as possible before the walls are built upon them.

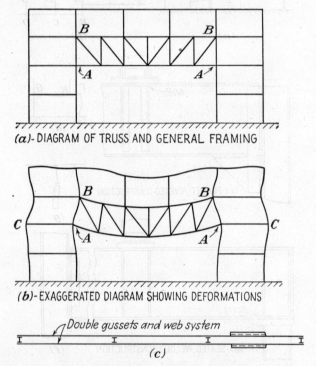

(a)- DIAGRAM OF TRUSS AND GENERAL FRAMING

(b)- EXAGGERATED DIAGRAM SHOWING DEFORMATIONS

(c)

Fig. 10·7.   Illustration of truss action in a multistory structure.

When a heavy interior column must be omitted in some lower story, it may be possible to provide the missing support by a beam, a girder, or a truss; perhaps the last can be made one story deep and the diagonals hidden in partitions. Such a truss may be especially desirable when two or more columns must be carried by it, as shown in Fig. 10·7(a). A deep girder holding these columns might cut down the clearance below it excessively, whereas the chords of the truss may constitute a part of the framing of the floors, and they are relatively shallow.

Even with a truss like that of Fig. 10·7(a), the rotation of the ends of the truss may cause severe stressing of the structure. If the truss is built with a camber to allow for future sag and rotation, it may be difficult to erect the structure because parts must be distorted in order to fit them together. The cambering does not eliminate the future movement under load. If the truss is not built to allow for future deformations, the stresses produced in the surrounding structure by these movements may be severe, as shown to exaggerated scale in Fig. 10·7(b). It is therefore desirable to permit movement at such a point as A in the lower chord until after the dead load is on the structure. This will at least reduce some of the distortion at such points as C.

Fig. 10·8.   Steelwork of the New Jersey ventilation building of the Lincoln Tunnel.
(Courtesy of the Port of New York Authority.)

Point A may be seated temporarily and connected firmly later on, or it may be permitted to act permanently as an expansion and contraction joint if the framing is made accordingly. The entire load is thus carried through the connections at points B, Fig. 10·7(a). Such heavy trusses should be made similar to bridge structures—gussets in two planes instead of one, somewhat as indicated in (c). It is not difficult to visualize the distortions that such framing causes in multistory structures; it is far more difficult to make sure that harmful cracking will not result.

In one heavy building, two rows of columns were carried by a pair of deep plate girders in order to span a wide opening. The intermediate columns were turned so that their webs were parallel to those of the girders, whereas the end columns were placed so that the

FIG. 10·9. A multistory industrial plant of modern design. It has a structural-steel frame and brick walls. (*Design and construction by the Austin Co.*)

FIG. 10·10. A modern steel, concrete, and brick power plant. (*Courtesy of the Phelps Dodge Corp.*)

connection angles of the girders came into the column webs. The end columns were too heavily loaded to make it practicable to seat the girders and then to place the upper columns on top of their ends. The rotation of the end of a girder necessarily bent the rigidly connected column and caused secondary stresses of large magnitude. Therefore, the columns were reinforced with heavy web plates in order to make allowance for the inevitable local overstressing of the tips of the column flanges. In some special cases, it may be possible to seat such girders on auxiliary columns, somewhat as is done in the case of the crane girders in Fig. 9·35. This double column, however, probably uses more space than is desirable.

Chapter 11

CONCRETE STRUCTURES

11·1 Introduction. Reinforced concrete is an excellent building material, adaptable to many uses. It is strong, fire-resistant, and durable when well made. On the other hand, it is a heavy material, and its use generally results in rather bulky members so that its greatest field of usefulness is in relatively low buildings and in structures where its mass, rigidity, and strength are advantageous. Tall buildings may be made of reinforced concrete but, when they are more than six or eight stories high, it is desirable to question the economy and advisability of such construction for industrial purposes.

Structures built of concrete should be planned upon the basis of the characteristics of the material itself, and upon the essential nature of the construction processes. Concrete is not a substitute for structural steel in terms of member for member. Architects and engineers, figuratively, should throw away many of their ideas derived from experience with steel-framed structures, then tackle the project at hand on the basis of utilizing the concrete to the best advantage. Many have done this and are now producing plans for concrete structures that are both attractive and practical.

Here, as elsewhere, the designer should make sure that concrete is the most desirable material for a structure and should give careful consideration to the general proportions of the structure and to the uses for which it is intended. Because of the nature of concrete construction, careful planning is needed in the first place because extensive alterations and radical changes of future use are likely to be both difficult and expensive.

11·2 Some General Principles. The planning and the detail designing of concrete structures are so influenced and circumscribed by practical procedures and considerations that the engineer should attack such problems entirely upon the basis of the best use of this particular material. He should remember constantly that, except for possible precast members, he is creating a structure to be made of "artificial stone," of material placed in position in a plastic state so that it must be supported temporarily by something other than itself, and of a material that will and should conform to every detail of the surfaces with which it is in contact when the plastic concrete is deposited.

Not only does concrete improve with the use of good materials, but its quality depends largely upon the excellence of the workmanship used in its manufacture, the adequacy and thoroughness of its placement, and the care with which it is cured. The attainment of the intended high quality is almost completely in the hands of the artisans who, in the field, convert heaps of aggregates, barrels of cement, and gallons of water into a structure for the use of man. Not only does its strength depend upon highly skilled labor, but the quality of its surface and the beauty of its appearance do likewise. It is foolish to forget these obvious truths. Yet occasionally such important operations are delegated to unskilled, inefficient workmen. Fortunately, this is the exception. Expert workmen produce surprisingly fine results.

When planning concrete work, an engineer should consider the following matters, along with many others:

1. Concrete should be placed in the forms within $\frac{1}{2}$ to $\frac{3}{4}$ hr. after it is mixed; thereafter it should remain undisturbed for a few days or weeks, depending upon the rapidity of its setting, in order to allow the chemical action to proceed without any fracturing of the partially set material.

2. Since every detail of formed surfaces must be provided in advance in the forms themselves, the cost of the forms and their actual construction should be considered when the shape and details of the members are planned. Portions of concrete projecting *out* from the main surfaces, therefore, cause difficult form work, whereas recesses may be made easily by attaching special pieces to the inner surfaces of the main forms.

3. The character and capacity of the mixing equipment inevitably affect the quantity of concrete that can be placed in a given time. It is obvious, of course, that the structure and its parts must be planned so that pours that should be monolithic can be made so.

4. Small miscellaneous parts that must be poured separately often retard progress; and they are likely to increase unit costs.

5. It is desirable to plan structures and equipment so that the concrete can be lowered vertically into place. Dropping concrete through long distances, chuting it at flat angles, moving it horizontally inside the forms by means of shovels or vibrators—such procedures tend to cause segregation and so should be avoided deliberately. Pumping may be advantageous when concrete is to be placed in large, monolithic pours at reasonable distances from the source or mixer, or at great altitudes above it. Generous proportions should be used for parts to be built under water by the use of a tremie or of tight buckets in order to allow for uncertainties of placement as well as for dilution of the cement paste.

6. Forms should be left in place long enough for the concrete to attain sufficient strength to support itself and any loads to be applied to it immediately and in the near future. With ordinary portland cement, this may require 2 or 3 days for vertical members such as walls and piers, or 2 weeks for heavy slabs and beams.

Other principles to be borne in mind in the planning of reinforced-concrete construction are the following:

1. Poured-concrete structures ordinarily try to act largely as continuous frames. This is inherent in their nature. In fact, if continuity is to be avoided without detrimental or objectionable cracking, special measures generally must be employed. Hence, the advantages of continuity can and should be utilized.

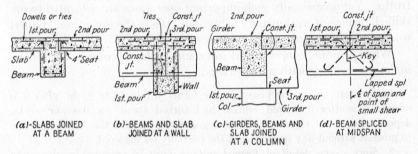

(a)-SLABS JOINED AT A BEAM　　(b)-BEAMS AND SLAB JOINED AT A WALL　　(c)-GIRDERS, BEAMS AND SLAB JOINED AT A COLUMN　　(d)-BEAM SPLICED AT MIDSPAN

FIG. 11·1. Details at junctions of pours in floor construction.

2. Since concrete is especially advantageous in resisting compression, its use is more desirable for columns and walls than for long-span beams. The arch, the dome, the cylindrical barrel, the rigid frame, the flat slab, and beam-and-girder construction are among the types most suitable for the use of concrete.

3. So-called "framed" connections are difficult to make in reinforced concrete. Junctions of beams to beams should be made by pouring the adjoining members monolithically if possible because, otherwise, it is difficult to provide for transverse shearing forces. When beams rest upon walls or columns, the construction joints should be located so that each beam has adequate bearing upon the supporting member. Some suggestions for planning these details are shown in Fig. 11·1.

4. Not only is simplicity of shape desirable in order to minimize the cost of formwork, but the duplication of parts permits the reuse of forms. It is obvious that heavy forms high in the air are costly.

5. Architectural details should be planned with consideration not only for the fabrication of the forms but also for the removal or stripping of them without damage to the concrete, or undue harm to the forms themselves. The details should also be such that the concrete will conform completely and easily to all the contours, projections, and recesses of the forms without spalling,

honeycombing, slumping, air-trapping, and surface imperfections.   Figure 11·2 illustrates some of these matters.

6. As the desired surface texture of concrete structures is something to determine carefully in advance, the structure should be planned so that the desired effects will be attained. Good effects will not just happen of their own accord; the bad ones do that.

7. The sequence of pours and the location of construction joints should be determined during the general planning of a structure in order to ascertain that what is desired can be built practicably. The volume of concrete that can be placed in one continuous pour depends upon the capacity of the equipment and upon the nature and details of the structure.   It is very important to avoid the incomplete placing of a pour by depositing a portion of the concrete

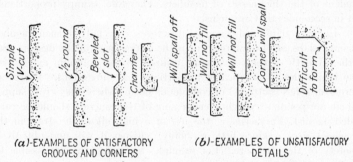

(a)-EXAMPLES OF SATISFACTORY   (b)-EXAMPLES OF UNSATISFACTORY
GROOVES AND CORNERS   DETAILS

FIG. 11·2.   Illustrations of principles of good and bad details for markings and offsets.

at one time, then pouring additional concrete alongside or on top of the first part after the latter has only partly set.   Settlement or displacement of forms, an attempt to vibrate or otherwise compact the concrete, and any other operations that disturb the original material after it has partially set but is not yet strong will generally damage the concrete.   After the first part has hardened, there is likely to be an unexpected plane of weakness at the junction with that deposited later.   Of course, a tall pier shaft may be poured almost continuously and over a period of many hours if the work is performed properly.   However, this is seldom easy of accomplishment in the case of extensive foundations, walls, and floors.

8. When specifying the live loads that a structure is designed to support, one should not be too niggardly because, once the structure is built, little can be done to strengthen it in the future. As stated before, the history of the use of structures shows that changes in use and equipment often increase the actual loads, or the owner often wishes that an increase were permissible. When life and property are at stake, it behooves one to be careful and conservative.   Within reason, good quality and long, safe service far outweigh any saving of money which may have been effected but which later handicaps the use of a structure, not to mention those "savings" that result in disaster.

It is a natural, psychological reaction of an owner or operator to believe that concrete construction is strong because it has such a splendid record of performance.   He therefore uses it for his purposes and seldom stops to consider whether or not the loads exceed those so carefully provided for by the designer who has long since left the scene.   It is not right to set traps for such unwary persons by "skinning" the design and construction.

9. The cost of a concrete structure is not directly proportional to the volume of concrete used in it.   The forms alone for thin floors and walls may cost from 40 to 100 per cent of the value of the mixed concrete as a raw material, because the expenditure for the forms depends upon the areas of formed surfaces, the weight to be carried, the necessary shoring, and the complexity of the details of the forms. The finishing of surfaces, too, is generally rather independent of the thicknesses of members. Therefore, skimpy proportions may result in economies that are delusive.

10. In most reinforced-concrete structures, especially in such members as beams and slabs, steel reinforcement is the critical part of the design.   Seldom can the strength of the concrete be utilized to the optimum extent because of the limitations of practicable proportions and dimensions.   However, the compression zones (bottoms) of continuous beams where they cross supporting members are points at which overstressing of the concrete should be carefully guarded against. Furthermore, the use of a high allowable stress in the reinforcement may produce little economy, whereas it will undoubtedly affect the safety of the structure.   For example, increasing the permissible tensile stress from 20,000 to 25,000 psi may seem to reduce the amount of steel required by 20 per cent.   It does so at the critical points, but such a large amount of the reinforcement very properly has to be used for various purposes and throughout the length of the member that, practically speaking, the total tonnage is surprisingly independent of the allowable unit stress, and the real saving of steel in the case previously mentioned may be scarcely 5 to 8 per cent.   Is the saving worth the extra hazard; and is the greater severity of tensile cracking of the concrete at critical regions detrimental, too?

11. Concrete shrinks after pouring because of the chemical action during setting and curing and because of the evaporation of water and the cooling down from the temperatures caused by hydration. The coefficient of shrinkage may vary greatly—possibly from 0.0002 to 0.0004—and this shrinkage is greater for "rich" mixes than for lean ones. As an approximate figure to bear in mind, one may assume that the shrinkage will be about $\frac{3}{8}$ in. per 100 ft. of length of structure. Thus, to avoid cracking, long structures should be cut into reasonably short units by contraction joints, which will act as expansion joints during future rises of temperature. The locating of these joints is a part of the planning of a structure.

A rather extreme example of the importance of remembering about the shrinkage deformation of concrete, but one that illustrates the basic action, is a proposal made for the spillway of a tailings dam. Flash floods required that the spillway have a wide crest and that it be placed in a channel cut in rock beyond one end of the dam. The impounding of the tailings made it desirable to raise the spillway crest in five successive increments of about 5 ft. each. The suggested plan called for a circular, arched section similar to that shown in Figs. 11·3(*a*) and (*b*). Assume that the first lift was poured 2 years ago, that the concrete *really* did slide on the base under it (a doubtful probability), and that the pressure of the water has thrown the arch into compression. A new lift is to be poured. Even though it is poured in alternate blocks first and then the intervening ones are filled in, shrinkage may cause a

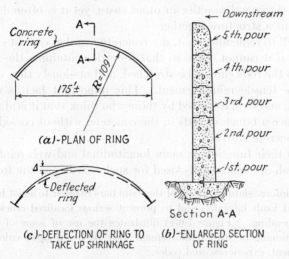

FIG. 11·3.   Extreme example of effect of shrinkage on horizontal arch.

total shortening of at least ½ in., as pictured in Sketch (*c*). For the new section to act as intended, it must be brought into compression also. The take-up of ½ in. in the length of the arc would mean that the "crown" of the new strip of the arch should move horizontally. How can it do this unless the lower pour does likewise and is correspondingly stressed more highly, or unless the top leans downstream? What happens as still more lifts are added? Is it not apparent that shrinkage will entirely change the intended action of the structure, whereas it might not have been so harmful if the entire spillway had been built initially?

If concrete is heated for placement during freezing weather, the total shrinkage may be even more than usual. If it is heated and poured upon existing cold concrete, the shrinkage cracking is aggravated.

12. As stated previously, the quality of a concrete structure depends largely upon the skill and carefulness of the workmen who build it. The planners and designers may have many ideas about refinements of design and detail, but they might be greatly disillusioned if they tried to do the work themselves

with the labor available—and do it at a profit. Planning and design should be such that a structure can really be built that way, efficiently and well.

11·3 Function of Reinforcement. When the sizes of columns must be minimized or when the concrete at some localized section must be strengthened without an increase of the cross-sectional area, steel reinforcement may be used to resist compression; otherwise, its function is primarily the resistance to tensile forces that the concrete itself cannot withstand safely. Seldom is the use of compressive reinforcement economical as a general practice in other cases, yet it is often desirable in order to knit a structure together.

It is well to remember that, if a concrete member cannot elongate as a whole or if it cannot curve so that the side containing the steel elongates, then the rods cannot be stretched, and obviously they cannot act as effective tensile reinforcement. This important fact is sometimes overlooked, and steel is wasted by those who think that it is always beneficial to place a bunch of rods in the concrete, without consideration of how the concrete is to act.

Besides their function as main longitudinal and web reinforcement, rods or mesh are customarily used for such services as the following:

1. To reinforce slabs crosswise of the main bars in order to assist in spreading concentrated loads laterally, and to prevent serious localized cracking caused by lateral bending.   Figure 7·6(e) illustrates the use of some of these rods. The proportioning of such reinforcement may be based upon calculations or upon judgment, experience, and codes.

2. To act as tiny columns to support other rods in place before and during concreting, as illustrated by the vertical reinforcement A that is to hold up the horizontal temperature reinforcement shown in Fig. 11·4(a). Naturally, these rods must have sufficient stiffness, but they need not be closely spaced.

3. To act as spacers to which the main reinforcement is to be wired and thereby held in position during the placing of the concrete. Such rods are the longitudinal ones in the footing of the wall shown in Fig. 11·4(a). These rods may also act as tiny beams to hold the weight of the main bars from chair to chair, or from one precast block to another, keeping the steel high enough for proper encasement.

4. To serve as dowels to tie two pieces of concrete together, or as little posts to which other steel may be wired in order to prevent its horizontal displacement during concreting. Rods B at the bottom front edge of the stem of the retaining wall in Fig. 11·4(a) serve the latter purpose.

5. To become "shrinkage reinforcement." This term is deceptive. The rods in the concrete do not magically cause shrinkage action to vanish; their purpose is to ensure that shrinkage will not cause harmful localized cracking. In fact, the steel itself tries to prevent shrinkage of the concrete. Therefore,

compressive stresses are caused in the rods by the shrinkage of the concrete except that, if the concrete really cracks, the rods should then prevent these cracks from becoming large enough to be noticeable. Therefore, adding steel to stop shrinkage may actually produce hair-cracking of the concrete. For example, assume that the simple foundation wall shown in Fig. 11·4(b) is to be poured in units 60 ft. long. If the coefficient of shrinkage is 0.0003 and if the wall does shrink accordingly and assuming it to be 5 ft. by 1.5 ft.,

Total shrinkage $= 0.0003 \times 720 = 0.216$ in.

Compressive f'_s in steel $= 0.0003 \times 30,000,000 = 9,000$ psi $\pm$

Tension in concrete $= \dfrac{A_s f'_s}{A_c - A_s} = \dfrac{2.64 \times 9,000}{1,080 - 2.64} = 22$ psi $\pm$

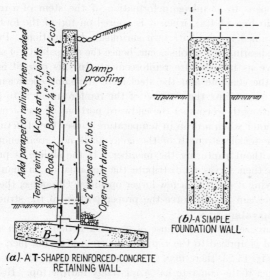

(a)-A T-SHAPED REINFORCED-CONCRETE RETAINING WALL

(b)-A SIMPLE FOUNDATION WALL

FIG. 11·4. Examples of reinforced-concrete walls.

Assuming the wall to slide symmetrically with respect to the center of its length, and assuming that the coefficient of friction is 0.75, then the tension at the center is

$$T = (1.5 \times 5 \times 150)\, 0.75 \times 30 = 25,200 \text{ lb.}$$

Therefore,

Additional tension in concrete $= \dfrac{25,200}{1,077} = 23$ psi

If the steel tries to help resist this latter tension, the effect is the relief of compressive stress already in the rods.

Total tension in concrete $= 22 + 23 = 45$ psi (approx.)

This is such a low stress that the concrete can probably withstand it. However, if the concrete cracks at the center, then the local stress in the rods at this section to stop the opening of the crack is

$$f_s = \frac{25,200}{2.64} = 9,600 \text{ psi (approx.)}$$

On the other hand, assume that the longitudinal rods are made ten times as large. Then their resistance to compression as the concrete shrinks may be

$$\text{Force} = 9,000 \times 26.4 = 238,000 \text{ lb.}$$

$$\text{Tension in concrete} = \frac{238,000}{1,080 - 26.4} = 226 \text{ psi (approx.)}$$

Hence, under this stress, the concrete may crack in order to relieve the tension and the heavy reinforcement actually causes hair-cracking.

What happens to shrinkage deformation of the stem of a retaining wall, such as that in Fig. 11·4(a), when it is poured on top of the footing after the latter has attained much of its own shrinkage deformation? Probably hair-cracking and shearing distortions occur, hence the advisability of short sections.

6. To serve as temperature reinforcement. In this case, it is sufficient to assume that the concrete and the steel have the same coefficient of thermal deformation. Therefore, the purpose of the reinforcement is to provide sufficient tensile strength to compel the endward portions of the structure to slide toward the center when a drop in temperature causes the structure to shorten and when the tensile strength of the concrete is not great enough to cause the motion without rupturing the member. If the sliding is prevented, the reinforcement then serves to distribute the deformation in many hair-cracks instead of having it occur at a few larger openings. Of course, the compression in the concrete can usually force the proper portion of the structure to slide when the temperature rises.

7. To minimize spalling because of shearing action. When a heavy, concentrated load is applied to the top of a concrete pedestal, pier, or abutment, as shown in Fig. 13·23, there may be a tendency to crack off the edges outside the loaded area if the concrete has a relatively narrow top. Rods hooked or bent around the corners may help to prevent spalling but they may not stop the cracking entirely. Circular hoops around the top may have some value, but rectangular ones will probably avail little.

8. To knit concrete encasement to the member it covers, or to prevent disintegration of that encasement. This is shown in Fig. 7·6(b)—the beam wrapper and the ties. Gunite encasement is usually tied together similarly, or by the complete wrapping of the member with wire mesh.

11·4 Position of Reinforcement in Exposed Walls. When a concrete wall is subjected to rather sudden changes of temperature on one side, there is a tendency for it to expand or contract, as the case may be. On the side that is affected first, there may be set up severe tensile or compressive stresses, and there may be high shearing stresses in the concrete. For instance, assume that a retaining wall is cold at night and then is rather quickly subjected to a rise in temperature in the sunshine the next morning. The outside surface will expand and tend to cause the wall to assume a curve that is concave on the back. This tends to crack the concrete in the rear surface because the wall is not generally free to assume its natural and desired curvature for the given conditions. In such a case it seems that reinforcement should be near the inner surface. On the other hand, when the conditions are reversed and the rear is relatively warm whereas the outside surface is subjected to a cold wind, it would seem that the reinforcement should be on the outside surface. When the walls are thick, the reinforcement is desirable on both faces. If they are very thin, the most satisfactory compromise may be to place the steel in the middle. However, placing concrete in thin walls is rather difficult. If one row of steel is to be used, it is generally advisable to put the rods near the outside rather than the inside face, because this is the one usually subjected to violent cooling and shrinking. It is not possible to design such reinforcement accurately because results will depend entirely upon the assumptions regarding the rate of heating and cooling, the differential in temperature between the two faces, the thickness of the wall, and the rate of transfer of heat through the concrete.

Another situation, causing unfortunate conditions and perhaps resulting in severe spalling of the concrete, frequently occurs in industrial plants. For instance, a concrete wall may be located near a place where heat is generated intermittently or temporarily, such as from a ladle of hot metal, slag, or similar materials. The sudden heating of the surface of a heavy wall will almost inevitably cause the expansion of the outer surface to set up shearing and tensile stresses which cause that surface to break away from the concrete behind it. Reinforcement of this surface will do little or no good except to knit the concrete together and reduce the falling away of the spalled portions. When such a situation can be anticipated, it is advisable to protect the wall with a layer of brickwork or similar fairly good insulating material, which can be replaced readily if it disintegrates. There is little that can be done to repair one of these walls, once it has spalled.

An illustration of the harmful action of localized heating of concrete is the cracking that occurred at a small boilerhouse. The structure was founded upon a heavy mat that rested upon plastic soil. The mat was stiffened by heavy ribs under the walls and also along all column rows, forming a checkerboard pattern of 5-ft.-deep cells under the floor. One of the central cells along one side of the structure was to be used for a sump. One day considerable hot water was admitted to this sump. Shortly thereafter, a few cracks were noticed in the exterior rib opposite the sump, and even in some lightly reinforced foundations of compressors that rested on the mat and across a previously poured rib. The pressures from localized expansion of the concrete apparently caused the unheated parts to be stressed excessively in tension.

11·5 Shrinkage Cracks along Window and Door Openings. It is very difficult to avoid some shrinkage cracks near the upper corners of window and door openings. Special reinforcement should be used across these points, the main reinforcement being horizontal just above their tops. Some additional reinforcement diagonally across the corners may be useful, but to a lesser extent.

The reasons for the preceding statement may be explained as follows:

1. If the wall below the windows is poured with a construction joint at the level of the window sills, the concrete will have time to shrink considerably during its setting and before additional concrete is poured above it.

2. It may be that the whole portion through the height of the window from sill to head will be placed as the next pour. If so, it, too, will have a tendency to shrink somewhat.

3. If the next pour is a continuous section across the tops of the windows, it will tend to shrink also. The lower portions between the windows will have developed considerable shearing strength by this time and will tend to act as anchors holding the concrete next to them in position. Any shrinkage cracks are, therefore, likely to occur above the opening of the window itself, because this point is restrained the least.

11·6 Expansion and Contraction Joints. Any expansion joint is, of course, a contraction joint also. However, a contraction joint may be looked upon as a plane of weakness that will permit the shrinkage deformation of the concrete to cause a slight opening at a predetermined point. In a way, such joints may also serve partly as expansion joints because a subsequent rise of temperature may not be so great that the expansion will take up more space than did the previous shrinkage. Even though the future expansion may be greater than the shrinkage deformation, contraction joints are very useful because the excess of increase in length will merely set up compressive forces in the concrete, and these are not likely to be serious. Some details of expansion joints are shown in Fig. 13·19.

Contraction joints, as well as expansion joints, should be located at the most advantageous places. No specific rules should be stated for this because structures vary so greatly in their dimensions and details. The general principle to be used is to visualize the deformations as greatly exaggerated, then to imagine where tensile stresses are likely to crack the structure.   These locations are then the ones at, or near which, the joints should be placed.   If it is impossible to place a contraction joint at such a place, reinforcement should be provided to prevent noticeable cracking.   It is obvious that reinforcement should not pass through a contraction joint if the latter is to work properly.

Keys to transmit shear are often needed at expansion, contraction, and construction joints.   They are generally more useful in vertical than in horizontal joints because the friction that exists at the latter because of the weight upon it is often sufficient to resist ordinary shearing forces. If the first pour at a horizontal construction joint is roughened slightly, the mechanical bond will offer considerable resistance to shearing forces between the lower and the upper portions of the wall.

It is generally advisable to make keys rather wide but shallow.   Too deep a key at a contraction joint is likely to be pulled off because of the friction along its sides.   In all contraction joints it is best to paint the first pour with asphalt, oil, or some material to prevent bond when the adjoining concrete is poured.   Joints with cork or premolded mastic fillers should have these fillers on the flat surfaces adjacent to the keys and on the main face of the key itself, but not on the edges of the key because this would prevent the transmission of large shearing forces. It happens sometimes that these prefabricated fillers outside of the keyway in a vertical joint will squeeze outward, slump or work loose, and present an unsatisfactory appearance; hence they should be mechanically fastened to the concrete by a few copper nails through the filler or by some other device, and embedded in the second pour.

Figure 11·5 shows some typical cases of how to plan the locations and details of contraction joints.   The following should be noticed, referring to the sketches by letter:

(a) This rectangular abutment for a small concrete T-beam bridge is filled with earth.   When the walls and front of the abutment contract, they tend to squeeze the earth, and the abutting power of the latter causes tremendous resistance.   Therefore, the concrete is likely to crack.   If there is a contraction joint at A, each half of the abutment may act as an independent, angular structure that is inherently stable.   On the other hand, if the bridge itself is made of concrete, it should have a longitudinal joint to match that in the abutment.   A steel bridge will usually adjust itself to the small motion of the abutment.

Another way to plan this abutment is to locate two contraction joints at B so that none will be needed in the bridge itself.   This, however, makes it necessary to consider each part as a separate retaining wall.   Keys at these joints in the wing walls would destroy much of the effectiveness of the joint because they would resist contraction of the main abutment.

(*b*) This pictures a corner of a long retaining wall. One keyed contraction joint is at *C*, in line with the rear of the footing of *CE*. The joints at *D* and *E* cut the wall into units whose lengths will depend upon what seems to be best for the particular situation. One should resist the temptation to mini-

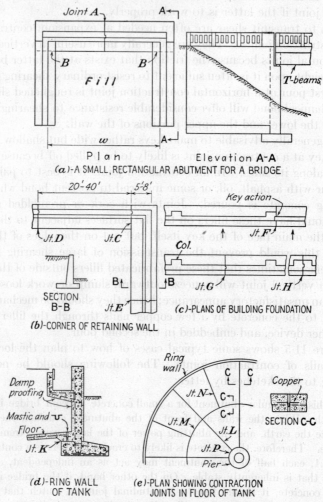

Fig. 11·5. Some locations and uses of contraction joints.

mize the number of joints just to save a little troublesome work and a relatively small amount of money.

(*c*) Assume that this shows the foundation wall under a concrete-frame building. The pilasters are naturally under the columns. If the contraction joint in the foundation is at *F*, it will interrupt the continuity of the wall in spreading the adjacent column load. Intermittent keys in the wall and a horizontal key in the footing will be of some assistance in the transfer of load to the right of F. With a joint at G, this spreading action is simplified. However, this location may cause difficulties when one tries to have the joint in the superstructure line up with that in the foundation. The use of joint H between adjoining columns will generally be the most simple and the best for the structure as a whole.

(*d*) This pictures a section through the ring wall of a settling (dewatering) tank about 230 ft. in diameter. In this case, it seemed to be desirable to pour the wall in alternate sections approximately 30 ft. long so as to minimize the harmful effects of shrinkage. On the other hand, the wall was reinforced circumferentially so that it could have no real contraction joints (to reduce the probability of leakage). The junction of the floor with the wall, however, was designed to permit horizontal movement by sliding of the slab on the footing. The top of the latter was made smooth and coated with tar or asphalt. Such sliding joints as these are not reliable when they are subjected to large pressures.

(*e*) This sketch shows the way the joints in the floor of a 230-ft. tank were laid out. The main radial joints L were made so that the slabs near joint P were not too narrow because sharp, long corners are likely to crack. Then the intermediate circular joint M and the additional joints N were used to break up the slabs into units of reasonable size. The sections were poured alternately, and all joints had copper waterstops that were soldered at junctions.

Thin members like balustrades, parapets, and concrete platforms that are affected quickly and severely by changes in the temperature of the air should be cut into small pieces. Provisions should be made to enable the necessary movements to occur without cracking of the parts. Furthermore, even thick members that are exposed to serious changes of temperature will be affected quickly. If they are supported upon short, thick walls or piers that strongly resist movement, enough contraction joints should be provided to avoid harmful cracking.

The relative action of connected parts should also be studied. For example, a thin concrete apron on or attached to a heavy stone-masonry bulkhead will crack to accommodate itself to unequal deformations and to movements at joints in the masonry. Such an apron attached to a heavy gravity type of retaining wall or bulkhead is also likely to crack because it is affected by temperature changes more quickly than is the massive structure.

11·7 Continuous Girders. When continuous, reinforced-concrete girders are used for heavy, moving loads, such as cranes, the varying positions of the loads will inevitably cause a shifting of the location of the points of contraflexure. When the loads are located so as to cause maximum negative bending moments near the supports, the positive moment near the center of the girder will be small and the points of contraflexure will be relatively far from the supports. On the other hand, when the loads are near the middle of the span so as to produce maximum positive moments, the points of contraflexure will be relatively near the supports.

When the tension is a maximum at a support, there will be hair-cracks in the concrete where the tension is sufficiently high; when the tension at the bottom of the beam is a maximum, the hair-cracks will

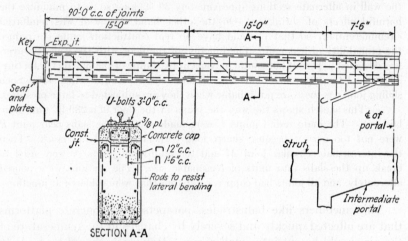

SECTION A-A

FIG. 11·6.   Reinforced-concrete girder for 10-ton crane.

naturally be in the lower portion of the beam. During the passage of the loads from one extreme position to the other, it can be seen readily that there is the likelihood of hair-cracking in the top of some portion of the beam under one condition and then in the lower part at the same general cross section under the second condition. These are the portions of the member that are subjected to reversal of bending moments. This means that there is a tendency to disintegrate the concrete in the region where the stresses vary from tension to compression and the reverse. Of course, the pressure caused by the compression will close any cracks that might have existed previously when that portion of the beam was under tension. The irregularity of the cracked surface and the friction under the pressure action may be suitable and strong enough to withstand the transverse shear. However, it seems wise to be particularly conservative in the design of the web reinforcement used in these general portions of the beam. It is advisable to design the stirrups to withstand the entire shear at a high unit stress in the steel so that the beam cannot possibly disintegrate.   At such points it is particularly valuable to have the main bottom rods bent up, or the top ones bent down, so that, if it should become necessary, they will knit the entire beam together across this critical section.   These bent rods may not be designed as stirrups, but they are very useful.   Figure 11·6 shows the details of one girder that was designed in accordance with these ideas.

In computing the bending moment at a support of such a continuous girder, it may be inadvisable to use the center of the support itself as the point of application of the reaction, and then to draw the bending-moment diagram and, from it, assume that the bending moment at the edge of the support is the ordinate of the moment diagram at that edge, considering the center of the support as a knife-edge.   It seems wiser to assume that the span is approximately the clear distance between the edges of supports, or a few inches back from them when the supports are reasonably stiff columns and walls, then to compute the bending moment accordingly and use it with its full computed magnitude.   If the first procedure is used, it will be found generally that the theoretical maximum negative bending moment is much less than if it is computed upon the second basis.   In any case, the negative reinforcement should not be cut off too quickly.

As an approximation for use in making preliminary designs of continuous beams and crane girders, it may be helpful to assume that the construction is similar to a cantilevered bridge with simply supported spans between the points of contraflexure, these being assumed at about 0.2 of the span from the edges of the supports.   The general section and reinforcement may be computed upon this basis; then more elaborate analyses may be made with these sections as a starting point.

11·8 Columns and Piers.   It is sometimes difficult to differentiate between a column and a pier.   According to the American Concrete Institute's code (and common sense, too), the longitudinal reinforcement in columns should be well tied together, somewhat as shown in Fig. 11·7 (a).   However, if the ties are larger than $\frac{1}{4}$ in. in diameter, they are difficult to bend by hand in the field.   If they are larger and must be bent in advance before they are placed, it is apparent that they are difficult to erect unless they are dropped in series over the tops of the long rods after the latter are placed.   The arrangement in Sketch (b) is better for such ties.

A column may be looked upon as a member that is round, square or rectangular, and which is relatively slender and highly stressed in compression; its safe load may also be limited more or less by the buckling tendency of the member.   On the other hand, a pier may be considered as a relatively heavy, massive shaft that is not very highly stressed and in which the reinforcement is used more to resist bending moments and to tie the structure together than it is for the resistance it offers to longitudinal compressive forces. In this case, it is not always necessary to tie the rods in as thoroughly as they should be in the case of real columns.

Figure 4·11 shows some reinforced-concrete columns about 35 ft. high, used in an industrial plant that was built during the recent war. These columns support heavy crane girders with maximum spans of

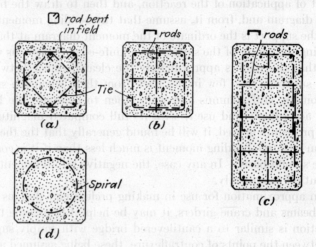

Fig. 11·7.   A few reinforced-concrete columns.

30 ft., carrying a 150-ton crane, also a 5-ton crane at the lower level. These columns must resist wind loads and lateral crane loads, too. The reinforcement is determined largely upon the basis of the cantilever action of the columns, which are really vertical beams fixed near their bases. The longitudinal forces in this crane runway are resisted by the rigid-frame action of the columns and crane girders, with haunching of the members in certain bays to provide strong portal bracing, somewhat as shown in Fig. 11·6. Figure 11·7(c) shows an arrangement of reinforcing that may be used for such column construction. Note that the main hoops can be placed around the vertical reinforcement without having to be dropped over it. The intermediate cross ties are merely rods with 90° bends at each end and arranged so that they can be dropped on top of the main ties. They are then wired in place. This arrangement is easy to erect, and it provides clear central portions through which an elephant's trunk may be placed in order to facilitate the deposition of the concrete.

In order to tie in the longitudinal reinforcement of a column in the most effective manner, spirals are used, as illustrated in Fig. 11·7(d). The desired architectural treatment, however, may require the use of square or rectangular columns. The latter are most suitable in outer walls or partitions, whereas circular columns may be preferable in the clear. Nevertheless, spiral reinforcement may be used in both types.

FIG. 11·8.   Precast beams in the yard after stripping of forms.   The rods are for bonding into other work.   (*Westcott & Mapes, Architects and Engineers, New Haven, Connecticut.*)

Longitudinal rods of themselves may not be economical in resisting compression except when heavy reinforcement will save space by reducing the sizes of columns. Some reasonable amount of steel is desirable; too much may interfere with proper placement of the concrete.

11·9   Precast Concrete.   The use of precast-concrete members and parts of members is a matter that warrants careful study. The possible savings in formwork are obvious, but the handling of heavy pieces in the field may require special equipment. If portions of a structure are to be precast, the original planning should be based upon this fact, and all details should be worked out accordingly. Precast parts can be incorporated in an otherwise poured-in-place structure, but provision should be made for the support of these heavy pieces during construction. Most poured-concrete structures gain much from the stiffness derived from the continuity secured at the junctions of parts, whereas a building

made of heavy, loosely connected, precast parts may be inherently undesirable. It is possible, however, to connect precast parts by means of
poured sections at the junctions if proper bonding of reinforcement is
provided. Although such procedures have not been common in the
past, their use should be investigated with an open mind. Because of
the possibility of appreciable economies, the use of precast parts will
undoubtedly increase in the future. One application of precast members
is shown in Figs. 11·8 and 11·9.

F‌IG. 11·9. Precast beams set in place as part of the bulkhead and deck construction at the Steel Point Station of the United Illuminating Co., Bridgeport, Connecticut.
(*Westcott & Mapes, Architects and Engineers, New Haven, Connecticut.*)

11·10 Prestressed Concrete. Prestressed-concrete members are
useful for certain structures. Their basic purpose is to avoid harmful
deformation and cracking when the intended loads are applied. Two
different principles that may be used in prestressed concrete are illustrated in Fig. 11·10. The following comments may help to clarify them:

1. In Sketch (*a*), a smooth rod is coated with a substance that prevents
bond of the concrete to the steel when the former is poured, or the rod may
be inside a mastic-coated cardboard tube. After much of the shrinkage of
the concrete has occurred and when the concrete has sufficient strength, the
nuts at the ends of the rod are tightened until the steel has the desired tensile
unit stress. Of course, the steel stretches inside the concrete, and the latter
compresses slightly. Thereafter, it is intended that further shrinkage of the

concrete will merely relieve part of the tension in the steel but that the rod will continually cause some compressive stress in the concrete so that cracks cannot open up.   Furthermore, when external forces try to elongate or bend the member, they may be considered to substitute for the compression in the concrete, but they should not annul the compression entirely.   Since the compression in the concrete generally is a low unit stress, little deformation occurs during its relief, and the increase of tension in the rod is not usually excessive. Only when the tensile stress in the steel is balanced by the effect of the external forces is the compression in the concrete relieved completely; thereafter, an increase of the tension in the rod will cause elongations that might crack the concrete.   Since the initial tension in the rod is supposed to exceed any that will be applied by the action of external loads, and because the original tensile strain in the steel should exceed the shrinkage and compressive deformations

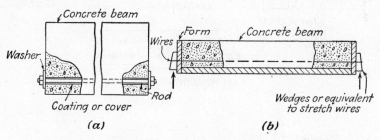

Fig. 11·10.   Illustrations of principles of prestressed concrete.

of the concrete, the rods should be made of a steel which has a high elastic limit and which can be used at a high unit stress.

This type of prestressing may be applied helpfully to such structures as water tanks.   The original tension in the steel is obtained by tightening turnbuckles, couplings, or nuts bearing on some kind of distributing beam, as illustrated in Fig. 11·11(*b*).

2. A second method of prestressing a member is illustrated in Fig. 11·10(*b*). Here the reinforcement is generally high-strength wires or small rods that are tightened until they have the desired tensile deformation and unit stress, using the form or some external anchorage to resist the pull. The reinforcement is then embedded while in this stressed condition, and the bond of the concrete to the steel grips the latter so that, when the member is later removed from the form and when the tightening force is released, the tension in the steel causes a compressive stress in the concrete, but without slipping of the reinforcement. This method is useful in the manufacture of precast, prestressed beams and slabs.

There are many practical matters to consider in the planning of prestressed-concrete structures, *e.g.*, the details to be used for a circular tank.   Various arrangements may be used for such structures, some of

which are pictured in Fig. 11·11. If the side walls of the tank are
connected rigidly to the floor, the tightening of the lower curved rods
by means of the nuts or turnbuckles cannot squeeze the cylinder inward
appreciably in order to remove shrinkage cracking and to compress the
concrete, and the tension in the rods causes vertical bending moments

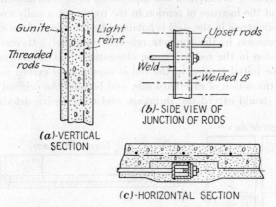

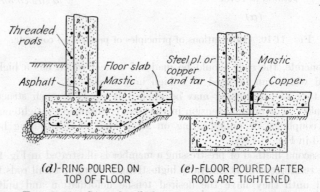

FIG. 11·11. Some details for prestressed-concrete tanks.

in the walls at and near the floor. If the walls are permitted to rest
upon the floor and to slide with respect to it, special details may be
needed to avoid leakage. The junction between the roof and the walls
may cause similar difficulties. Figure 11·11(d) pictures one arrangement
in which the wall of the tank rests upon the thickened edge of the floor
slab. Sketch (e) shows the wall resting upon a footing, with the floor
poured after the circumferential rods were tightened.

11·11 Vacuum Concrete. Because more water is necessary to
secure the desired plasticity of concrete for practicable placement than

is needed for chemical action, a patented vacuum process has been developed for removing much of the excess water prior to the setting of the concrete. The air pressure compacts the plastic concrete while the vacuum cover sucks out this water. The process has some special advantages where the desire for density, early strength, high strength, quick removal of forms, and speed of construction justify its use. One such case is illustrated in Fig. 11·12.

11·12 Concrete-frame, Multistory Buildings. When a fireproof building is desired, one might ask with good reason why structural-steel members encased in concrete might not be replaced by those made of reinforced concrete in which the concrete itself helps to carry the load. There are many times when the latter type of construction may and should be used.

Buildings with reinforced-concrete framework, concrete beam-and-girder floors, and some type of curtain walls have a wide range of usefulness. Their beams and columns may be of almost any sensible size and arrangement; their height and general dimensions may be made to accommodate all except extreme conditions; and

FIG. 11·12. Precast-concrete culvert sections over piping at the University of Connecticut, Storrs, Connecticut. By means of the vacuum process, these sections could be removed from the forms in 24 hours. Notice the invert slab, edge keying, and rollers. (*Westcott & Mapes, Architects and Engineers, New Haven, Connecticut.*)

their framing is more adaptable to unavoidable irregularities than are most other types of concrete buildings.

Once the type of floor and wall construction for a particular building has been selected, the general layout of columns and beams should be developed along with the making of the floor plans. Assuming that the floors of a heavy, multistory building are to be some variety of slab-and-beam construction, the use of bays exceeding 30 to 35 ft. in length is generally uneconomical because of the large sizes of the beams and girders. Bays shorter than 18 to 20 ft. are likely to result in beams that cannot well utilize the available strength of the materials because of minimum practicable sizes.

In such buildings the simplicity and regularity of the column arrangement are even more important than they are in steel construction. Offsets in column rows, inequality of bays, and side-stepping or omission of certain columns can be accepted, but the planner should not require such things until he is sure that nothing better can be done. When extensive complications cannot be avoided and when they cause serious uncertainty of design and of safety, probably he should revise the general layout or consider changing the framing to structural steel in the interest of economy and ease of construction as well as of structural determinacy and reliability.

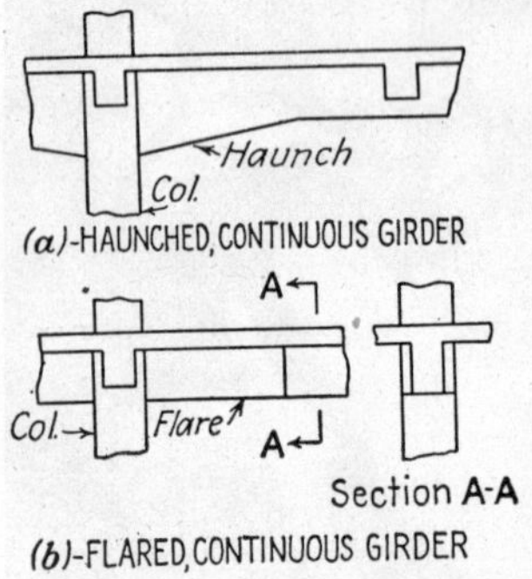

(a)-HAUNCHED, CONTINUOUS GIRDER

(b)-FLARED, CONTINUOUS GIRDER

Fig. 11·13. Two methods of increasing areas at supports of continuous beams and girders.

In concrete-frame structures, the continuity of the beams and girders, combined with their T-beam action near mid-span, frequently make it desirable to use haunched members like that shown in Fig. 11·13(a) because of the greater depth to resist the large negative bending moments at the supports compared to the small positive moments at the centers of the spans. On the other hand, the attainment of some desired architectural effect and clearance may practically compel the use of members with straight bottoms. The sides of these members may be flared as in Sketch (b) when this is essential to secure adequate strength, even though the forms will be more expensive. Therefore, approximate sizes of critical beams and girders should be found during the early planning of a building so that clearances, story heights, and architectural treatment may be determined correctly.

Generally, the beams of such skeleton construction are heavy and stiff. Inequality of loads, unbalanced negative moments, unequal spans, and the effect of adjoining portions of a continuous beam generally cause it to rotate slightly at its junction with a column. The latter will offer whatever resistance it can to this rotation but, unless cracks or overstressing occur, both column and beam will rotate together. Therefore, certain bending moments should be provided for in both beam and column. When one of these beams terminates, as at an outer column or wall, it is probable that the latter cannot restrain the beam so fully as does the framing at an interior column. Therefore, it is often theoretically desirable to use outer bay lengths that are 80 to 90 per cent of those used for inner bays where full continuity is possible, thus avoiding the existence of larger bending moments near the center of the outer bays and at the first interior columns than exist at the centers of other spans and at the other interior columns. This is for the purpose of using the same size of beam and reinforcement at similar points throughout the length of the beam. However, the architectural appearance of the exterior of the structure and the desired uniformity of dimensions will influence one to make these end bays the same as the other ones. These last requirements undoubtedly should outweigh those of theoretical calculation, and all members should be made suitable for their purpose.

With large panels carrying heavy floor loads (especially concentrated loads), it is usually desirable to subdivide the panels by using intermediate beams, if a beamed ceiling is not objectionable. The slabs may then be designed as one-way beams. In other cases with shorter, nearly square panels, large two-way slabs with beams along the column rows may be more desirable. When the loads are sufficiently small, long-span one-way slabs may be used with large beams running along the column lines and in one direction only. In any case, the framework can be varied readily to suit special conditions.

When thin one-way slabs are used with beams 6 to 10 ft. on centers, the girders (or headers) that support these beams and extend crosswise from column to column are likely to be much heavier than the beams themselves. It is therefore preferable, when the bays in one direction are considerably longer than those perpendicular thereto, to have the girders run the short way in order to minimize their sizes and to reduce the resultant detrimental effect upon clearance and story height.

The sizes of columns may decrease from the lower to the upper stories. The ordinary columns generally can and should remain concentric, but those in outer walls, adjacent to elevator shafts, and at similar positions should be located with one face in a vertical plane, unless offsets are desired. This facilitates the uniformity of wall and spandrel-beam details, whereas the effect upon other beams and girders is slight. In many cases it may be economical to specify columns of the same dimensions in several consecutive stories in order to use the same forms repeatedly. The reinforcement may be varied as necessary. In general, the extra volume of concrete used costs little compared to the expenditure for extra forms. Again, when tied columns are used, it may be feasible to maintain one dimension for their cross section, then to vary the other one, in order to use standard panels and to adjust the distance between two opposite faces to suit each case. Of course, this assumes that rectangular or square columns are best suited to simplify formwork at the junctions of the beam haunches and the columns.

The skeleton framework of such a multistory building may be designed to resist lateral loads through the rigid-frame action of beams and columns. Seldom, however, are practicable industrial structures made of reinforced concrete so tall and narrow that this action causes serious trouble, except in the case of earthquakes. It is sometimes advisable to analyze a framework upon the basis of this rigid-frame action in order to make sure that failure cannot occur in this way. Nevertheless, as with steel buildings, the stiffness of walls and partitions (parallel to the horizontal forces) and the rigid-diaphragm action of the floors to deliver loads to the walls are so great that these last parts must crack or distort before sidesway can cause much bending resistance at the junctions of columns and beams. When spandrel beams are poured as deep members extending from the window heads in one story to the window sills in the next higher one, these spandrels will be so stiff that the bending in the columns may be computed safely upon the assumption that the ends of the columns are fixed. This type of spandrel construction may be very useful when poured-concrete walls are desired.

In the planning of change houses and office buildings, it may be both practicable and economical to locate beams along the lines of partitions and walls, with some type of flat, long-span floor between them. The planning should be done carefully in order to minimize the conspicuousness of beam haunches. In this connection, the designer should remember that shallow, wide beams as well as deep, narrow ones can be made to carry loads when they best serve his purposes. Furthermore, he should remember that concrete columns and floors are so stiff and strong that small eccentricities of beam reactions upon the columns may not cause harmful bending moments in the latter.

Cantilevering of beams to support other beams, brackets on the sides of columns to support beams, eccentric column capitals, beams and headers balanced across a single column, and many other special arrangements may be used when the columns can provide sufficient bending resistance. However, the designer should question such specialties until he has made certain that they are essential and that unpredicted loads, unbalanced loads, and unanticipated construction joints will not cause failure of the structure.

It is possible to utilize inner partitions, the walls of stair wells, elevator shafts, and other concrete parts as interior supports for floors when one is sure that there will be no practical reason for wanting them relocated in the future, provided they have sufficient stiffness as vertical diaphragms to avoid buckling, and if they can be made strong enough and vertically continuous enough to carry the accumulated loads safely to the foundations.

11·13 Flat–slab Construction. The combination of flat slabs and columns has been developed to utilize the particular advantages of reinforced concrete poured in place. The slabs can transmit shears and bending moments in various directions to points of support if the rein-

FIG. 11·14. A flat-slab, reinforced-concrete warehouse equipped with a ceiling-suspended belt conveyor, portable chute, and adjustable-height portable bag piler for handling bags of cocoa beans from the railroad siding to the storage pile. (*Courtesy of the Link-Belt Co.*)

forcement is adequate and properly placed. Actually, the slabs try to serve somewhat as continuous, heavy plates that are "dished" concave downward at the columns, somewhat like inverted saucers. Between these regions of negative bending, the slabs act to resist positive moments and to transfer the loads to whatever places can and will support them. Truly, these floors are very indeterminate, but that does not mean that they are correspondingly unsafe and impracticable.

Flat-slab construction is especially well suited to such structures as warehouses, plants for light manufacturing, and buildings requiring large, continuous, open floor areas. The provision of smooth, nearly flat ceilings is automatic. This type is not well suited to structures that are very narrow, irregular in shape, and cut up with partitions and large openings in the floors.   Although a flat-slab floor can distribute concentrated loads of moderate proportions, it is not the most desirable type for the support of large trucks and heavy machines unless the slab is made unusually thick.   Two different uses of flat-slab construction are shown in Figs. 11·14 and 7·22.

It is obvious that column capitals and drop panels are needed for the purposes of reducing the effective spans of the slabs, spreading the regions of critical shear over a sufficiently long perimeter to render them safe, and bringing enough of the slab into negative bending action to ensure safe stresses and permit the proper placing of reinforcement.   The diameter of the top of a capital should be approximately 0.2 to 0.25 of the span length between centers of columns; the width of the drop panel should be about one-third of this span length.

When planning a flat-slab structure, the designer should be very careful to see that the columns are arranged in rows so as to provide a regular pattern with nearly uniform bay lengths in both directions; that successive columns are directly over each other; that spandrel beams and others can pick up the edges where the slabs are discontinuous; that openings will not perforate and damage the system; and that the partitions will not interfere with the intended action of the structure by applying heavy local loads on the one hand or unwanted lines of support on the other.   The interior, freestanding columns may properly be circular; the wall columns may appear more satisfactory if rectangular.   Cantilevering of the floors and walls beyond the outer columns is possible when this feature is desired.   The bays should seldom be less than 20 ft. long; they may exceed 30 ft., but that is a good upper limit for ordinary structures.

The story heights of flat-slab buildings may be limited by various features such as the following:

1. Clearance beneath the slabs and drop panels for equipment and use.
2. Clearance beneath interior beams, as at elevator shafts.
3. Clearance under beams over doorways in exterior walls.
4. Clearance beneath luminaires, pipes, ducts, monorails, and other objects connected directly to or suspended from the ceiling.
5. Space required for proper windows, spandrel beams, and wall construction.
6. Height required for adequate ventilation and air space.
7. Height required to avoid the visual and psychological effects of too-restricted headroom.
8. Height required for proper illumination by daylight and electricity.
9. Requirements in some critical story affecting the others in order to secure uniformity of external architectural appearance.

The actual saving in dollars when one minimizes the story heights of a structure is small because about all he saves is a narrow strip of walls, partitions, glass, and column shafts. The most expensive parts are the floors, roof, and foundations. Furthermore, in buildings that are so large in floor area, restricted headroom may cause perpetual annoyance.

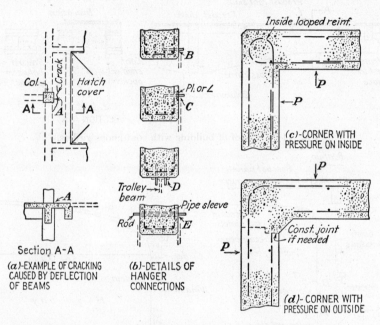

FIG. 11·15. Some miscellaneous details of concrete construction.

11·14 Concrete Mill Buildings. Reinforced concrete can be, and has been, used for the framework of single-story mill buildings. This construction received considerable attention during the war because of the scarcity of structural steel for such use. To be answered is the question of whether or not it can compete successfully with steelwork in the future.

Concrete rigid-frame mill buildings are generally limited to those requiring not over 50- to 100-ft. clear aisles, those having no crane runways or those of small capacity, and those needing moderate vertical clearance (perhaps 30 to 35 ft.). It is possible to extend these uses much further, but the cost is likely to be excessive.

Concrete framing for a large mill building with a flat roof is shown in Fig. 11·16. This utilizes long-span, continuous girders about 15 ft.

apart in one direction with columns under each girder.   Poured-concrete
cross frames and a few intermediate struts are used for stiffening the
structure.   The purlins are precast joists that rest upon a continuous
shelf; the roof slabs are precast-concrete planks.   It is possible to set
these joists in pockets in the sides of the main girders and to mortar

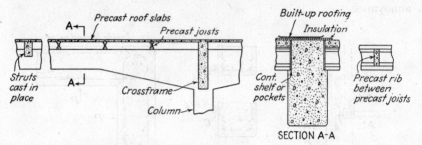

FIG. 11·16.   Roof of building with continuous girders.

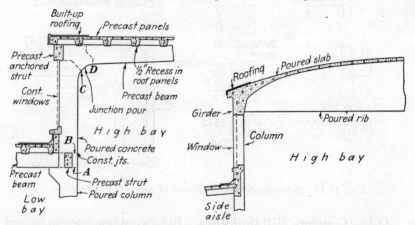

FIG. 11·17.   Rigid-frame high-low-
bay construction partly precast.

FIG. 11·18.   Tied, ribbed, arched roof.

them in place.   It is also possible to use a poured-concrete "tin-pan"
or beam-and-slab roof if desired.

When proper study is given to uniformity and simplicity of construction, the use of steel or wooden forms that may be moved and reused
repeatedly may reduce the cost of a reinforced-concrete structure more
than one might suppose.

Figure 11·17 shows another type of construction that utilizes the
rigid-frame action of the columns and roof beams.   It is an illustration
of the use of precast parts of members in order to minimize the cost of

formwork.   The junction piece between construction joints A and B is poured in place with the horizontal members resting on the lower joint. The upper portion of the column is then poured.   With the main rib supported upon falsework, the junction at the knee between joints C and D is then poured, thus splicing the reinforcement that is left pro-

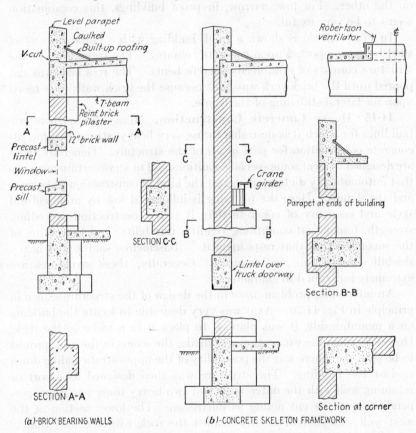

FIG. 11·19.   Small structures made of concrete and bricks.

jecting from the column and rib.   The tensile steel may be welded in the field if desired.   The roof slab consists of long, precast, channel-shaped panels.

Still another type, designed for the use of movable forms, is shown in Fig. 11·18.   This may be used for a series of high-low bays if desired. The thrust of the thin roof slab is partly resisted by the horizontal edge girder; part of the action is that of a wide T-beam.

A combination of concrete roof construction and reinforced brick walls is pictured in Fig. 11·19(a).   This type of construction has proved to be very satisfactory.   The brick walls are of ordinary construction, whereas the pilasters are reinforced vertically, the rods being doweled to the foundation on the one hand and extending into the concrete top band on the other.   For low, narrow, fireproof buildings, this combination seems to be very useful.

In Fig. 11·19(b) is shown a small building with a crane runway of steel beams supported upon concrete columns.   The framework of the structure consists of reinforced-concrete bents.   The roof slab was not poured until the brickwork was built because the brick walls were relied upon for lateral stiffening of the frame.

11·15   Heavy Concrete Construction.   Many times there are buildings for which it is desirable to use very heavy, strong, reinforced-concrete construction for part or all of the structure.   Generally these are designed to meet some special conditions and to serve certain purposes that automatically dictate or suggest the kind of construction to be used and the details.   Here the planning is influenced less by architectural style and economy of concrete than it is by construction procedure, strength, foundation conditions, rigidity, durability, and the nature of the superstructure that rests upon it.   Basements, shafts, and heavy sidehill construction are examples.   Generally, these structures are extremely individual in character.

An interesting problem arose in the design of the structure shown in principle in Fig. 11·20.   As it was very desirable to locate the building on a mountainside, it was planned to place it in a niche in the rock.   However, when the excavation was made, the seams in the rock proved to be such that there was the possibility of the upper strata sliding down against the building.   The structure was then designed as a sort of retaining wall with the outer walls and two heavy inner partitions perpendicular to the cut acting as buttresses.   The lower section of the west wall was poured directly against the rock with the idea that it would require relatively little force to prevent the rock from starting to slide, whereas a large resistance would be needed to stop it after motion had begun.   Ribs of plain concrete were extended westward to the upper rock faces for this same general purpose as well as for use as foundations for part of the structure.   The rest of the heavy concrete work was then incorporated into this buttress scheme.

Another example of a heavy concrete structure having a crane runway is illustrated in Fig. 11·21.   For resisting lateral forces, the columns act as cantilevers that are fixed at their junction with the main struc-

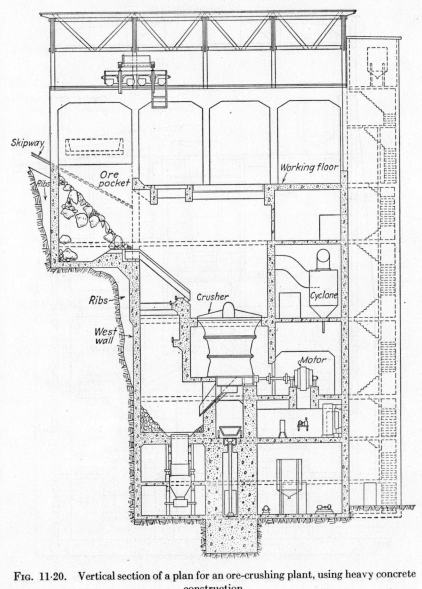

Fig. 11·20.   Vertical section of a plan for an ore-crushing plant, using heavy concrete construction.

ture; for longitudinal forces, one bay is braced as a rigid-frame portal whereas the other columns are tied to it by the crane girders and the intermediate struts.   The building is planned to act as a large strong

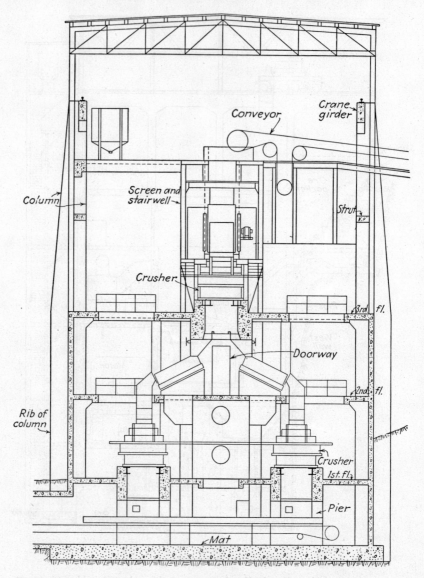

FIG. 11·21.   An ore-crushing plant built of reinforced concrete.   It is designed
as a boxlike structure supported upon a heavy mat foundation.

box that consists of heavy exterior and interior walls, which are in turn
steadied by the floors.   The entire structure is supported upon a heavy
mat to spread the load over compressible soil.

The planning of pours and the locations of construction joints are matters of especially great importance when such heavy construction of reinforced concrete is designed.

11·16 Concrete Subjected to Shock. Because of its lack of ductility, concrete itself is not a desirable material to absorb violent shocks from hard, falling objects; reinforced-concrete beams will serve this purpose to a moderate extent only. Special study should be given to problems of this nature.

In an ore-reduction plant, carloads of ore were to be dumped into a large pocket. It was desirable to divide this space with a central concrete wall to support the track girders. The detail shown in Fig. 11·22(a) was tried, but the impact gradually shattered the concrete in spite of the metallic guards. The wall was later rebuilt as pictured in

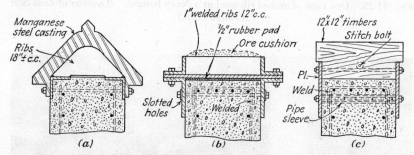

FIG. 11·22. Examples of protection of wall against shocks and abrasion.

Sketch (b). The rubber cushion has enabled the wall to endure a severe battering. Another method of protecting such a wall is pictured in Sketch (c). The timber cover is replaceable, and the pipe sleeves allow the steel side plates, and the threaded rods also, to be renewed.

When dealing with concrete under shock, this principle of cushioning the blows may be applied by so planning the structure that a thick blanket of loose material will continually overlie the concrete. This blanket is also useful in reducing grinding and wearing down of the surface. Corners and edges that are subjected to pounding and grinding should, however, be protected by wooden buffers or metallic guards.

11·17 Special Concrete Structures. Concrete is especially well adapted for the construction of arches and domes. These are specialized structures, yet the principles of their action may be applicable in industrial construction. Their proportioning and the details of their design are matters requiring special knowledge and skill.

The use of long, ribbed arches to hold a roof is illustrated in Fig. 11·23. This is unusual, however.

Fig. 11·23.   One type of arched rib used at a Navy hangar.   (*Courtesy of Lone Star Cement Corp.*)

Fig. 11·24.   Special, heavy, reinforced-concrete construction.   Notice the concrete supports and the hangers for piping.   (*Courtesy of the Cast Iron Pipe Research Association.*)

Fig. 11·25. The ring walls and bottom of a 300-ft. dewatering tank, showing the arrangement of joints. (*Courtesy of the Phelps Dodge Corp.*)

Fig. 11·26. The construction of movable forms for a 35-acre, one-story, reinforced-concrete war plant for the Wright Aeronautical Corp. (*Courtesy of Lone Star Cement Corp.*)

FIG. 11·27.   An all-reinforced-concrete building.   The Fairchild Aviation Corp. (*Courtesy of Lone Star Cement Corp.; photo by Albert Rothschild.*)

FIG. 11·28.   Building a wall of high-pressure steam-cured cinder blocks with a cream-colored pigment, unpainted.   The plant of the West Disinfectant Co. in the background is reinforced-concrete-skeleton construction with brick curtain walls. (*Courtesy of Lone Star Cement Corp.*)

Arched construction is often used for culverts, conveyor tunnels, and underpasses.   In planning such structures on plastic soil, and when supporting varying depths of fill and large live loads, one should consider the longitudinal beam action of the entire structure as well as the arch action of a typical cross section.

Thin-shelled domes of concrete with circumferential rods to prevent bursting outward may be used as covers for concrete bins and tanks. The use of gunite instead of poured concrete may be economical for building such specialized structures.

The Z-D construction for cylindrical roofs, somewhat like the thin slab of Fig. 11·18 without the transverse ribs, is another specialized use of concrete.   It may be substituted for the bowstring, steel-truss type of construction if the dimensions of the structure and the cost permit it. The horizontal thrusts at the interior junctions of several such arched roofs set parallel to and adjoining one another will counteract, but special care should be exercised in planning the supports to be used at the outer edges of the building.

The planner of industrial structures does well, however, to remember continually that the experiences of engineers and builders through the years can and should be a source of much benefit to him.   Unusual and highly specialized construction may have some advantages in certain cases, yet economy of construction, familiarity of contractors with a particular type of structure, adaptability for other uses, and the simplicity of the structure itself are important matters to one who plans reinforced-concrete construction.   What is really best for a given case? It is the engineer's duty to study carefully the many features involved when he prepares to answer such a question.

Chapter 12

WOODEN STRUCTURES

12·1 Field of Usefulness of Wood. Wood is a combustible material and cannot be considered as truly permanent; yet it is exceedingly useful in making industrial structures,. particularly small buildings, trestles, towers, tanks, conveyor galleries, platforms, etc.   In such locations as the middle South, northern New England and New York State, the Great Lakes district, the Rocky Mountains, and the West Coast where timber is available and may be more economical than are steel and concrete, it may be advisable to use wood even for large buildings.

Wood is a crop, a renewable resource, a material upon which many of our ideas of architecture and construction have been based.   Undoubtedly it will continue to have an important role in the building and general-construction industries of the future.   Its insulating quality, availability, adaptability, ease of transportation and fabrication, and the fact that people like it are strong influences in favor of its continued use.

On the other hand, wood is a material that should be used with proper consideration for its special characteristics—both advantages and limitations.   Too often it is employed thoughtlessly, and there seems to be a tendency for young engineers to overlook the fact that it is a major building material with the use of which they should become thoroughly acquainted.   Undoubtedly, modifications of the form and qualities of structural materials made of wood will occur, as has been illustrated already in the case of plywood.   These improvements will extend the use of wood, but they probably cannot replace ordinary commercial lumber.

12·2 Some Characteristics of Wood. Structures made of wood, like those made of other materials, should be designed to utilize the material in an efficient, economical way with due consideration for what should and should not be done with it.   For instance, the following are points to bear in mind:

1. Commercial sizes of lumber, except for boards and thicknesses under 4 in., are generally given in multiples of 2 in. Planed or finished lumber is

reduced in size about as follows: $\frac{3}{8}$ in. for sizes 4 in. or less; $\frac{1}{2}$ in. for larger sizes. These dimensions must be used for calculations of strength and for the fitting together of pieces.

2. The ordinary length of commercial lumber is 12 to 16 ft. Heavy timbers like 8 by 10 and 12 by 12 may be secured in lengths up to 20 or 25 ft. (sometimes more), but it is not wise to rely upon using such lengths unless southern yellow pine or West Coast Douglas fir are obtainable. Even then, it is advisable to make sure that one can obtain these long timbers before designing structures that depend upon their use. Therefore, it is advisable to make the layout of a structure on the basis of using 12- to 16-ft. stock, or less, meaning that spacing of columns and heights of stories should be from 10 to 15 ft., in general.

3. Timbers over 12 in. in width or depth are likely to be difficult to obtain. Wide boards such as 1 by 10 or $1\frac{1}{4}$ by 12 may also be unavailable or, if they can be purchased, a premium may have to be paid to secure them, and delays in delivery are likely. Wide, thin boards may warp and split objectionably.

4. Wooden members are relatively weak in longitudinal shear, parallel to the grain. As they are unreliable in resisting heavy tension crosswise of the grain, they should not be used in such a way. They are also rather weak in resistance to large compressions perpendicular to the fibers. These facts have much influence upon the planning of wooden structures.

5. Framed connections between timbers carrying large transverse shearing loads are difficult to make. As a general principle, it is desirable to plan a structure so that one timber rests upon its supporting one, and this in turn rests upon its column or another beam. The difficulties encountered, owing to this tendency to pack up in depth, will soon be apparent to one who starts to design wooden structures.

6. Wooden structures can be fabricated readily in the field. It is easy to cut wood into a multitude of different shapes. When loads are light, ordinary connections can be made on the job by nailing or bolting.

7. Trusses of many varieties can be made from wood. It is often possible to fabricate them completely in the manufacturers' shops and to ship them to the site as units; when too large, they can be shop-fabricated, then assembled in the field. However, they should be designed as *wooden* trusses, not as substitutes for and copies of steel construction.

8. Wood is light and relatively easy to handle by hand. Great skill in carpentry is not needed in using it as a structural material except for fine cabinet work and other special things not representative of most industrial construction.

9. Wood shrinks crosswise of the grain (perhaps as much as 2 per cent when used green), but the longitudinal shrinkage is not likely to exceed 0.2 per cent. It also expands when damp and shrinks when dried again. Air- or kiln-dried lumber should be used. He who builds with green, unseasoned lumber should not blame the material when shrinking, warping, and cracking occur; neither

should he condemn others when they disregard some basic conditions that are as the Creator made them.

10. Wood permanently under water is long-lived; when permanently dry, it is fairly durable; when alternately wet and dry, it rots in a few years. Creosoting and certain other chemical treatments will usually retard the decay of wood, perhaps more than double the useful life of the material. It is unwise to rest wooden posts or sills directly on or in moist ground; to extend wooden columns into concrete foundations; and to use wood where it is likely to be covered with leaves, rubbish, or dirt that hold moisture and facilitate decay. Dry

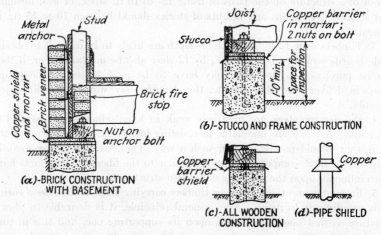

FIG. 12·1.   Some details of guards against termites.

rot occurs sometimes when timbers are set in pockets in masonry walls, placed within small foundations under a floor, or otherwise sealed in small spaces that do not have proper circulation of the air. Ordinary decay is due to fungus growths, which need the right conditions of mild temperature, proper food, moisture, and air. If any one of these conditions is unfavorable, the growth of fungi is eliminated, or at least retarded.

11. Wood under water is subject to destruction by the teredo, limnoria, and other salt-water marine life. Creosoting helps to prevent this; covering the wood with metallic casings or burying it in mud will keep out the destructive creatures; encasing piles with reinforced-concrete shells is helpful, but the coverings usually crack and disintegrate after a time.

12. Wood is also subject to destruction by termites. This must be guarded against, and it can be avoided generally. It is essential to keep wood off the ground; to use copper flashing to form ant guards at the tops of foundation walls and pipes as shown in Fig. 12·1; to raise these foundations high enough so that termites cannot build up their mud shafts to form covered passageways from the ground to the wooden structure; to prevent cracks and any holes through foundation and basement walls; to avoid dark and inaccessible spaces

under wooden floors; and to maintain careful inspection to ascertain the existence of any threatened damage in time to take preventive measures. Treatment of wood with creosote will be helpful but it is not sufficient alone; mechanical prevention is needed.

13. Really select, sound, and "perfect" lumber may not be so available on a big job as it would seem desirable to have it. Therefore, one should use allowable unit stresses which are not overly optimistic but which can probably be justified for the material as it is. First-class wooden members, which are graded for strength, are well seasoned, and are used properly, are surprisingly strong and reliable. The designer is often justified in varying the allowable unit stresses—and the safety factor—to suit conditions if the applicable building code will permit it. If a member is likely to receive its design load and if its failure or excessive deflection is important, one should be conservative; if a member is designed for obviously improbable loads, one may relax the restrictions to suit the case. This is engineering, however—not a thing for the novice to abuse promiscuously.

14. Inspection of lumber prior to its use is exceedingly important. Too often almost anything is accepted, and used wherever it happens to come. This is not good engineering. When pieces are used as "architectural" members for appearance more than for anything else, the quality requirements for strength may be relaxed; when the pieces are to become important load-carrying members, care should be exercised in their selection. A danger to be avoided is that of carpenters failing to carry out the engineer's intentions in these respects.

15. When lumber is purchased, the question of random lengths should be investigated. If the pieces are supposed to be of a certain length, will the underrun permitted by the seller's terms render many pieces useless?

16. Much can be done when planning structures to minimize the waste of lumber because of cutting off ends that will be of no value; much should also be done in the planning to reduce the amount of labor required in the carpentry.

17. The fact that wood is combustible need not eliminate consideration of its use in industrial structures. The basic principle to bear in mind is that large wooden members will not burn rapidly; neither will large, tight, flat surfaces of heavy planking. This is the idea behind the so-called "mill-building" construction. Fire spreads rapidly in a wooden building that has many small pieces which serve as kindling wood and across which there can be a natural draft. Heavy members are slow-burning and often hold up the structure for a few hours before they are dangerously weakened. Exposed steel members under the same conditions might soften and cause collapse. Although modern chemical treatment will retard the burning of wood, it is best to use simple, heavy construction, and to minimize situations that permit natural drafts and the spreading of a fire through floors, platforms, walls, and roofs. Then protection of the structure by means of an adequate sprinkler system and hose stations is advisable. Obviously, timbers should not be rested upon or close to chimneys and other possible sources of high temperatures.

18. Protection of wood by proper painting is essential, especially for parts that are exposed to weathering.

12·3 Connecting Devices. Before one starts to plan wooden structures, it is well to consider some of the typical means of making connections when framing pieces of lumber together because, to a surprising extent, such matters have an important bearing upon the planning. Many and varied are people's ideas as to the best methods of fitting the pieces together, and numerous variations of details are useful in practice.

Nailing or spiking pieces of lumber together is an old but widely used method of connecting them. This is suitable for small pieces and light loads. However, the strength of such connections is small and highly problematical because it depends so much upon the workmanship and the particular conditions. There is seldom any real design of such connections.

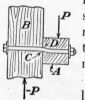

Fig. 12·2. Action of bolted connection in shear.

Lag screws are merely large wood screws with heads like bolts so that they can be tightened by the use of a wrench. To avoid splitting the wood, it is advisable to bore holes about ⅛ in. smaller than the lag screws (not larger than the body of the screw at the base of the threads) before the latter are "driven." Space at the connection must be provided to enable a workman to use a wrench.

Bolted connections have been used for many years. Figure 12·2 shows the action of a bolt connecting a horizontal beam A to a column B. The shear causes a concentration of the bearing on the side of the hole in the column at C and in the beam at D. This crushing action on the wood, especially perpendicular to the grain, usually limits the strength of the connection, but the latter may also be affected by the bending of small bolts and splitting of the wood, particularly if the member is subjected to longitudinal tension. The holes in wood are generally drilled to the same size as the diameter of the bolts.

Washers should be used generally under the heads of lag screws and under heads and nuts of bolts in order to spread the pressure when they are tightened, also to avoid "chewing up" the wood. These washers may be small rectangular plates, thin standard machine washers, or even large cast-iron ones, depending upon the forces to be withstood.

Split-ring connectors are much stronger than bolts for making shear connections in wooden construction. Figure 12·3 illustrates their action. Sketch (a) shows a typical steel ring with a keyed joint to that it can be expanded or opened slightly. In (b), the beam is fastened to the column

with a ring connector and bolt.   In order to make the connection, the
two timbers must be fitted together and the bolt hole drilled through
them, or else they must be drilled separately with the bolt holes carefully
located in advance.   By means of a special rotary cutter with the bolt
hole as a guide (taking the connection apart if drilled assembled), an
annular groove is made in each timber, the grooves being slightly larger
in diameter than the rings.   When the bolt D is tightened, the timbers
are brought together firmly and the ring is forced into both grooves.
When a load is applied as in Sketch (c), the ring bears against A along
both surfaces E whereas it also bears on B along surfaces F.   This
brings a large area of wood under compression at the surface of the ring

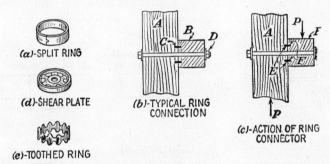

(a)-SPLIT RING

(d)-SHEAR PLATE   (b)-TYPICAL RING
                           CONNECTION

(c)-ACTION OF RING
    CONNECTOR

(e)-TOOTHED RING

FIG. 12·3.   Ring connectors.

and in shear within and behind it.   Malleable-iron half rings, sometimes
called "shear plates," such as that shown in Fig. 12·3(d), are used in
connecting timbers to steel.   Their strengths may be considered to be
the same as those of split rings.

Another type of steel connector is the toothed ring, shown in Fig.
12·3(e).   It requires no cutting of grooves in advance but is partly
driven into the wood around a bolt.   Then, generally with temporary
high-strength bolts, the timbers are drawn together and the teeth embedded in both timbers; then ordinary bolts are placed in the connection.

In heavy work like trestles, steel rods are sometimes used as driftpins by driving them through drilled holes about ⅛ in. undersize.   They
have little tensile value but are of some use in resisting shear, as for
holding heavy stringers on the tops of columns.

Adequate end and edge distances are necessary for any of these
connecting devices.   If these distances are not sufficient, splitting of the
wood is probable.   Through experience, standards and codes controlling
these requirements have been established, and they should be adhered to.

12·4 Beam Connections.   The most desirable and simple way to hold up a wooden beam is to seat it directly upon its support. Nevertheless, connections of many sorts are used under conditions for which each is particularly suitable. Figure 12·4 illustrates some connections of beams to other beams (headers); and the following comments refer to the respective sketches:

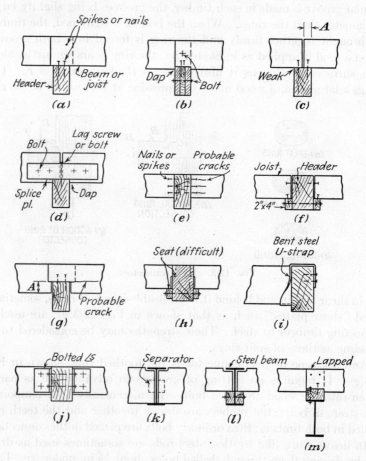

Fig. 12·4. Some connections of beams supported upon wooden and steel beams or headers.

(a) It is preferable to lap the beams across the header so that each has adequate bearing area to transmit the reaction without crushing the fibers. The beams may also be connected to each other. In this case, all three members are shown spiked together, which may be sufficient in many instances.

(b) The beams are dapped so as to clinch the three-plank header, the lapped portions of the beams are bolted together, but both are merely nailed down to the header.

(*c*) Here the beams are assumed to be necessarily in line. Unless they are dapped, they do not steady the header effectively. The transfer of longitudinal forces through the nails from one beam to the other is not satisfactory. Even though the nails are strong enough at first, they may not remain so. The length of bearing of the beams at *A* is likely to be inadequate.

(*d*) The two dapped stringers are in line. However, a splice piece is bolted to them and is connected to the header by a large lag screw. The latter avoids the loss of section that the header would suffer if a through bolt were used. This connection fastens all the pieces together sufficiently for most purposes.

(*e*) In this case, the tops of the beams and header are flush, and the former are toenailed to the latter. This is inadvisable. Unless diagonal holes are bored in the beams for the nails, small cracks may occur, then drying and shrinkage may enlarge them, and the weathering of an exposed structure will soon cause rusting of the nails.

(*f*) The header is deep enough so that the beams can be seated upon long pieces that are bolted to the header. The loads should be spread enough to avoid splitting the header along the plane of the bolt holes. The beams are nailed to the seat and header just to keep them in place.

(*g*) These beams are cut deeply so that they can be seated upon the header. When the distance *A* exceeds 25 per cent of the depth of the beam, it is probable that a crack will develop as shown and the shearing strength will be greatly damaged.

(*h*) In this case, the header is notched (mortised) to receive a portion of the beams, and seats are bolted on in addition. As it is very difficult to obtain simultaneous bearing upon these two surfaces, one or the other will tend to carry all the load alone.

(*i*) Steel strap hangers are effective in supporting beams upon the sides of headers. The straps may be for one side, as shown, or for both sides.

(*j*) This is an attempt to frame the beams to the header as might be done in the case of structural steel. Seldom is this arrangement desirable. The boltholes weaken the members, and expert workmanship is required if the parts are to fit properly. Furthermore, the number of bolts or ring connectors required for strength, and the end distances needed, may cause large eccentricities and bending moments that will damage the members.

(*k*) Since these beams are not attached to the steel member, lateral displacement of the beams is likely; hence it may be advisable to bolt on separators, as shown by the dotted lines.

(*l*) In this case, the beams are supported upon wooden pieces that rest upon the steel flange but are bolted through the web of the header. Nailing the beams to the seats may or may not be adequate.

(*m*) Here the beams are carried upon a nailing strip that is bolted to the top flange of the steel header. If it is necessary to resist uplift, the bolts may pass through clip angles or blocks that fasten all three members together. Steel straps and nails may serve the same purpose.

When beams are seated upon brick or concrete walls, there are a few basic principles to bear in mind; Fig. 12·5 shows some of them. In Sketch (*a*), the end of the beam is encased as the brick wall is built. This is likely to facilitate decay of the covered end of the beam, and deflection is likely to cause the beam to act like a lever and crack the

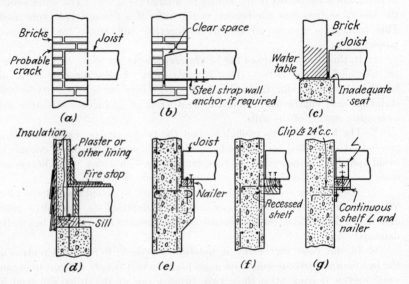

FIG. 12·5.   Beams supported upon walls.

wall.   Furthermore, the brickwork cannot be built in advance of the erection of the floor.   In Sketch (*b*), these difficulties are overcome because the beam rests in a niche in the wall.   The top of the beam is cut to clear the masonry, and the space beside it permits the circulation of air.   It is often desirable to anchor a beam to the masonry, and strap anchors or some other type can be used when needed.   In Sketch (*c*), the bearing length of the beam is inadequate, and the member is not held in position properly.   To remedy this, it is customary to bolt a wooden sill to the masonry, then to place the joists and studs upon the sill, and to attach all these together.   There may be cases in which corbeled or offset shelves are provided along walls in order to support floors and platforms.   If so, Sketch (*e*) is suitable for heavy loads, whereas (*f*) is capable of resisting small loads only, unless a shallow recess or shelf is provided as shown by the dotted lines, thus permitting the timber seat to bear upon the concrete. A modification of this idea is shown in Sketch (g).

12·5 Beams and Girders. Heavy wooden members are generally relatively wide, and the low unit compressive stress in beams does not cause as much sideward buckling tendency as does the customary high stress in steel. Nevertheless, excessive unsupported lengths should be avoided.

The ordinary floor with narrow wooden joists should have bridging every 4 or 5 ft., partly to steady the joists but primarily to spread concentrated loads so that several joists will participate in the resistance, and excessive local sagging will be prevented. When a heavy, fixed, concentrated load must be supported, it is often desirable to use grillage-

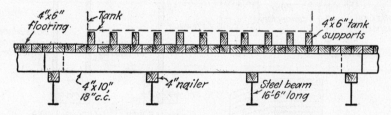

Fig. 12·6. Grillage-type support for a tank.

type framing, as shown in Fig. 12·6. The beams in the lower set will not all be equally loaded but, if some at the center sag much more than the others, the upper set will spread the load to members farther away.

The longitudinal shearing strength of wooden beams is something to be investigated always. It is likely to be especially troublesome in short, heavily loaded members. When wooden members are obviously unsuitable because of the need for greater shearing resistance, one need not hesitate to consider the use of a few steel beams, even though they are incorporated in a wooden structure. However, one must guard against excessive crushing of the supporting timbers under the ends of the steel members.

To be avoided also is the mutilation of wooden beams. Wood is so easy to notch out and to bore holes through that workmen are likely to do so excessively when installing utilities and equipment, or when making alterations. Wooden members have withstood so much abuse in the past that persons are inclined to think that they can take just a little bit more the next time. Not only do these cuts decrease the effective section of a member, but they cause high localized stresses that are especially harmful to a fibrous material like wood.

Because of the limitation of commercial sizes of lumber, there is the natural tendency for one to try to build large beams out of two or more timbers.   Of course, two large timbers of the same size and material set side by side or one on top of the other are, if equally loaded, twice as strong as one alone, except for crushing at the ends of the latter case. When they are to be connected as in Fig. 12·7(a) to constitute a beam twice as deep as one timber, the longitudinal shearing stress along their junction may be resisted by bolts or by some type of timber connector, as pictured in Sketch (b).   In both cases, the reduction of section caused

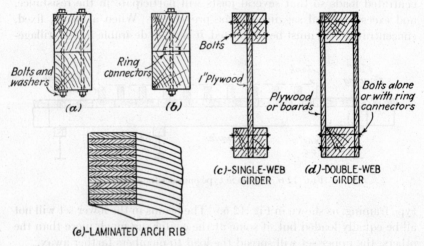

Fig. 12·7.   Built-up beam and girder sections.

by the holes should be allowed for.   Mortised shear blocks are difficult to install, and they necessarily remove part of the section of a beam that would otherwise resist longitudinal shearing forces and bending.

Often there are places where the clear spans must be 25 to 35 ft.— too long for single pieces of lumber, but not long enough to justify the use of trusses.   Furthermore, the appearance of a solid section may be preferable to that of a lot of small truss members.   Then a wooden girder may be made as in Figs. 12·7(c) and (d).   The former has its flanges composed of timbers bolted to a central web, whereas the latter has them between two webs.   Heavy plywood or two layers of oppositely sloping boards are suitable for use as single webs; the plywood seems to be more efficient for the double-web arrangement.   Both types can generally be fabricated in the shop and shipped to the field as complete members. The development of resistance to longitudinal shear, transverse shear, and web buckling should be provided somewhat as for steel girders. The flange sections will probably require splicing because of their length. One such girder is pictured in Fig. 12·8.

Long members, such as beams, columns, and truss chords may be built up by using shorter lengths of planks bolted together so that only one layer has a joint at any given point, and the remaining pieces are sufficient to serve as a splice for it.

A modern development in large wooden members is laminated or "unit" construction. Figure 12·7(e) shows how a heavy solid member is built up by gluing thin boards (about ⅞ in.) together under pressure, thus making a long, sturdy member. These shallower, solid members

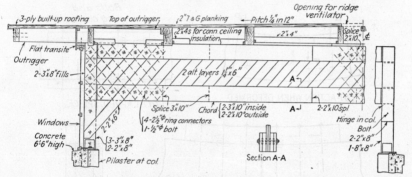

FIG. 12·8. Wooden roof girder for a change house.

save in depth of roof construction, are more fire-resistant than light pieces, and look much neater than trusses. However, if the span is 50 ft. or more and if the member is straight, its flexibility and cost may be excessive. It is also wise to investigate the probable effect of variations in moisture and temperature when these variations are severe, in order to make sure that the laminations will not eventually separate. Thorough protection by painting is desirable. Because of the thinness of the constituent pieces, laminated members can be fabricated in curved shapes, such as arch ribs and rigid frames. Their appearance is generally neat and attractive.

The splicing of large wooden beams to resist bending moments is difficult and should be avoided as much as possible. Figure 12·9(a) pictures a case wherein two abutted timbers are to be spliced by means of "scabs" on the sides, these being attached by bolts alone or by bolts and ring connectors. In Sketch (b) the deformed beam is shown to exaggerated scale. Not only does the bending moment cause the bolts to deliver compressive and tensile loads to the splice plate as indicated, but the shear and the resultant twisting in a vertical plane cause them to exert forces that try to split the splice piece along or between the bolt holes, thus aggravating the splitting tendency caused by longitudinal shear.   It would be better theoretically, for bending alone, to place the splice pieces as in Sketch (c), but the resistance to shear is not satisfactory.   Furthermore, this arrangement is seldom desirable in floor construction because of the projection of the top splice piece.   If the

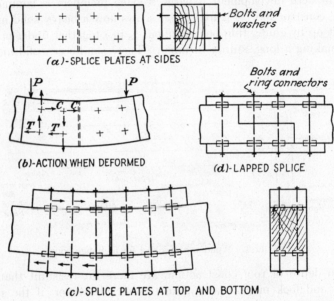

(a)-SPLICE PLATES AT SIDES

(b)-ACTION WHEN DEFORMED

(d)-LAPPED SPLICE

(c)-SPLICE PLATES AT TOP AND BOTTOM

FIG. 12·9.   Some details of beam splices.

main timbers are overlapped as in Fig. 12·9(d), the advantage gained is probably not worth the labor and loss of material.   About the best that can be done is to make the side splice pieces amply long, and to locate the splice where the bending moment is small.

12·6 Wooden Trusses. Small trusses are built easily out of wood, but those with spans over 50 ft. supporting the usual floor or roof loads require careful attention in their design and details.   The supporting of heavy concentrated loads such as cross trusses and offset columns is still more difficult.   This is due not so much to low allowable unit stresses in the timbers as it is to the difficulty of making connections and splices. One type of wooden truss used in the past is that having a double latticed system of web members with bolted connections; another is the Howe truss with vertical rods as tension members and diagonal solid timbers as compression ones, as pictured in Fig. 12·10.

The use of ring connectors has greatly facilitated the construction of wooden trusses and extended their usefulness. Figures 12·12 and 12·13 picture two trusses that are so fabricated. Although these are not substitutes for the construction shown in Fig. 12·10, the reader should compare the details of the two types carefully. Has the ring-connector type replaced the latter entirely, and should it do so? This question may cause much argument, but it seems that each type should be used wherever its peculiar advantages make it the most desirable. Furthermore, a designer should combine various features of these types when such action will produce the desired and best results.

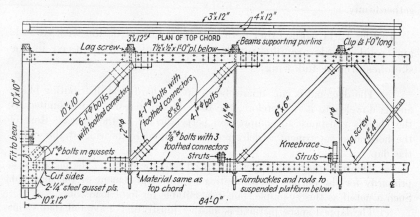

FIG. 12·10.   A roof truss with tie rods.

In Fig. 12·10, the following features should be noticed:

1. Each chord is composed of four planks, bolted together to constitute one long, heavy member. The ends of the various pieces are staggered so that the remaining ones passing any such junction serve to splice the discontinuous pieces. In this case, toothed connectors are used between the planks to increase the shearing resistance between them.

2. The diagonals are solid timbers that are dapped into the chords, having a recess chiseled out of the latter so that the diagonals cannot be displaced sidewise. In order to increase the bearing area and to decrease the local shearing unit stresses near the daps, bearing blocks are bolted onto the chords and the diagonals. For simplicity of details, the working point for the diagonals in the central panel is offset from the theoretical panel point. This is not harmful when these web members carry such small loads and when the chords are so large. These diagonals are designed as compression members. The lag screws at their ends have very little strength in resisting tension.

3. The verticals are tie rods with turnbuckles for the attachment of a platform suspended below the truss.

4. The connection to the column is made through two steel gusset plates. In this structure, the clear height of the columns made it desirable to use two timbers as shown. Theoretically, the combination of bearing of timber on timber and the transfer of loads to the gusset plates is satisfactory; practically, however, simultaneous action is difficult to secure and requires very accurate work.

5. The purlins are in line, with the end of each one bearing on one-half of the top chord except for the counterbore to clear the nut and the end of the tie rod. The washer used with the tie rod is a steel plate that is large enough to serve as a seat for the purlins. Clip angles are bolted to the purlins and are connected to the chords by lag screws, thus fastening all three pieces together firmly.

In Fig. 12·11, some other details of bolted construction with tie rods and solid chords are illustrated. Some points to be noticed in the sketches are the following:

(a) The diagonal is cut square, bears upon a hardwood distributing block, and is doweled to it. Therefore, the force in the diagonal is not limited by the chord's resistance to compression perpendicular to the fibers. Most of the horizontal component is delivered to the chord by bearing at the end of the dap.

(b) The solid diagonal is merely dapped into the chord. The lag screw is primarily for the purpose of preventing lateral displacement of the diagonal. Such a detail as this is simple, but it is suitable for light loads only.

(c) The lapped splice pictured is another illustration of a detail that seems to be efficient and economical. However, it is difficult to secure equal bearing at the ends of the overlapped portions, and the transfer of loads by simultaneous action of the bolts and two end bearings is uncertain. This is also true if the splice plates shown by the dotted lines are added. A compression splice is likely to be better if the ends of the main timbers are cut square, abutted, and joined by two (or four) splice pieces to hold the main members in line.

(d) This shows a detail that is designed to splice a tension chord made of solid timbers. The main chord sections are dapped, and the splice pieces are supposedly cut to fit so that most of the load is carried by the locking action of the splice plates. This is also a piece of workmanship that is exceedingly difficult to perform. It is generally more desirable frankly to abut the pieces, or to overlap them as in Sketch (c), then to use two or four splice pieces with enough bolts or connectors to transfer the required load.

(e) Here is shown a pitched roof. The solid top chord is dapped deeply into the lower chord, weakening the latter considerably. The extension of the lower chord beyond the cut provides enough material to prevent splitting caused by the horizontal thrust. The truss bears upon the ends of heavy timbers (plates) that run across the top of the column. These tie the building together, and the top ends of the studs are nailed to the plates. All these

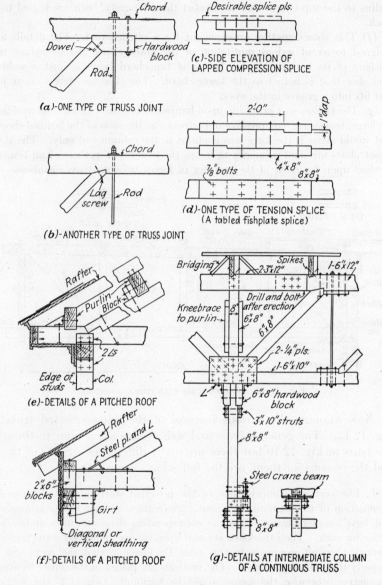

FIG. 12·11. Some details of wooden trusses.

main members should be connected securely; here this is accomplished by bolts and clip angles. It is also possible to extend the column up to the truss, and to connect the plates by the angles and bolts alone. In order to connect the purlins to the top chords and to support them laterally, both are bolted to a block.

(*f*) This shows another arrangement for a pitched roof. The details are designed to avoid serious mutilation of the lower chord and to reduce the crushing of its bottom fibers. The solid top chord bears against a welded steel shoe that is bolted to the lower chord. The shoe also has a shear lug that fits into a groove in the wood.

(*g*) The trusses rest primarily upon hardwood bearing blocks, thus avoiding the large, transverse, compressive unit stresses at the ends of the bottom chords that would occur if the force was confined to the column end only. The steel gusset plates are used primarily to fasten the members together. End bearing is relied upon for most of the transfer of forces between truss members.

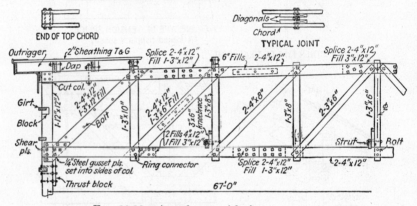

FIG. 12·12.   A roof truss with ring connectors.

Now examine the various features of the ring-connected truss in Fig. 12·12. The general shape and web system are similar to those of the truss in Fig. 12·10 but there are many differences. Some of these, and the reasons for them, are the following:

1. The verticals comprise one of the principal starting points for the determination of the basic arrangement. Since these are the shortest members and have smaller stresses than the corresponding diagonals, one timber will suffice for each. Their thickness is based upon the size required for the heaviest vertical; then all are made to this same thickness so that the parts will fit properly throughout the truss. The verticals are placed in the center to attain symmetry, otherwise the joints would be harmfully twisted if the vertical pulled on one side and the diagonal pushed on the other. Since the pull of the end connections tends to split the ends of the verticals, these ends are long, even though they project above and below the chords. Even if the stresses permitted the use of 2-in. lumber, this is too thin for use with ring connectors cutting into both sides.

2. The diagonals are made double for symmetry and strength. Two timbers 4 in. thick are needed for the end diagonals; therefore this thickness is
used for the others, except at the center where the packing of the members
makes it advisable to move the working points out. Since the stresses are
small, this can be done. These center diagonals are placed outside of the
chords in order to permit a strong splice at the middle of the top chord. Since
the end diagonals would be too thin for the heavy compression, a filler is bolted
between the halves to make a stiff member. The second diagonal is partly
stiffened for similar reasons. Since the ring connectors deliver compressive
loads to the diagonals, the end distances need not be so long as for the tension
members, although generosity in this respect is almost always good policy.
The diagonals are placed between the verticals and the chords in order to have
the vertical components of the diagonal stresses taken directly by the vertical
members, whereas the horizontal components are delivered directly to the
chords. These various forces cause a crosswise shearing action in the ends
of the diagonals that may split them; hence ample end distances and·even
stitch bolts, as in Fig. 12·13, may be advantageous. In this case, having the
diagonals inside the chords also causes the latter to fit better where they cross
the columns. Furthermore, the straight-band effect of the chords appears
neater than would a series of diagonals connected outside them, and the transfer of stresses in the latter case is not so direct.

3. The top chords are made of two heavy planks throughout the truss. A
splice is necessary at the center because of the change in direction, and an
intermediate splice is required to reduce the lengths of the pieces. Technically,
the end sections of the chords could be thinner than the middle ones because
of their smaller compression. The chords, however, must withstand the bending caused by the intermediate purlins, and little material would be saved by
making the end pieces thinner.

4. The bottom chords are likewise two heavy planks of the same section
throughout. Two splices are sufficient, and these are made by using filler
pieces between the planks. If needed, outside splice pieces could be used also.

5. The end shear must be delivered to the column at the bottom of the end
diagonal. Although a thrust block is connected to the column under the
diagonal, two ¼-in. steel gusset plates are inserted between the diagonal pieces
and the bottom chord. By means of half-ring shear plates on one or both
sides of these gussets, the forces are delivered from the wood to the steel and
thence into the column, the latter being cut out to fit the gusset plates. Boring
the holes so that both gussets connect satisfactorily requires excellent workmanship, and this is one of the chief reasons why steel plates as gussets in
wooden construction are far less advantageous than they might seem to be.
Nevertheless, there are places where they are almost indispensable. Lag
screws may be suitable and more convenient than bolts in some cases.

6. The column is a long timber that is to resist transverse forces by bending,
being gripped by the truss chords. The top chord is merely bolted to the
column because this is adequate. It is important, however, to make sure that

the truss deflection will not bend the columns seriously. In this case, the column at one end has a hinge effect provided just below the gusset plates so that harmful impressed bending could not be caused by truss deflection. Knee braces between the truss and columns are not used here because they would interfere with the required clearance or would cause the truss to be placed higher, adding to the over-all height of the structure.

7. Alternate purlins are bolted together and to the top chord; those at the panel points rest on one-half of the top chord, are cut to clear the vertical member, and are bolted where they overlap.

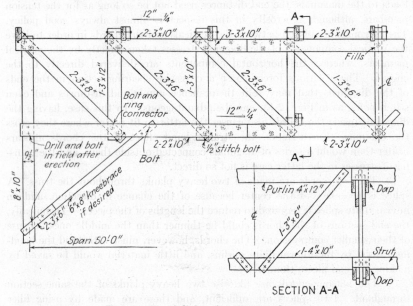

FIG. 12·13.   A light, ring-connected truss.

Another roof truss with ring connectors is pictured in Fig. 12·13. The verticals are in compression and the diagonals in tension. Therefore, the former are made of single timbers with the two parts of the heavier diagonals fitting against them. The vertical nearest the end is made wide enough to accommodate two ring connectors. The purlins are fastened by bolting to the tops of the vertical members. The knee brace is for the purpose of reducing the lateral bending moment in the column and is, therefore, fitted and connected after complete erection of the roof.

Some miscellaneous details of ring-connected trusses are shown in Fig. 12·14 in order to suggest a few of the many ways of arranging the parts of such construction.

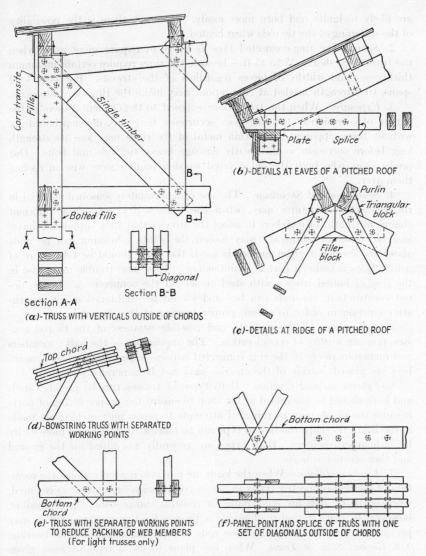

Fig. 12·14. Details of some trusses with ring connectors.

What factors should be considered before one adopts the type of truss construction to be used in a particular case? Some of them are these:

1. *Fire Resistance.* The members of the ring-connected type are more open and the pieces are generally smaller than in the tie-rod type; therefore the former

are likely to ignite and burn more easily. However, there is the possibility of the softening of the tie rods when heated.

2. *Span.* The ring-connected type is likely to require more wood when the trusses are short—35 to 45 ft.—because the rings require certain minimum thicknesses and widths of pieces regardless of the stresses. For very long spans, the strength needed at connections may make the rings advantageous.

3. *Exposure.* When the trusses are exposed to the elements, there is the danger of corrosion of the rings—an occurrence that may develop harmfully without being apparent. The thin metal of the rings may lose its strength long before corrosion would greatly damage heavy tie rods and bolts. Our predecessors who built the old covered wooden bridges were wise in roofing them over.

4. *Seasoning and Shrinkage.* The use of inadequately seasoned material in ring-connected structures may, when the timbers dry out, cause sufficient change in lengths of members to affect the stresses that they supposedly have, and the crosswise shrinkage may loosen the joints. Nothing can be done about the former if green lumber is used; the latter should be taken care of definitely as a planned part of maintenance. This same trouble may arise in the case of bolted trusses with steel gussets at the connections. In the tie-rod construction, the rods can be—and should be—tightened a few months after erection in order to ensure proper bearing of the diagonals.

5. *Appearance.* The simplicity and possible neatness of the tie-rod construction are worthy of consideration. The appearance of the bulky members and numerous pieces of the ring-connected trusses—especially when web members are placed outside of the chords—may not be generally pleasing.

6. *Fabrication and Erection.* Both types of trusses can be prefabricated; and both should be assembled at the shop to ensure the proper fitting of parts because the pieces may be ruined if attempts to repair mismatching are made in the field. Perhaps the tie-rod type can be fabricated in the field more easily by ordinary carpenters. Both types are generally assembled on the ground and then erected as units.

7. *Load Conditions.* When the loads are movable concentrations, the members of the ring-connected type can act in compression or tension, as required, whereas the tie rods are inadequate for resisting compression. It is possible, however, to place a timber alongside a tie rod for this purpose, but it may prevent the future tightening of the rods to force the diagonals into bearing.

8. *General Style of Truss.* When one plans to use a truss of some given style or type, this may of itself make it desirable to build that truss with ring connectors or with tie rods. For example, a large bowstring truss like that of Fig. 12·15(a) has heavy chords but light web members. It might be desirable to build the top chord out of several layers of planks (or laminated construction) that could be assembled in curved positions and bolted together. With the width of the planks placed perpendicular to the plane of the truss, the tie rods are advantageous whereas a ring-connected system may not be. Furthermore, single, sturdy timbers are the most suitable for web members that are

subjected to compression. As another example, moderate-sized trusses for steeply pitched roofs, as in Figs. 12·15(*b*) and (*c*), do not require heavy chords, and the web members are long but carry small loads. These trusses can be made with solid chords, then the members composing the web system may be connected to the sides of these timbers. On the other hand, tie rods do not fit well into many varieties of such trusses. In the case illustrated in Fig. 12·15(*d*), the roof over a large bin is carried upon trussed members of a three-hinged arch. The arch thrust combined with inward wind pressure at some times and outward suction at others, with resultant alternation of web stresses, made a ring-connected truss seem to be preferable.

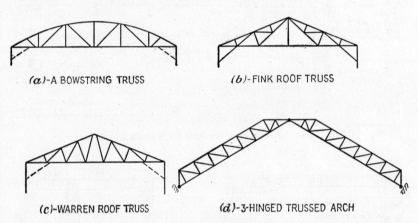

(a)-A BOWSTRING TRUSS   *(b)*-FINK ROOF TRUSS

(c)-WARREN ROOF TRUSS   *(d)*-3-HINGED TRUSSED ARCH

Fig. 12·15. Some types of wooden roof trusses.

A designer need not believe that he is compelled to adhere exclusively to a single type of construction. He can and should use whatever serves him the best; when combinations of tie rods, ring connectors, bolts, or gusset plates are advisable, they should be used.

Continuous trusses of wood are not commonly used because it is difficult to make the necessary connections and to make these structures truly continuous. However, one such use is shown in Fig. 12·11(*g*). In this case, the trusses were erected as simply supported ones, then the upper chord section across the column was fitted, drilled, and bolted in the field to ensure proper adjustment.

Many times it is possible and desirable to make wooden trusses that are not of any ordinary standard type but are designed to meet special conditions or to secure certain desired results. Such a case is illustrated in Fig. 12·16, where the roof construction is a sort of trussed and knee-braced purlin with the parts bolted together. The trusses are knee-braced to the columns to secure lateral stiffness of the building; hence the bolt holes in the bottom of the outer knee braces may be drilled in the field after the structure is erected.   This avoids the forcing of undesirable bending stresses into these columns.   The thrusts at the central column are assumed to counteract each other.

For moderate spans, heavy beams may be knee-braced alone, or knee-braced and tied, as pictured in Fig. 12·17.   The action of such construction will be discussed further in connection with Fig. 12·18.

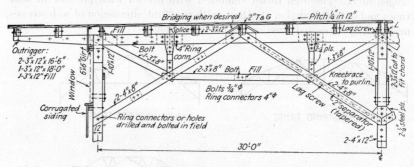

Fig. 12·16.   Portal-type trussing for a small warehouse.

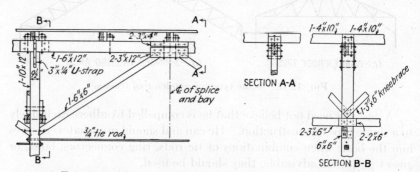

Fig. 12·17.   Roof construction with knee braces and tie rods.

When wooden trusses are under consideration, some of the first decisions that should be made are the following:

1. The span to be used.
2. The shape of the roof, whether pitched, flat, or rounded.
3. The spacing and locations of purlins.
4. The depth desired at the center of the truss.   This depends upon the loads, but it should not be less than approximately one-eighth of the span if the chord sections and deflections are not to become unduly large.
5. The depth desired at the ends of the truss in order to be able to make suitable connections.
6. The locations of any trolley beams, suspended equipment, piping, and

other concentrated loads that may automatically make it desirable to have a panel point or an open space at a specific location.

7. The positions of any monitor construction or other things that will rest upon the main truss.

8. The positions of struts or vertical cross frames that may make it desirable to have a panel point or a vertical member in any special location.

9. The use of ring-connected or solid-timber and tie-rod construction.

10. A system of chord and web members that will be consistent with the needs of all these various requirements.

12·7 Wooden Supports for Cranes.

Light bridge cranes can be supported upon wooden beams and columns, but their capacity may be limited to 5 tons, with bridges 30 to 40 ft. long.   Practically, such cranes are usually floor-controlled or hand-operated.   Even when light cranes are to be used more or less continuously, it is advisable to question the use of wood for the beams.   One might try to substitute steel beams supported upon wooden columns, somewhat as shown in Fig. 12·11(g).

Crane beams should be single, solid timbers if members of sufficient size are obtainable.   A 12 by 12 beam is shown in Fig. 12·18(a).   Incidentally, the following details in this sketch should be noted:

1. The rail is not set directly upon the top of the timber but rests upon a thin, steel wearing plate.   The use of intermittent steel plates under the rail would merely concentrate the pressure at local spots.   The rail itself is used to spread the wheel load along the timber in order to avoid crushing of the wood; the longitudinal distribution caused by the rail is problematical but it seems to be safe to limit the maximum wheel load to the following:
Wheel load = (width of rail flange) $\times$ (4 $\times$ depth of rail) $\times$ (allowable unit stress in wood perpendicular to grain)
All quantities are to be expressed in pounds and inches.

2. Steel plates with two lag screws in each to prevent twisting are used as clips.   Square plate washers with eccentric holes for adjustment of the rail are used under each clip.

3. Lag screws are used instead of through bolts in order to minimize loss of area in the beam due to the holes.   If the lag screws are removed and replaced several times, their grip on the wood may be impaired.

4. The beam must be wide enough to have adequate lateral stiffness and to permit the use of the lag screws without splitting the edges of the member.

5. The 1/4-in. wearing plate is to protect the wood against wear caused by any longitudinal movement of the rail as the beam deflects.   It also prevents the washers around the lag screws from cutting into the wood.   This plate should have several separate lag screws attaching it to the beam.

6. The rail splice material should fit against the rail head and flange in order to avoid pounding and crushing of the wood near the splices.

It is possible to make a crane beam by using two timbers side by side and bolted together. However, with the rail over the longitudinal junction of the two pieces, there is a tendency to spread and to twist the beams. The deflection of such shallow beams is likely to be harmful to the rails when the loads are heavy, and the details at the columns may be very troublesome. If one timber is insufficient, it may be more advisable to use two pieces connected as in Fig. 12·18(*b*). Note the following features in this figure:

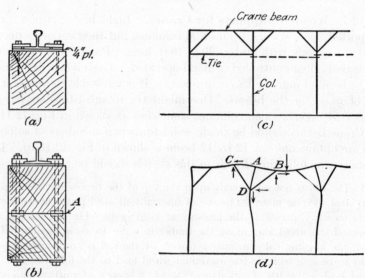

Fig. 12·18.   Action of knee braces and details of crane beams.

1. If the member is built as two independent beams—say two pieces of 12 by 12—with no resistance to longitudinal shear between them, there will be relative motion and wear along the junction *A*.

2. When the combined member is to act as a unit with twice the depth of one piece, the longitudinal shear at the center should be computed, ring connectors used to withstand it, long bolts run through as shown, and a sufficient number of rings used to allow for repetition of stresses.

3. Some of the through bolts may be located so as to hold the rail clips, too.

Wooden crane beams should be designed generally as simply supported ones spanning from column to column, or with joints at the columns and with supporting knee braces as shown in Fig. 12·18(*c*). It is usually inadvisable to attempt to make these beams continuous. Of course, a knee-braced system is statically indeterminate. When knee braces are used, they should be really capable of carrying the load. A horizontal tie near the bottoms of the knee braces may be used throughout the system as shown by the dotted lines, but it is especially desirable in the end spans to prevent undue bending and deflection of the end columns.

The action of a knee-braced beam under a concentrated load is indicated in Sketch (d). Notice particularly that there is a tendency to lift the beam off the column at A owing to continuity of action across the top of the knee brace at B, and also to the upward pressure at C. The arrows show some of the forces. An exact analysis of a system like this will seldom be justified because of the yielding of joints, and other uncertainties. The size of the main beam will generally be determined by the shears; if not, an estimate should be made of the safe reduction of the simply supported beam's bending moments due to the assistance of the knee braces, and the beam may be designed accordingly.

Figures 12·19(a), (b), and (c) show some arrangements for the details of a crane runway made of timber beams with knee braces. Attention is called to the following points:

1. The beams are supported directly upon the ends of separate crane columns A. The difficulty of making strong wooden brackets on timber columns, and the resultant bending in the latter, make this advisable.

2. The beams and the column are steadied laterally by filler blocks B and through bolts connecting to the building column C, which must be steadied at its top and must be strong enough in bending to resist the lateral forces.

3. The bearing pressure at the end of the beam may be critical at D, Sketch (b). If so, a bearing block as shown in (c) may be inserted under the beams to help spread the load.

4. The blocks F and B tie the beams together and resist the upward kick. Ring connectors may be used if the bolts are not strong enough, but this generally requires assembling the parts, taking them apart, cutting the grooves, and reassembling the parts. Toothed connectors are easier to apply and may be sufficient.

5. In this case the knee braces G, Sketch (b), are fitted into daps in the column and are tied with a through bolt. The connection of the knee brace under beam H is made so as to avoid cutting and weakening it, hence piece I is fastened under H to resist the horizontal force. The lag screw at this point in G is used to resist a little tension and to hold G in line; such a connection, however, is worth very little in tension.

6. Another arrangement of knee braces is the use of double timbers like J in Sketch (c), with bolts or connectors used to carry the load.

An arrangement of framing at the bases of the columns is also shown in Fig. 12·19(a). Column A is connected directly to the foundation by

small angle clips, bolts, and anchor bolts.   Column C bears directly on
the concrete instead of on the sill K but is connected to the latter by
angle clips or short, bolted blocks, the sill itself being anchor-bolted to
the concrete.   Building columns may be carried directly upon sills when
the loads are small.   In any case, one should be sure that flashing or
other provisions are made to cause storm water to drain outside of the

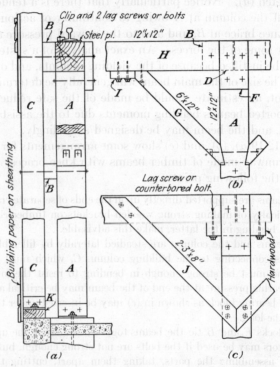

FIG. 12·19.   Some details of supports for cranes.

foundation.   When the woodwork or other siding (or the copper flashing)
stops on top of the foundation wall, wind is likely to drive the rain against
the sill and aggravate decay of the wood.

12·8   Bracing Wooden Buildings.   A wooden building, like a steel
one, should be braced.   If it is small, the sheathing of the roof, the siding
and its inner sheathing, and the general stiffness of the structure are
sometimes adequate to resist wind and other lateral forces; if the building
is large, a special bracing system may be necessary.   When the roof
boards are put on in herringbone fashion, the construction is surprisingly stiff.   (The sheathing for one-half of the roof, from center line or

ridge to eaves, is laid at a 45° slope across the purlins or rafters; the other half is sloped 45° in the opposite direction.) Tongued-and-grooved sheathing is better than plain boards for bracing action as well as for tightness.   The same idea may be used in the side walls if inner sheathing is employed and if the walls are not cut up too much by windows and doors.

When a strong bracing system is needed, the use of one of the following may be satisfactory:

A. Roofs:

1. Nail strongly a few diagonal boards or planks under the sheathing and between the purlins to give a small amount of shearing resistance.
2. Spike, or lag-screw, diagonal planks under the purlins or rafters to form a sort of truss across and lengthwise of the roof, using somewhat the same principles as previously described for bracing steel structures.
3. Use double sheathing—one set perpendicular to the purlins and the other at 45° thereto. This is very strong if well nailed together; it is also very simple but requires the use of considerable lumber.
4. Incorporate a lateral truss system to act with the main vertical trusses. It is generally very troublesome to do this but, when necessary, it is preferable to locate the trussing directly under the purlins so that they (or some of them) become a part of the system, and the diagonal members can be supported under the purlins to avoid sagging and flimsiness. Figure 12·20(*a*) shows one way of arranging the details at a panel point of such a bracing system. This construction is like that used for steelwork. The use of a Warren type of web system is for the purpose of avoiding the crossing of two diagonal braces. In Sketch (*b*), the diagonals are not connected directly to the truss chords but, if the purlins are stiff laterally and if they are connected strongly to the trusses, the eccentricity of the connection is not likely to be harmful. The Pratt type of web system is used to avoid the intersection of two bracing diagonals at the same point on the truss. In cases such as these, one bay out of four to six is supposed to have a complete bracing system, then the intervening trusses are steadied and connected to the braced bay by means of the purlins. Obviously, the attachments of the purlins to the trusses and to other purlins in the same line should be strong.
5. A series of knee braces between purlins and truss chords may be entirely satisfactory if the chords are solid, stiff members or if the two slender portions are stiffened by "web" fillers forming an H section or by plank cover plates making a U-type member. Two different details of such knee braces are shown in Figs. 12·20(*c*) and (*d*).
6. Roof trusses should have some sort of cross frames and struts, or knee braces to the purlins, to steady the lower chords and to prevent

lateral overturning of the trusses. When these members are sufficiently strong to brace upper chords, a lateral system may be attached to the lower chords and cross struts. Such a system, however, is likely to involve much troublesome detail. Figures 12·10 and 12·12 indicate some arrangements for struts and cross frames between trusses. In

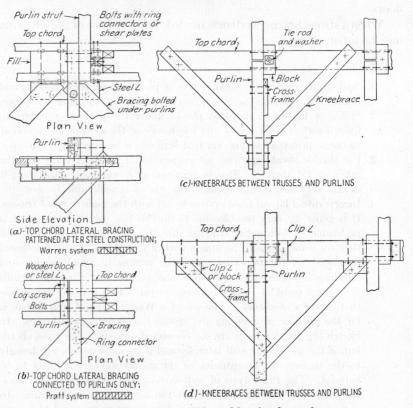

FIG. 12·20. Some details of lateral bracing for roof trusses.

these cases, the diagonals of the cross frame start near the lower chords of the trusses and slope up to the central portions of the purlins. In Figs. 12·13 and 12·20(c) and (d), the slope is reversed. It is desirable to use whichever one produces the most simple details—generally, the avoidance of many members intersecting at the same joint.

B. Walls:

1. The principles given in items 1 and 2 for roofs may be used for bracing walls, but their appearance is undesirable; item 3 makes a neat, strong, and well-insulated structure. Even a single layer of diagonal sheath-

ing is surprisingly strong if it slopes at 45° in one-half of a wall whereas it slopes at 90° thereto in the remainder of the wall.

2. Knee braces may be used in conjunction with the studs, girts, any horizontal struts, and columns. If the building is not too tall and narrow, such a system is very effective even though it may not be completely trussed in itself. The connections of the knee braces should develop tensile resistance if feasible, otherwise one brace will resist in compression when the wind blows in one direction, whereas only an oppositely sloping one acts if the wind is reversed. The columns must be able to resist any bending moments caused in them by the thrust· of the braces. When knee braces or diagonal struts are merely nailed or spiked to their connecting members, shrinkage and corrosion are likely to impair the effectiveness of the joint. Some such framing is indicated in Fig. 12·21(a) and (b). It is desirable to arrange the short diagonals in line so as to form, in effect, long compression members. The ends of these members should have a strong point or member against which to react; otherwise bending of the latter will destroy the effectiveness of the diagonal. The intermediate girt A in Sketch (a) is used to avoid excessively long and flimsy studs; the small stud B in (b) is to prevent sagging of the girt under the window sill.

3. A more positive truss effect may be attained by adding long diagonals to the system of columns and girts or studs, but this usually requires a lot of detail trouble when making the connections. One such scheme is shown in Fig. 12·21(c).

When planning a bracing system composed of timbers, one is wise to consider the knee-brace principle as one of the most desirable systems because it is especially well suited for construction in wood. It is best to cut and fit these diagonal members in the field whenever they are to bear against the main pieces, and to wedge them into place with thrust blocks. Seldom will a carpenter be able to dap or mortise them and still attain the desired initial (though small) compression. An attempt to pattern the bracing after steel construction is usually inadvisable. An example of the knee-bracing of trusses and columns at an interior column is given in Fig. 12·21(d).

Vertical bracing in the walls should be used at and near the corners of wooden buildings, near large doorways, near offsets, and at such intermediate points as may seem to be desirable. However, it is seldom necessary to brace all bays if the intervening ones are steadied by struts to the braced points.

12·9 Trestles and Piers. Timbers are useful for the construction of many things besides buildings; e.g., highway and railroad trestles, piers and other water-front facilities, bins, water towers, pipe-line supports,

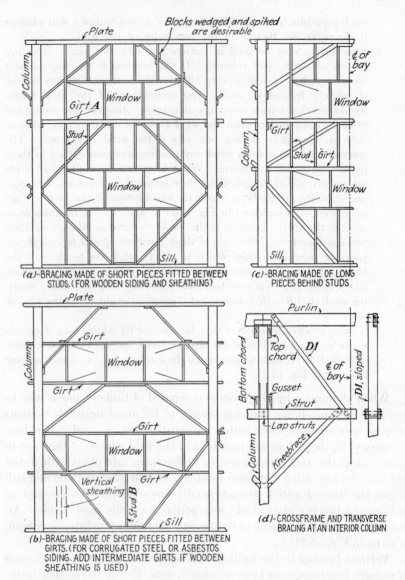

(a)-BRACING MADE OF SHORT PIECES FITTED BETWEEN STUDS.(FOR WOODEN SIDING AND SHEATHING)

(c)-BRACING MADE OF LONG PIECES BEHIND STUDS

(b)-BRACING MADE OF SHORT PIECES FITTED BETWEEN GIRTS.(FOR CORRUGATED STEEL OR ASBESTOS SIDING. ADD INTERMEDIATE GIRTS IF WOODEN SHEATHING IS USED)

(d)-CROSSFRAME AND TRANSVERSE BRACING AT AN INTERIOR COLUMN

FIG. 12·21.   Some schemes for vertical bracing of walls and columns.

and conveyor galleries.   In general, it is desirable to make these structures as simple as possible, yet sturdy and well braced.   Those members carrying heavy loads should be designed so that the timbers bear upon each other if it is possible.

The railroad trestle shown in Fig. 12·22 has the ties dapped in order to clinch the stringers; the bolts are used to hold the ties in place.   In

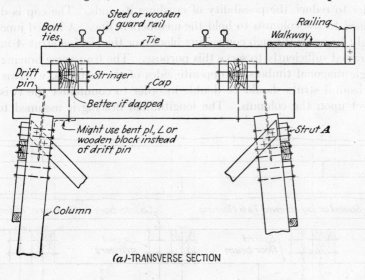

(a)-TRANSVERSE SECTION

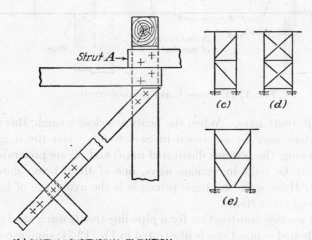

(b)-PARTIAL LONGITUDINAL ELEVATION

FIG. 12·22.   One type of trestle construction.

many cases where the trains move slowly, bolting alone is sufficient. The stringers are made of alternate, lapped, single, and double timbers in order to maintain the same effective axis for them, and to use the same size for all ties.   Stringers should be dapped and connected by bolts; the single one is then bolted to the cap or floor beam to knit the structure together. The heavy cap extends beyond the columns in order to reduce the possibility of crushing its ends. The cap is drift-pinned to the columns to hold the members in line. A bolted junction might be made through connecting blocks, or the bracing strut A might be raised sufficiently to serve this purpose. The transverse bracing has single diagonal timbers on opposite sides of the columns, whereas the horizontal struts should be double in order to counteract the twisting effect upon the columns. The longitudinal bracing is assumed to be

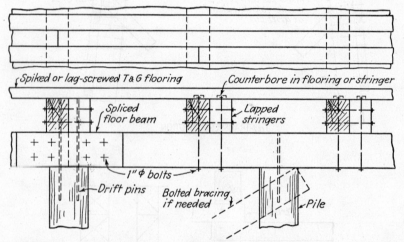

FIG. 12·23.   Some heavy pier construction.

placed in alternate bays. When the bents are close enough, this longitudinal system may be as shown in Sketch (c); when the diagonals become too long, the systems illustrated in (d) and (e) are preferable.

Piers may be built in various ways, one of them being shown in Fig. 12·23. Here again the basic principle is the avoidance of heavily loaded framed connections.

Framed wooden construction for a pipe-line trestle using steel gusset plates and bolted connections is illustrated in Fig. 12·24; similar connections are also pictured in special parts of several of the other drawings in this chapter where such details seemed to be advantageous. This tower shows the planning of a wooden structure patterned after a steel one. Such construction is serviceable for light loads. As stated previously, however, it may be difficult to match holes properly through the double gussets and the intervening timbers.

Figure 12·25 shows a more conventional type of bolted tower construction that seemingly could and should be used as a substitute for that of Fig. 12·24 because it is planned specifically for the use of wood and for complete fabrication in the field.   The double struts are used

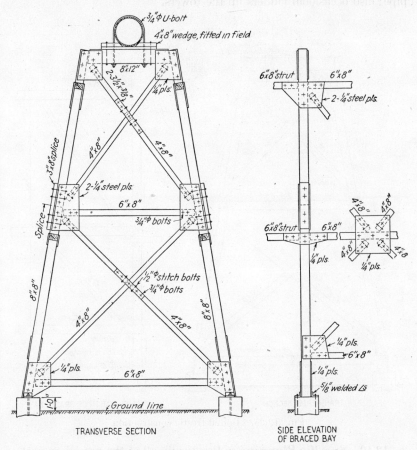

TRANSVERSE SECTION

SIDE ELEVATION
OF BRACED BAY

Fig. 12·24.   Bolted trestle construction with steel gusset plates.

here, too, to reduce any twisting of the columns that might be caused by the single diagonals on opposite sides of the posts.   The K-type of longitudinal bracing is used so as to reduce the required lengths of timbers and to avoid the necessity of splicing them.   In most such ordinary timberwork it is unnecessary to insist that all members at a joint have their axes intersecting at a common working point because the columns are so stiff that the effect of eccentricity at the connections is unimportant. In wooden structures particularly, a system that is practical is also likely to be good.

When such a trestle as that shown in Figs. 12·24 and 12·25 is planned, it might be advisable to provide an inspection walkway alongside the pipe; also occasional ladders up the towers.

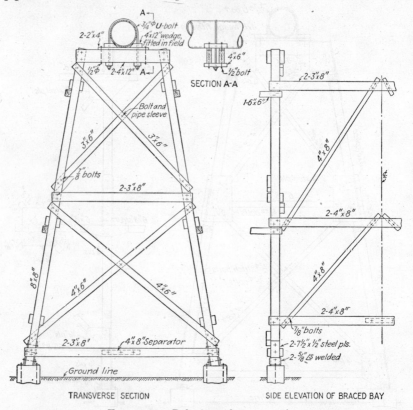

Fig. 12·25.   Bolted trestle construction.

12·10   Specific Planning. Practically all of the preceding part of this chapter has been used to explain and illustrate the details of various members and connections in structures built of wood. Why? Because such details should have a tremendous influence upon the planning of anything that is built of timber. As with structures made of other materials, it is essential to consider the equipment to be housed and the specific parts to be supported. However, the designer is so much more restricted by the lower strength of the material, the short lengths and small sizes of commercial lumber, and the limitation of what can be

Fig. 12·26. The erection of parallel-chord, ring-connected trusses that are lifted into place with the columns attached. (*Courtesy of the Timber Engineering Co.*)

Fig. 12·27. Ring-connected bowstring trusses, showing purlins, knee braces, cross frames, and struts. (*Courtesy of the Timber Engineering Co.*)

done to make connections that he should plan wooden structures automatically with proper consideration for these detail matters.

It is unwise for a person to draw upon a piece of paper a series of lines representing the beams, columns, trusses, bracing, and other members that he wishes to have, then to puzzle about how these parts can be connected. It is far better to plan the structure specifically for the utilization of wood and to consider these detail matters carefully as he lays out the structure, doing so not on paper but in his mind sufficiently

FIG. 12·28. Glued, laminated, tied arches in a small hangar. (*Courtesy of the Timber Engineering Co.*)

to assure him that, when he or someone else develops these things later on, practicable, economical members and connections can be obtained. The skill and facility with which he does such planning are a gauge of his ability as an engineer. Experience and study enable a man to develop the ability to judge quickly the feasibility and appropriateness of a proposed framing scheme, and such expert ability is valuable.

Chapter 13

FOUNDATIONS

13·1 Character of Foundation Problems. The foundations of
a structure are extremely important, and the problems to be solved in
planning them are often beset by a wide range of uncertainties.   In this
field, design certainly approaches closer to an art than to an exact
science.   Many of the conditions are indeterminable, assumptions must
be made, a suitable type of foundation must be selected, the final dimensions and details must be chosen, and good judgment based upon both
experience and theory is required.

A foundation must be able to support a structure without failure.
If it is inadequate, the consequences are obviously serious and the
situation is generally both difficult and costly to remedy.   On the other
hand, the construction should be as economical as it is practicable to
make it.   Almost anything can be made unquestionably safe if enough
money is spent to attain this objective alone, but the job may be unduly and wastefully expensive.   Hence, the engineer is faced with the
task of securing adequate safety and optimum economy simultaneously.

Foundations on soils almost inevitably settle more or less under the
load of a structure.   What constitutes more than an acceptable deformation?   What less?   What pressure will the soil withstand safely?
How much will this particular structure settle?   These are serious questions.   If one waits for the answers to be given after the structure is
built, the consequences may be serious for the engineer as well as for
his structure. Here again the expenditure of enough money may result
in very slight settlement.   Is it worth the cost?

The real engineering comes in the answering of such questions as
these, and in the selection of the basic type and proportions of the
foundation to be used.   After these decisions are made, the detailers
and the builders of the structural work of the foundation can do little
to effect important economies.

The need for all reasonably obtainable information regarding ground
and water conditions at the site is too obvious to be argued.   There have
been some, nevertheless, who have planned foundations upon data rang-

357

ing from hearsay to a glance at the surface of the ground to see that there really was some there.   It is obvious, too, that the justifiable expenditure for soil investigations bears some relation to the importance of the structure and to the seriousness of failure or excessive subsidence.

When studying the logs of borings and the soil profiles plotted therefrom, an engineer should bear in mind the conditions under which the data were obtained.   When something appears on paper there is a natural tendency to believe that it is authoritative, whereas it may be the interpretation of some draftsman.   However, in this sort of case, one should remember that various strata may not have sharp dividing lines that can be located to 0.01 ft., that wash borings may not yield data that are easily interpreted, that undisturbed soil samples are not undisturbed but are far more helpful than washed ones, and that the profile shown between borings is an assumption.   Intangible though the exact conditions may be, the work done by experienced, careful workmen in making soil explorations should be commended, and it probably yields as reliable information as the uncertainties of the composition and characteristics of the soil justify.

A foundation can be planned completely only after the structure and its loads are determined.   Nevertheless, the general requirements of the foundation should be investigated in the original planning to see that satisfactory construction can be made for both the superstructure and the substructure.   Often the contractor must start excavation long before a complete design can be made.

13·2 Soils.   Soils are generally classified into certain broad groups: hardpan, gravel, caliche, sand, loam, silt, clay, and mud.   These names denote special but rather broad characteristics.   In nature, soils classed in any one group may differ widely; many soils are a mixture of materials from various groups; and the ground at any site may be composed of many strata of various materials in different states of compaction.   In many cases, conditions vary greatly in different portions of a large site because of erosion and deposition by wind, water, and glacier.

Stating the safe bearing pressure for any general kind of soil is, therefore, a hazardous undertaking.   The data in Table 13·1 are given as a general guide, not as a sedative to ease the doubts of the user.   Local building codes may specify allowable pressures that are based upon years of experience with the soils in the district.   Customary practice that has proved satisfactory under similar conditions may be a good guide if adequate comparison is possible.   At any rate, one should investigate such things.

Table 13·1 Approximate Allowable Bearing Value of Foundation Materials

Material	Bearing capacity, kips per sq. ft.	
	Approximate depth 3 ft.	Approximate depth 6 to 10 ft.
Soft silt and mud........................	0.2–0.5	0.5–1
Silt (wet but confined).................	2–4	3–4
Soft clay.............................	2–3	2–4
Dense, firm clay......................	4–5	5–6
Clay and sand mixed..................	4–6	5–7
Fine sand (wet but confined)..........	4	4–6
Coarse sand..........................	6	6–8
Gravel and coarse sand...............	8–10	10–12
Cemented gravel and coarse sand......	10–12	12–14
Poor rock............................	15–20	15–20
Sound bedrock.......................	40–60	40–60

A brief discussion of the characteristics of various soils as foundation materials is given as a general guide:

1. *Hardpan and Caliche.* Very strong when conditions of air and water are such that the binding or cementing agents will not be broken down.

2. *Gravel.* Generally excellent when not subjected to scour. The particle size is usually classed as over ¼ in.

3. *Sand.* Coarse sand is nearly as good as gravel, but fine sand may wash out, blow away, or even become "quick" when saturated with water under the right conditions. Sand is classified as particles ranging from ¼ in. to 0.05 mm. in size.

4. *Loam.* The topsoil that is so valuable for agricultural purposes but, because of its compressibility, variability, and organic matter is unsuitable for heavy foundations. It may have clay, silt, or sand as its chief constituent, or it may have a mixture of them.

5. *Silt.* Rather compressible and likely to flow under load when saturated. The size ranges from 0.05 to 0.005 mm.

6. *Clay.* Relatively compressible, of low strength, likely to flow under pressure, and showing considerable shrinkage when dried. The size of particles is generally taken as less than 0.005 mm.

7. *Mud.* Of slight or no value for supporting loads.

In nature, these soil materials often occur as mixtures. A soil with less than 20 per cent of clay with sand may be called "loamy" sand; it acts largely as a sand, and the clay may be a binder. When the clay is 20 to 30 per cent, this soil may be called "clayey" sand or "sandy" clay loam; the claylike qualities will become more apparent.   When the clay exceeds 30 per cent, the material is a sandy clay; and the qualities of the clay will affect it prominently.

One should consider the entire body of the soil under a structure from the footings to rock, or to such a depth that the effect of the loads can be assumed to be negligible.   Hence, a good surface stratum of sand may be strong in itself but, if underlain by compressible materials like silt and clay, it may be dangerous as a foundation.

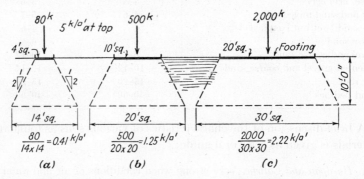

FIG. 13·1.   Effect of size of loaded area upon average intensity of pressure at lower level.

13·3   Some General Principles.   As a starting point, it is generally desirable to plan a foundation so that the intensity of pressure on the soil is uniform for all portions of the structure.   This is satisfactory in the case of gravels and good sands, but it may cause differential settlements when the soils are compressible silt or clay.   The reason is illustrated in Fig. 13·1.   It is satisfactory to assume that granular materials will distribute the superimposed loads over areas that increase with the depth on the basis of a slope of 2:1.   Although the intensity of pressure is customarily assumed to be uniform at any given horizontal plane, the maximum near the center may actually be nearer $1\frac{1}{2}$ times the average. Soft and medium clays may not have the shearing strength to spread the loads so rapidly.

A study of Fig. 13·1 shows at once the effect of the size of a loaded area upon the pressures at some lower depth, even though the initial intensity is uniform.   If the settlement caused by an intensity of pressure of 0.5 kip or less per square foot is assumed to be negligible, the subsidence of the small footing will be caused by the total compressive deformation of a column of soil 8.7 ft. high; that of the 10-ft. square one,

21.8 ft. high; and that of the 20-ft. square footing, 43.5 ft. high.   It is
clear that the settlements will not be uniform in these three cases.

From the preceding illustration, it appears that the soil directly under
a small footing can be loaded more heavily than the same material under
a large one as far as settlement is concerned.   The small footing indicates that the structure is light anyway and probably relatively unimportant, whereas the large footing is under a heavy and probably valuable structure.   The more dangerous situation thus accompanies the
larger and more costly structure.   From this standpoint alone, a bearing
pressure that is allowable under a small footing on compressible soil may
be unwisely high for a large one.

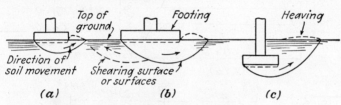

FIG. 13·2.   Character of shearing failure.

A soil may fail by shearing, *i.e.*, by flowing out from under the loaded
area, as illustrated in Fig. 13·2(*a*).   In this case, an increase of the area
of the footing causes the area of the surface of rupture or sliding to increase as in (*b*), hence improving the probable resistance to movement.
This means that narrow footings may fail by shearing of the earth more
easily than wide ones.   An embedded or deep footing, as in (*c*), also has
greater resistance to shearing than does the same one at the surface.

Granular materials like sand and gravel become firmer under pressure
than when loose.   For them, the pressure is beneficial if the soil is
steadied laterally.   This cheerful statement does not apply to clays, and
it should not be trusted for silts.

The bearing areas of a foundation should be proportioned to resist
the maximum loading upon the structure without exceeding the allowable pressure on the soil.   The structural parts of a foundation should
also be designed to resist the greatest probable load.

The settlement of sands and gravels under load occurs almost entirely
when the load is applied; that of clays and silts may continue for long
periods as water is squeezed out slowly and the soil is compacted, or as
the material moves gradually.   Therefore, live loads, wind, traction, and
other temporary loads cause little or no settlement because movement
cannot occur so rapidly.   However, warehouses that hold goods for

several days at a time may be assumed to cause a pressure equal to the dead load plus one-half or some other portion of the live load.

An approximation of the settlement caused by a plastic soil under a structure may be estimated as follows, referring to Fig. 13·3(a):

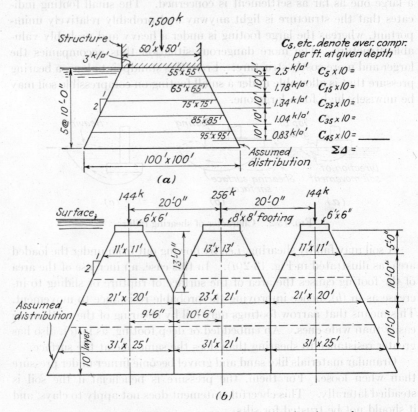

Fig. 13·3.   Assumed distribution of loads for approximating settlements.

1. Draw the 2:1 assumed cone of distribution.

2. Divide it into slices of some chosen thickness; *e.g.*, 10 ft.

3. Compute the assumed average pressure at the centers of these slices.

4. Use as many slices as the pressures seem to justify.

5. From curves of compressibility made from laboratory tests of "undisturbed" soil samples taken at or close to the centers of the slices, find the settlement per foot of earth for an intensity of pressure equal to the assumed average at the given point.

6. Multiply each of the settlements computed in item 5 by the height of the slice, and add the products.

If the foundation is considered to be separate footings, as in Fig. 13·3(b), the settlements may be approximated as for Sketch (a), except that the cones of distribution need not be assumed to overlap. Naturally, great accuracy is impossible in such problems as these; nevertheless, one may obtain a helpful scale for use in determining what action to take in his basic planning of a particular foundation.

When a footing is to be alongside or near an area that is excavated to a lower depth, the cone of distribution of the pressure should not be assumed as in Fig. 13·1, because the earth at one side is likely to slump off. It is advisable to locate the elevation of the footing as pictured in Fig. 13·4(a) if the soil is granular, or as in (b) if it is plastic. However, if local pits are dug, shoring is used, the soil does not slump, and the pit

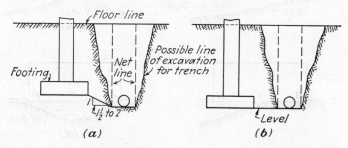

FIG. 13·4.　Footings alongside excavations.

is permanently lined with adequate masonry, footings may be used alongside and at higher elevations than shown in Sketch (a), especially when the soil is a good sand or a stiff clay. Unfortunately, however, the foundations must be planned before the adequacy of shoring and the absence of earth slippage are known; hence conservatism in placing the footings sufficiently low may be a virtue. Fine sands and silts are especially likely to become disturbed by excavation. In any of these cases, good judgment is essential.

Newly placed earth fills are undesirable as foundations for important structures unless special conditions exist and the workmanship used in placing the fill gives a reasonable guarantee of adequate compaction of the material. This subject will be discussed further in Art. 13·11.

Soil conditions that vary greatly under a given structure are especially dangerous. A few possibilities are illustrated in Fig. 13·5. Of course, the buildings should be relocated if better conditions can be found and if the plant layout will permit such changes. The following principles should be studied in connection with the sketches shown in this figure:

(a) *Hard Material at One End, Gradually Increasing Depth of Soil to the Other End.* If the soil is sand or stiff clay and the building is not too heavy, the worst that will probably happen is a slight rotation of the structure about A. If the soil is soft silt or clay, end-bearing piles or caissons to a firm bearing should be used.

(b) *Hard Material under the Center, Gradually Increasing Depth of Soil toward Both Ends.* This case is likely to break the back of a structure by cracking the top above C. When the ground is firm sand or gravel, it may be sufficient to use a complete "deformation" joint through the structure at C, letting the

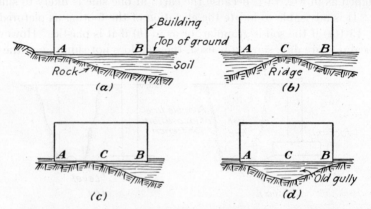

Fig. 13·5. Possible subsoil conditions causing unequal settlements.

slight rotations about C open the joint instead of cracking the building. When the soil is plastic or relatively compressible, a joint may be used if the settlements at A and B will be small, as for a light structure, but the foundations should be carried down to a firm bearing when the building is heavy.

(c) *Hard Material under One-half, Gradually Increasing Depth of Soil to the Other End.* This case should be treated the same as for (b) except that portion CB is the only one in danger of rotation.

(d) *Hard Material under Both Ends, Gradually Increasing Depth of Soil toward the Center.* If the soil is firm, the settlement probably will do no more than compress slightly the top of the structure above C. If the soil is soft and the building is heavy, it is advisable to carry the foundations down to firm bearing.

When a heavy structure with masonry walls, such as a warehouse or an office building, has small wings or other parts that produce much smaller intensities of pressure under them than exist under the main structure, and when this structure rests upon deep, plastic soils, it may be desirable to provide a complete joint at the junction of the light and the heavy portions. In some cases, it may be possible to make the light extension strong enough to transfer loads from the main structure, but this is unusual. It is even more desirable to change the basic plan so as to avoid such a situation. A heavy building on plastic soil should load that soil as uniformly as possible; since settlement will occur, let it be uniform. If its magnitude is not excessive, no one may notice it.

Trouble from settlement and cracking may not be serious in the case of framed structures of the mill-building type with corrugated or other relatively flexible siding. However, there is a limit to how much one should rely upon this flexibility.

It is good policy to have the center of gravity of the bearing areas of a foundation coincide with the resultant of the applied loads. Since varying live loads affect the sizes of these areas and since live loads may occur at different places at different times, this goal is seldom attainable. Nonuniform pressure under a footing may be accepted when the soil is firm; it is to be avoided when the building is on deep, plastic clay except when caused by temporary loads. Retaining walls are, of course, a different matter, and it is desirable to provide lateral supports for the tops of basement walls by means of the construction of the first floor itself.

A planner should look for the danger signals to be found in soil profiles. For example, look at Fig. 13·6. Sketch (a) shows a tapered stratum of plastic soil that will compress unequally and cause the structure to tilt; if this were sand, no harm would result. Sketch (b) pictures a uniform layer of plastic soil that is trapped below thick strata of sands and gravel. These serve as a heavy blanket to keep the clay from escaping, and they may distribute the load so that the resultant intensity of pressure on the clay may not be harmful. Whether or not the situation is dangerous depends upon the applied pressure, the thickness and rigidity of the upper strata, and the properties and thickness of the plastic layer. Sketch (c) shows a stratum of plastic soil that is free to move sidewise under pressure; if it were fine sand below the water table, there might be danger of quicksand.

How long can a foundation wall be made without having contraction joints in it? If it is reinforced adequately, joints need not be spaced closely because their presence and action would require a joint in the superstructure above them if cracking of the latter is to be avoided. Such walls are often made from 100 to 200 ft. long, or even more, without joints, but hair-cracks undoubtedly occur in them because of frictional resistance of the soil when the wall tries to shorten. If a wall has offsets, large sudden changes in section, or weak spots where pipes, doorways, and trenches cut through, these points are where cracking is likely to occur.

When joints are used, intermittent keys, as in Fig. 13·7(a), are often desirable to permit contraction, and even longitudinal rotation, without vertical or lateral offsets of adjoining parts. Sometimes it is desirable to seat one wall on an extension of the other, as in Sketch (b). Keys at a joint in a corner, as in (c), defeat the purpose of the joint. It might be wise to move the joint into the long wall and farther from the corner, as indicated on the drawing.

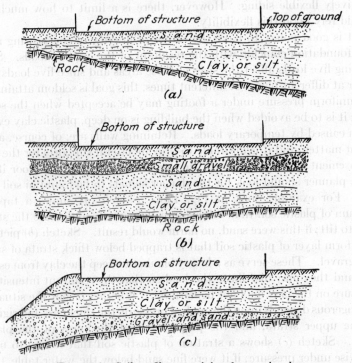

FIG. 13·6.   Soil profiles containing danger signals.

When considering either settlement or bearing pressure caused by a structure, it is the increase of pressure over the original condition that is important. As previously implied, a footing with its base 5 ft. below the surface will generally carry safely a larger load than it would if located at the top of the ground. Although the soil at the former level may have been under a pressure of 500 lb. per sq. ft. and although the load on the foundation and the weight of the backfill increase this pressure, the beneficial effect of embedment and compaction usually will exceed any detrimental effect of the initial compression. Otherwise, a soil that is safe for 2 tons per sq. ft. at the surface would seemingly be valueless at a depth of 40 ft., but this is known to be fallacious because the general action in nature is for pressure to consolidate the material. Hence, it is generally sufficient to plan a foundation upon the basis of the additional loads applied to the soil.

13·4 Water. Ground water may or may not be harmful. Coarse sands and gravels have about the same angle of repose when under water as when dry, and they will support safely practically the same load under either condition. Saturated fine sand, however, may become dangerous. Water usually is present in silts and clays and may be the source of much trouble. When such soils are disturbed in the presence of water, they are likely to soften and disintegrate.

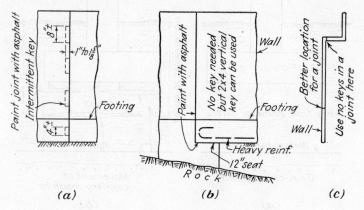

Fig. 13·7. Joints in foundation walls.

Capillary moisture tends to bind together the particles of a fine sand or silt, as illustrated by the moist sand of an ocean beach. When alternate cycles of complete drying and subsequent moistening occur, the latter condition may even cause bulking or swelling of the soil. Drainage to avoid complete saturation may be very desirable, but capillarity will hold the moisture in fine sands, silts, and clays many feet above the water table unless removed by evaporation; capillary moisture will rise only a very short distance through coarse sand and gravel.

Freezing under foundations in cold climates can be very dangerous, and the frost depth may reach 5 ft. in the extreme northern part of the United States, or 3 to 4 ft. in the vicinity of New York City.

The action of frost heaving is not that of expansion of the soil upon freezing, as occurs when water becomes ice. To illustrate, let Fig. 13·8(a) represent an assumed situation. Very fine sand and silt are porous, yet they permit capillary action to raise moisture many feet above the water table. Assume that the ground freezes to a depth of 3 ft. and that, at this level, the water in the soil at A freezes. Then, instead of the moist soil freezing lower down, capillary action sucks water up from the water table. This water then freezes upon contact with the cold front and gradually forms the ice lenses A. The action is again repeated lower down, forming ice lenses B but thereafter causing no increase in A. These lenses constitute a real increase in volume because they are formed from water *below* them, not from that previously existing in the soil at A and B. Therefore, heaving results. Upon

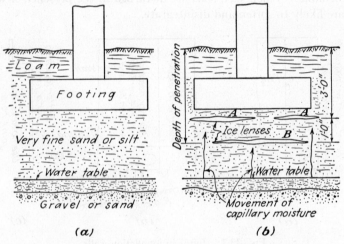

(a)   (b)

FIG. 13·8.   Frost action and formation of ice lenses.

thawing in the spring, the water in the lenses produces local softening and may cause subsidence of the foundation.

If the water table in Fig. 13·8 is too deep, the ice lenses cannot form. If the soil under the footing is dense clay, the latter is too impermeable to facilitate the formation of the lenses. If the soil is coarse sand or gravel, its capillary action will not raise the water more than a foot or two. This shows that a layer of 1 to 2 ft. of gravel or cinders—under a pavement, for example—when placed just above the frost depth, will prevent the formation of these ice lenses unless the water table rises well into or through the layer; obviously, such a layer must be positively and continuously drained.

The depth of the footing to reach below the probable effect of frost should be based upon the distance from the lowest or nearest surface exposed to the cold. Figure 13·9 illustrates some possible cases. Ordinarily, the foundations inside a building are not endangered by frost action except, for example, in a refrigerated warehouse, in which case special precautions should be used to avoid deep and harmful freezing.

Surface water, too, can cause trouble with foundations because of scouring and undermining. The transporting power of rapidly running water is surprisingly effective. The surface drainage should be planned so as to avoid any channels alongside foundations.

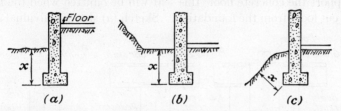

FIG. 13·9. Embedment to prevent frost heaving and subsidence. Distance x = 3 to 5 ft., depending upon climate.

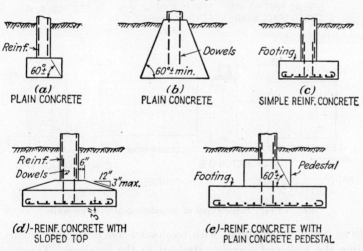

FIG. 13·10. Some simple concrete spread footings for columns.

13·5 Spread Footings. One of the most widely used foundations to distribute concentrated loads is the spread footing, several types of which are shown in Fig. 13·10. The plain concrete ones may be used for light loads, but the trapezoidal type in Sketch (b) requires complicated formwork. The simple footing in (c) is suitable for moderate sizes; those in (d) and (e) are better for large ones. If there is a large overturning moment combined with the vertical load, it is frequently desirable to use a rectangular footing with its long dimension parallel to the overturning tendency; in other cases, doweling the concrete floor to the top of the foundations will cause the floor to resist the lateral forces and to deliver them to suitable reaction points, or to the ground by means of friction.

Exterior masonry walls, and sometimes the edges of floors, need to be supported as well as the exterior columns; hence one of the arrangements shown in Fig. 13·11 may be useful. All the sketches show a ledge to support the concrete floor; this seat will be omitted when the floor is to be cut loose from the foundation. Sketch (*a*) shows individual spread

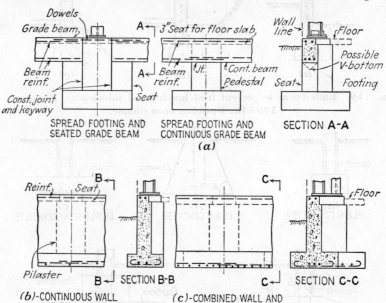

Fig. 13·11. Some types of foundation at exterior walls.

footings under the columns, with reinforced-concrete grade beams supporting the wall and carrying its load to the footings. These beams sometimes have a triangular-shaped bottom to reduce the heaving effect of freezing, but its efficiency is doubtful. These beams should be seated or made monolithic with the pedestal. When this system is used with heavy crane columns on plastic soil or medium clay, there is a tendency for localized settlement under live loads that may crack masonry walls. In Sketch (*b*) is shown a continuous foundation wall and footing, with pilasters at the columns. This is satisfactory when a foundation wall below frost is desired anyway, provided that the column loads are small and the effect of their eccentricity is not great. The walls can be designed as continuous beams that spread the concentrated loads along a line bearing. This type requires more concrete and excavation than does that in Sketch (a). The arrangement in (c) is a combination of (a) and (b); it may be desirable when crane loads are heavy and the eccentricity is large. The wall serves somewhat as a stiffening or distributing girder when heavy live loads on soft, plastic soils might cause "pumping" of individual footings.

One should choose a type of foundation that seems to suit the particular structure. He need not make all foundations of this same type when variations to serve special purposes are desirable, but he should not try to use every type in his repertoire just to show that he can do so. Reasonable consistency may be more sensible.

13·6 Mats and Floating Foundations. Conditions often arise that would require spread footings to be very large. It may then be practicable to use one large, reinforced-concrete slab or mat under the entire structure. This mat must be stiff and strong if it is to spread column and wall loads relatively uniformly over the soil; if it cannot do so, it may crack. In effect, such a mat can be planned somewhat like a flat-slab floor in reverse. Many of the details of such mat foundations have to be adapted to the particular problem; however, some general principles are shown in Fig. 13·12, as follows:

(a) This drawing illustrates a mat used as a basement floor. It is advantageous to have the slab cantilevered out beyond the foundation wall as pictured at A, but the pedestal at B may cause interference with use of the floor space. The mat may be designed as indicated by the main reinforcement shown in the figure. Better distribution of loads can be secured when the basement has walls, with doorways, along the column lines in one direction, thereby permitting the omission of the pedestals whose purpose was to reduce the shearing stresses.

(b) At C in this sketch, the foundation wall is assumed to be close to the property line, and the reinforcement is carried up into the wall to form a rigid-frame corner. The pedestal is replaced by a local thickening of the mat at the column D, and the intermediate portion of the slab is reinforced for tension in its top. This arrangement causes some complication of excavation and reinforcement.

(c) This pictures the arrangement used for supporting a small boilerhouse on deep, soft soil. The steel frame was three bays wide, with the heavy boiler in the central bay. A heavy wall E was carried around under the edge of the building, and cross walls F and G were placed along the column lines in both directions, forming a checkered pattern. With the column loads supported at the junctions of the walls, the ribs acted as inverted T-beams, whereas the mat was reinforced as a set of continuous two-way slabs. The hollow spaces were filled with tamped gravel in order to avoid the need for forms under the concrete floor. The floor slab was then seated on the walls and reinforced to prevent cracking along the edges. Foundations for compressors and pumps were carried down to the mat.

(d) Reinforced-concrete mats are often used under large equipment, such as this furnace. Structurally, they are not used to spread the load but to form a sort of pavement. However, in such a case, the concrete must be protected from excessive heat to avoid dehydration, because the insulation or brickwork of the bottom of the furnace reduces the transfer of heat but does not prevent accumulation or rise of temperature when the ground below

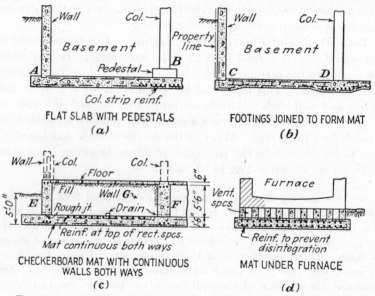

FLAT SLAB WITH PEDESTALS
(a)

FOOTINGS JOINED TO FORM MAT
(b)

CHECKERBOARD MAT WITH CONTINUOUS
WALLS BOTH WAYS
(c)

MAT UNDER FURNACE
(d)

Fig. 13·12.   Some uses of reinforced-concrete flat-slab mats.

the mat cannot conduct the heat away. A temperature of 600°F. or higher is likely to injure ordinary concrete; Lumnite cement may stand as much as 1000°F. The best protection is some sort of natural or forced ventilation between the furnace and the mat, as indicated in the sketch.

The term "floating foundation" will be used to denote a boxlike, hollow foundation that displaces approximately as much weight of soil as the dead load applied by the structure. For example, assume that the basement in Fig. 13·12(b) is 12 ft. deep, the mat averages 1 ft. 6 in., and the soil is soft clay. The weight of a column of soil 1 ft. square would be approximately 1,350 lb. If the complete structure averages this same amount per square foot, there is no increase of load applied to the soil; hence there should be no settlement other than overcoming the rebound caused by the excavation and unloading of the earth prior to the building of the structure.   Except in special cases, the live load is too temporary to cause harmful settlements.

An extreme example of the use of this principle of floating is shown in Fig. 13·13.   Variable soils with adobe under one side of the big footing, and with a puttylike soft clay some 30 ft. below the base, made this type of construction seem to be the best and worth its cost.   With a stack projecting 540 ft. into the air, unequal settlement would be serious. After 3 years of service, the observed settlement was uniform and not over ¼ in.[1]

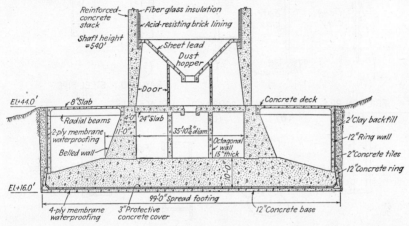

FIG. 13·13.   Design of foundation of stack on soft soil.   (*Courtesy of Phelps Dodge Corp.*)

13·7   Piles.   Water-front and marshy sites are frequently necessary for industrial plants because of the need for locations that can be served by water-borne transportation.   This often confronts the engineer with the problem of planning foundations to support heavy loads on soft material or on deep-lying strata.   For this purpose, piles are very useful.

A friction pile transfers its superimposed load to the surrounding soil by means of skin friction along its surface, whereas an end-bearing pile delivers its load primarily as a column to the material upon which its end rests.   There are many combinations of these actions in actual practice, and the distribution between friction and end bearing is impossible to ascertain with exactness.   As a rule, however, the compressibility of plastic soils is so relatively large that, if the tip of the pile rests securely upon or in a firm stratum, the latter will take the load if

[1] DUNHAM, CLARENCE W., Support for a Tall Stack on Poor Soil, *Engineering News-Record*, Sept. 21, 1944.

it can do so; only by yielding locally can it shift appreciable load to the higher strata.   Almost any type of pile can be used as a friction pile.

End-bearing piles should have tips of adequate area to prevent spearing into the bearing stratum; they should have adequate cross sections to resist the compressive forces; they should be straight and preferably parallel to the applied loads; and the soil around them may be relied upon to eliminate the slenderness and buckling troubles, even if the soil is only consolidated mud, silt, or soft clay.

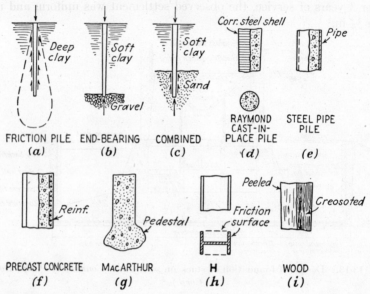

Fig. 13·14.   Load-bearing action of piles, and some ordinary types.

Some of the types of pile used ordinarily are shown in Fig. 13·14. A few comments about them and their uses follow:

1. *Wooden.*   These are light, can be floated to many jobs, are easy to handle and cut, are relatively weak in compression, are increasingly difficult to obtain in good quality and over 50 or 60 ft. long, are difficult to drive through an overlying hard stratum, must be under the water table to prevent decay, are combustible if exposed, are subject to the ravages of marine borers, are flexible and advantageous for fenders and dolphins, and are best suited for use as creosoted friction piles.

2. *Precast-concrete.*   These are heavy and difficult to transport, are strong as columns and good for end bearing, require considerable time for curing, are difficult to drive into firm strata without shattering the heads unless water jets are used, and are difficult to cut off or extend if the original length is not correct.

3. *Cast-in-place Concrete with Metallic Shell.* These are generally composed of a metallic shell, like the Raymond pile, which is driven into place by means of a retractable mandrel; then the space is filled with concrete with or without reinforcement. They are particularly useful as friction piles, easy to transport and drive, adjustable to any reasonable length, ensure complete and proper section of concrete, and are seldom used for piles projecting above ground. However, a contractor must be careful that adjacent driving does not damage piles that have not had time for the concrete to attain proper strength.

4. *Cast-in-place Concrete without Metallic Shell.* These are usually built by driving a pipe with a detachable cap at its bottom, or by sinking an open pipe that is subsequently cleaned out. The concrete is then deposited as the pipe is withdrawn. These piles are useful and economical if they can be constructed correctly, but there is the danger from surrounding granular material and from water running in as the pipe is withdrawn—something that is difficult to ascertain. Cleaning them out may be rather costly, and driving with closed end may be difficult because the uniform diameter automatically produces a large area of tip. The MacArthur or pedestal pile is made by ramming down the lower portion of concrete to displace the surrounding soil and to gain a large bearing area. There is, however, little or no control as to how large and of what shape the pedestal may be. Disturbance of inadequately set concrete by adjacent driving may be especially harmful; and so may be the use of a water jet.

5. *Pipes Filled with Concrete.* These are suitable for long, heavy piles and deep driving, are subject to the same problems of cleaning or driving empty as are those of item 4, are relatively expensive, are strong as columns and end-bearing piles, are easy to transport and adjust to almost any length, and are very useful when coarse gravel and soil containing boulders must be penetrated to reach rock. Instead of several of these piles in a group, one large caisson (one over 24 in. in diameter) may be used, constructed by similar means, and often inspected before concreting.

6. *Steel H-piles.* These are especially adaptable to conditions that require long piles to reach bedrock. They are relatively easy to drive through intervening dense strata and overlying gravel, and their compressive strength and column action are excellent. Of course, they are individually expensive but, under proper conditions, will support very heavy loads. In open water or in underground, flowing water, corrosion may be a problem; in clays and other dense soils, the passage of water may be so slow that the renewal of the oxygen supply is not sufficient to cause excessive rusting.

The best type of pile to use in a given case is a question to answer upon the basis of the relative economy, practicability of construction, availability of materials, desired durability, and adaptability to the service required. If any one type were the best for any and all conditions, the present competition between types could not exist.

13-8 Pile Foundations. A pile may be looked upon as a means of delivering loads through intervening weak strata to a suitable under-lying material, or it may be a means of spreading a locally excessive load downward and outward to bring into action an area that is large enough to support the loads without harmful consequences. Piles are almost indispensable in cases of soft soils where mat and floating foundations cannot be used. There are, however, certain principles to be borne in mind when planning pile foundations:

1. End-bearing piles resting upon a hard stratum with no underlying plastic materials may be designed as individually equal "columns." The total safe load on a group equals the safe load on one pile multiplied by their number.

2. Friction piles in groups tend to distribute the loads from numerous piles to the same area of soil. The total safe load on a group does *not* equal the safe load on a single test pile multiplied by the number in the group. This is seen easily by comparing Figs. 13·14(a) and 13·15(a). Exactly what the safe total load may be is utterly indeterminate, yet approximations must and can be made. The resisting value of the soil across some such position as C-C of Fig. 13·15(a) may be estimated. From tests of undisturbed soil samples, one can judge the allowable bearing value of the soil at this location; then he can estimate the area that can be reasonably assumed to be effective. This latter will vary with the shearing and cohesive strength of the soil, both of which may be determined by laboratory tests of samples at various depths. He may also estimate the frictional resistance that may be anticipated to exist along the surface of the piles. Some possible guidance for this is given in Table 13·2. Assume that AB represents the penetration into the soil, then

Table 13·2 Approximate Allowable Value of Skin Friction on Piles, Lb. per Sq. Ft.

Material	Approximate depth		
	20 ft.	60 ft.	100 ft.
Soft silt and sand...............	50–100	50–120	60–150
Silt (wet but confined)..........	100–200	125–300	150–400
Soft clay......................	100–200	125–250	150–300
Stiff clay.....................	300–500	350–550	400–600
Clay and sand mixed...........	300–500	400–600	500–700
Fine sand (wet but confined).....	300–400	350–500	400–600
Medium sand and small gravel...	500–600	600–800	600–800

the value of x in Fig. 13·15(a) to use as a basis for the distribution or spreading of the load, may be somewhere from 4 or 5 for soft clay and silt to 2 or 3 for medium clay and relatively firm silt. Naturally, the total load applied on any horizontal plane cannot exceed the frictional resistance developed safely above that plane. It is self-evident that close spacing of these piles and the addition of many more piles in a group are not efficient uses of friction piles. A minimum spacing of 3 to 4 ft. c.c. is desirable.

3. Piles that stop above plastic strata, as shown in Fig. 13·15(b), may deliver their loads to the upper clay and sand strata, but they do not prevent the settlement that the silt and lower clay layers may cause.

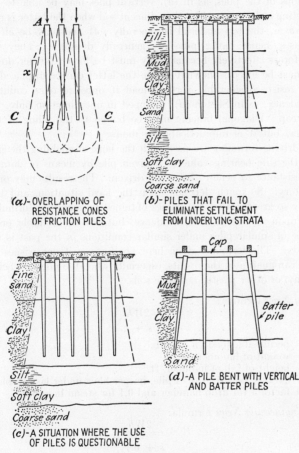

(a)-OVERLAPPING OF RESISTANCE CONES OF FRICTION PILES

(b)-PILES THAT FAIL TO ELIMINATE SETTLEMENT FROM UNDERLYING STRATA

(c)-A SITUATION WHERE THE USE OF PILES IS QUESTIONABLE

(d)-A PILE BENT WITH VERTICAL AND BATTER PILES

FIG. 13·15.   Groups of piles.

4. Fill applied after piles are driven, or even deposited soon before the piles are driven through it, may actually cause a downward load on the piles because of compaction of the mud and the fill itself, as illustrated in Fig. 13·15(b).

5. Assume that the piles of Fig. 13·15(c) are to be capable of withstanding an average load of 20 tons each and that they are 4 ft. c.c.   The equivalent uniformly distributed pressure on the footing due to the reaction of the piles is approximately 1.25 tons per sq. ft.   It is possible that the clay will stand

this pressure directly and that a mat foundation is suitable; any intervening sand stratum might be utilized as a distributing medium to spread the pressure over the underlying silt and soft clay.   This alternate, however, is not feasible for Sketch (b).

6. When there are lateral or longitudinal forces of large magnitude acting upon the tops of the piles, as in (d), vertical piles may be able to withstand them by acting as beams held by the adjacent soil when the latter is reasonably firm.   However, the top material is generally soft and may be air or water in some cases; hence batter piles are generally desirable.   They will resist horizontal forces effectively because they must be forced farther down or the structure must be lifted somewhat before the latter can be displaced very far. They also resist considerable vertical load if opposite ones counteract the tipping tendency, as in Sketch (d); if sloped in one direction only, they tend to tip the cap.   Diagonal bracing may be bolted to the piling of trestles in air or water, but it is impracticable in mud.

7. Pile-driving formulas are used with the hope of enabling the engineer to determine the safe bearing value of a given pile by means of data obtained from the resistance to penetration when driven.   The results may or may not be satisfactory.   So much depends upon the local situation, and these conditions vary so greatly, that the values obtained by means of formulas should be looked upon as one piece of evidence, but not as infallible proof.   The performance of similar piles under similar conditions in the past is worthy of careful study.   The formulas given here are for use if one wishes to do so, but no one can guarantee the results, especially when the piles are being driven into silt, clay, or other plastic, cohesive soils.

Engineering News formula:

$$R = \frac{2Wh}{s + c}$$

where R = permissible load on pile, lb.
W = weight of hammer, lb.
h = height of fall of hammer, ft.
s = average penetration of pile, in. per blow under last 10 blows
c = factor 1 for drop hammer and 0.1 for steam hammer

Modified *Engineering News* formula:

$$R = \frac{2Wh}{s + 0.1\dfrac{P}{W}}$$

where P = weight of pile and cap, lb., assuming that a steam hammer is used.

Simplified Hiley formula:

1. For drop hammer:

$$R = \frac{3Wh}{s + k} \times \frac{W}{W + P}$$

2. For single-acting steam hammer:

$$R = \frac{3.6Wh}{s + k} \times \frac{W}{W + P}$$

where k = half the total rebound of the pile hammer in inches, and the other symbols are the same as for the *Engineering News* formula.[1]

8. A concrete pile may weigh from 2 to 6 tons. Its weight should be included among the loads applied to the soil unless this is allowed for by the pile-driving formula or code used.

9. Piles driven into plastic, cohesive soils tend to become "set" after the driving ceases. In the case of sands, similar consolidation occurs even when a water jet is used during the driving. However, the use of a water jet in plastic soils may transform them into mud.

10. When trying to visualize the load being applied by any pile foundation, spread footing, or mat to unfavorable soil, the planner may be helped by converting the contemplated pressure into an equivalent column of earth; *e.g.*, 3 tons per sq. ft. is the approximate pressure of a 60-ft. column of earth. Such ideas may restrain one from unwise optimism.

11. Piles driven down to boulders may be broken in the process, and their end-bearing value may be unreliable.

What must be done in planning a pile foundation? Obviously, many decisions must be made in advance, such as the following:

1. Choose the type of pile preferred for the special situation.
2. Select the safe load to be used per pile for design purposes.
3. Determine the length probably needed, so that the piles or material can be ordered. A driving and loading test may be worth its cost in ascertaining this information.
4. Select the elevation for the tops of the piles.
5. Select a minimum spacing of piles.
6. Determine the preferred pattern or general arrangement of piles.
7. Specify the embedment of the pile tops in concrete footings.

The arbitrary assumption of a safe load per pile may seem to be impossible before the piles are driven; it is indeed a matter for the exercise of extremely good engineering judgment and is made only after thorough study of the conditions at the site. The contractor will then strive for the desired results. Preliminary test piles, or the test loading of some of the first piles driven in the permanent work, may yield results that are very helpful. If the piles cannot withstand the load selected for design, revision of the plans for the foundations will be necessary, but this will cause less serious trouble than will future harmful settlement of the structure. If the piles can withstand safely more than the assumed allowable load, some money is wasted in carrying out the original plans, but it is probably not an excessive amount compared to

[1] "Pile Foundations and Pile Structures," Manual 27 of Engineering Practice, American Society of Civil Engineers, 1946.

the total cost of the project.   Of course, plans can be revised downward as well as upward if unexpectedly favorable conditions are encountered.

Furthermore, it is very easy to plan a complicated pile foundation on paper; it is something else to build it in the field.   Hence, it is advisable to simplify such foundations as much as can be done practically, and to allow leeway for the minor inaccuracies of location that almost inevitably arise when the piles are driven.

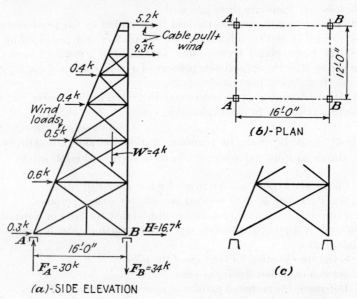

Fig. 13·16.   General data for one half of a dead-end tower.

13·9   Uplift and Overturning.   Tall, slender structures may cause severe upward and overturning forces to act upon their foundations, and these forces may be more troublesome than the downward pressures alone.   Anchor towers of transmission lines, dead-end towers at substations, crane runways supported upon A-frames, high conveyor bents, narrow towers enclosing bucket elevators, and elevated tanks when empty—these are a few structures whose foundations may have to be designed with special consideration for these upward and horizontal forces.

As an illustration of the planning of such foundations, assume the dead-end tower pictured in Figs. 13·16(a) and (b), which show the general arrangement of the steelwork, the magnitudes of the forces acting upon the structure, and the spacing of the bearings.   It is obvious that the dead loads of the tower and cables are small, whereas the horizontal forces resulting from the tension in the cables have both large magnitudes and large lever arms from the foundations. The safe bearing value of the soil, its angle of internal friction, the coefficient of sliding friction, and the desired safety factor have to be ascertained or assumed for each case. The safety factor should not be less than 1.5.

In Fig. 13·16(a) are pictured the shears and vertical forces applied to the foundations of this structure at A and B for one-half of the tower, assuming balanced loading on the steelwork. In this case, the forces are not reversible, and the shear is assumed to be resisted equally by A and B. If the tower diagonals are slender members capable of resisting tension only, as in Sketch (c), the shear would be largely concentrated at A. It is therefore desirable to tie A and B together by a bottom strut in the tower or by a strut in the foundation itself.

The safety factor for downward pressures is generally included in the specified permissible bearing value of the soil. Uplift, however, must be resisted by the weight of the foundation at A and by any earth above it; hence the actual effective weight to resist the uplift caused by the overturning forces must be $1.5 \times 30 = 45$ kips. The horizontal shears at A and B tend to overturn the individual parts of the foundation, or the foundation as a whole; thus the maximum edge pressures under the footings will be the critical ones. Unless the foundations are 4 or 5 ft. deep, the abutting resistance of the soil is not very reliable for preventing the tilting of the foundations because too much deformation may occur before the earth stops the movement; on the other hand, this abutting resistance may be very effective in preventing sliding.

What sort of foundations can be used for this structure, and what are the good and bad features of each? Figure 13·17 illustrates some possible types. Comments about them follow:

(a) This sketch shows separate pyramidal footings. The one at A must have an effective weight of 45 kips. This may be assumed to include the weight of the plain concrete itself at 145 lb. per cu. ft. and that of the surrounding earth represented by the portions CDE and FGH. The latter is questionable, however, in this special case. For a sudden upward yank, the earth might be displaced along some such lines as CJ and HK; for a steady pull, the wedging action along CE and HF might permit an objectionable amount of vertical movement of A (and tilting of the tower) before the footing wedges enough to stop the motion. Certainly, no more than the earth above CH should be included as resisting weight.

The front footing at B, even with an allowance of several kips, W, for the excess weight of the footing over that of the original earth, will need a relatively small base area. However, allowance must be made for the resultant high pressure on the front edges of both footings. To approximate this edge pressure, it seems advisable to assume that the resultant vertical force under *B* is the assumed weight of the footing plus 34 kips, whereas that under *A* is 15 kips. Neglecting the abutting power of the earth, the pressure diagrams under the footings may be about as shown in the sketch. It is obvious that this condition is too severe, that the horizontal shear will not be resisted equally by the front and rear foundations, and that the resistance of the earth to tilting of the foundations should be utilized. To get an idea of the resisting moment that the earth can offer, compute the abutting power of each 1-ft. layer of soil on the area of the portion of the footing that bears against it, multiply each such force by its lever arm above *H* or *M*, and compare the summation of these moments with that produced by the horizontal shear about the same points. If the resistance is two or three times the applied moment, the excess of vertical pressure under points *H* and *M* of Sketch (*a*) need not be worried about. The resistance to sliding may be computed upon the basis of the pressure under the footings multiplied by the coefficient of sliding friction, adding also the abutting value of the earth in front of the foundations. Of course, the foundations should be far enough apart so that the line *HN* is not over 30° or 40° above the horizontal if the abutting resistances on both *A* and *B* are to be relied upon. Obviously, such a plan as this requires a large foundation at *A* but a small one at *B*.

(*b*) This sketch shows the use of separate rectangular footings and pedestals. Their design is similar to that for Sketch (*a*) except that they utilize less concrete and more earth for resisting uplift. Here again, the foundation at *A* will be large; that at *B*, small. The weight of earth vertically over the footing of *A* is included in the resistance to uplift.

(*c*) In this case, the individual foundations at *A* and *B* are replaced by one elongated footing and pedestal under both *A* and *B*. This greatly improves the resistance to local and general overturning and seldom requires any reliance upon the abutting power of the earth in front of the footing to resist sliding and overturning. However, it requires more excavation and concrete but is well adapted for cases where the overturning forces are reversible.

(*d*) This type is a compromise between those shown in Sketches (*b*) and (*c*). The reinforced-concrete rib between *A* and *B* is to stop the local overturning of the footings. Although using less concrete than (*c*), its construction is more fussy.

(*e*) Here the continuous wall and footing of (*c*) are turned 90° in order to increase the effectiveness of its weight at *A*, to reduce the intensity of pressure under *B*, and to engage the lateral resistance of more earth. A rib can be used between *A* and *B* if desired. This type is especially useful on soft clay.

(*f*) It is possible to use a flat slab like this when there is no danger of frost, when a concrete floor is desired anyway, when the soil is weak, when groundwater conditions make it advisable to minimize excavation, or when the overturning forces and uplift are small. It is not suitable for the tower in this case because the necessary weight requires too thick a slab.

(*g*) This type is a modification of (*f*) and is more efficient, has better embedment, and engages more earth. Ribs are desirable between A and B, or along the back and front, when the forces and depth are such that individual piers cause too much localization of bending moments.

(h) When the tower is on bedrock lying at the surface, it is possible to use concrete pads with swedged anchor bolts grouted into drilled holes in the rock. Seams in the rock, cracks caused by blasting if the tower is in cut, breaking of rock around and between the drilled holes, possible disintegration of the rock, imperfect grouting, and eventual rusting of improperly protected anchor bolts —all these are possible troubles that make such a foundation less advantageous than it seems.

(i) When the cable pulls are very large, backstays may be desirable, as shown here. The anchorage at O, however, should be designed to resist the uplift and sliding. The latter may be especially troublesome. In this case, one column may replace the two shown in Fig. 16·13(a) if a stiff, structural member instead of a cable is used for the backstay.

(j) This shows a possible arrangement when a tower must be founded upon a hillside or sloping cut.

(k) In this case both pressure and part of the uplift may be resisted by the piles. It may be a question as to exactly how to evaluate the latter; if so, one is wiser to consider the piles only as a substitute for good firm soil. To resist uplift, the piles must be fastened securely to the footing.

If the forces on a tower may act in either direction, if these forces are large whereas the spread of the tower is relatively small, and if the bearing value of the soil is low, foundations of the types shown in Figs. 13·17(c), (e), and (g) are likely to be the most desirable. The general principles discussed for this dead-end tower may be applied also to other structures acting under conditions that are at all similar.

13·10 Waterproofing Foundations. Basements, pits, and trenches frequently need protection to guard against water seeping into them when the water table is above their bottoms; in other cases, it is essential to avoid dampness caused by moisture in the ground penetrating through the concrete even when the water table is lower. Troubles from these sources are difficult to remedy once they are found to exist after a structure is built. Discovery of the conditions causing such things, and steps to guard against these troubles, are essential in the general planning prior to construction.

Many are the conditions that may cause wet basements. The innocent-looking situation in Fig. 13·18(a) may cause trouble because wall B tries to act as a dam in stopping the flow of ground water along the top of the dense gravel stratum. If the latter were clay or rock, the action would be similar. The obvious remedy here is to install open-joint drains in trenches, partly filled with gravel or crushed stone, around

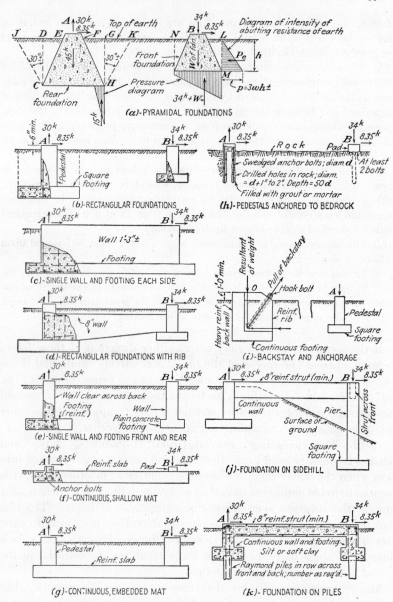

FIG. 13·17.   Possible foundations for a dead-end tower.

the uphill side and two ends of the basement, outletting the pipes into drainage lines that discharge the water down the hill. Furthermore, the surface runoff during severe storms requires adequate ditches if ponding is to be prevented. A concrete or stone-paved ditch may be located at C, but it is better to slope the surface down from C to a ditch at D, and the roof drainage may be carried locally across the areaway to this drain. These measures help to avoid temporary overloading of the subsurface piping.

Another source of trouble may come from a subterranean dam as shown in Fig. 13·18(b). During dry weather, the sandy clay may permit the seepage of sufficient water to avoid accumulation, but during periods

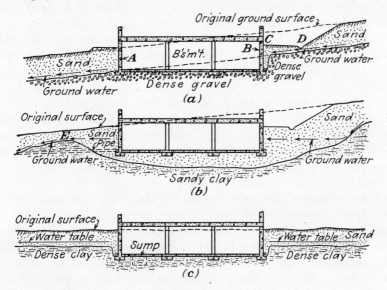

FIG. 13·18. Conditions that may cause wet basements.

of heavy rainfall, the ridge at E will act like a dam. Therefore, porous or open-joint drains are needed around the entire structure, and they should discharge through trenches cut across the obstruction.

Gravel alone without piping is not desirable for such important subsurface (French) drains because it is likely to silt up and become useless. Capped risers and T- or Y-connections in the pipe line at corners and about every 100 ft. are advisable for future cleaning of the piping. If these open-joint pipe lines are used for roof and surface stormwater drains, they tend to let water out into the surrounding soil, and they may have no capacity left for taking in seepage water during storms that last several hours. If straight pipes are used, the joints should be covered with tar paper or something to keep out solid materials; if loose, bell-and-spigot joints are used, the bell is generally sufficient protection, although tar-paper wrapping is helpful. Cast-iron pipes are stronger than vitrified clay ones.   Porous tiles or pipes are satisfactory if the openings do not silt up.

In flat territory like that pictured in Fig. 13·18(c), outside drains are useless when they have no place to discharge the water.   It is possible to use them if a sump and pump are provided.   However, the questions of the quantity of water to be handled, the duration of pumping, and the possibility of breakdown of equipment should be considered.

Even for situations like Figs. 13·18(a) and (b), poured-concrete walls are preferable to those built with cement or cinder blocks, and they should have enough reinforcement to prevent local shrinkage and temperature cracking.   Dense concrete helps to prevent seepage.   Integral admixtures may also improve the impermeability of the concrete but do not stop leakage at cracks, construction joints, and honeycombed places.

A thorough covering of dampproofing—bituminous coatings without fabric—on the outside of the walls is helpful in sealing them against percolation.   Such coatings on the inside surfaces are in a position of last resort and are therefore likely to be ineffective; these coatings are primarily for service against the penetration of capillary moisture in the soil.

When saturated ground surrounds the structure, even temporarily, an exterior covering of at least two-ply membrane waterproofing is desirable.   Some details of such construction are shown in Fig. 13·19. It is very important to have the fabric in such membranes lapped properly, sealed thoroughly, and free from air bubbles and water in or under the membrane.   Sharp projections may tend to puncture the membrane; projecting and reentrant corners should be chamfered or filleted to ensure proper contact; junctions between bottom and sidewall membranes are difficult to seal unless copper or other suitable flashing is incorporated at the splice; contraction joints in the walls should be accompanied by flexible flashed joints in the membrane or by water stops; and the completed waterproofing should be protected from damage during backfilling around the structure.   If the soil has, or is likely to have, oils, gasoline, or other solvents in it, the membrane may need the protection afforded by an outer covering of copper foil or a 3-in. layer of poured concrete knitted together with wire mesh.

When a basement floor is below the water table, hydrostatic uplift may heave or crack the floor.   Both the bending and the shear must be resisted.   Reliance upon surrounding drains to lower the water level will be unwise if these drains are permitted to freeze or clog up.

Membrane waterproofing under heavy concentrated loads should be

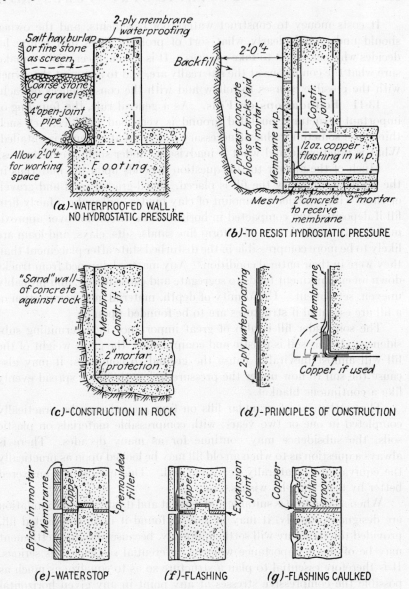

(a)-WATERPROOFED WALL,
NO HYDROSTATIC PRESSURE

(b)-TO RESIST HYDROSTATIC PRESSURE

(c)-CONSTRUCTION IN ROCK

(d)-PRINCIPLES OF CONSTRUCTION

(e)-WATERSTOP

(f)-FLASHING

(g)-FLASHING CAULKED

FIG. 13·19.   Some details of membrane waterproofing.

prevented from flowing or rupturing under pressure. Such membranes
are not rubbery enough to bend or stretch across joints where motion
occurs, and they will not resist excessive pressures unless confined.

It costs money to construct waterproof basements, and the owner should understand clearly what sort of problem faces him before he decides whether or not to take chances. It is the engineer's job to make sure what the conditions at the site really are, and to acquaint the owner with the possible courses to follow and with the consequences of each.

13·11 Foundations on Fills. As a general rule, the founding of important structures on filled ground is very bad practice, yet such things are sometimes almost necessary unless great expense is entailed. What is practicable and what is inadvisable under such circumstances?

Much of the answer to this question depends upon the materials in the fill itself, and how the fill is placed. Well-graded sand and gravel, or these with a moderate amount of clay binder, will make a fairly firm fill if deposited and compacted in horizontal layers of not over approximately 1 ft. in thickness. Uniform fine sands, silts, clays, and loam are likely to be more compressible in the disturbed state after placement than they were in their natural condition. Any material dumped from trucks down an embankment tends to segregate and cause future, and probably uneven, settlement. Uniformity of depth, material, and compaction of a fill are essential if structures are to be founded upon it.

The soil under fill is also of great importance in determining subsidence. If this soil is plastic and compressible, the great weight of the fill will almost inevitably cause the ground to compress; it may also cause the soil to flow under the pressure unless the fill is spread evenly like a continuous blanket.

The settlement of granular fills on firm ground may be practically completed in one or two years; with compressible materials on plastic soils, the subsidence may continue for as many decades. There is always a question as to when an old fill may be looked upon as practically the equivalent of naturally deposited soil. This question is answered better by tests than by wishes.

When a structure is suitable and when it and its structural foundation are designed properly, it may be safe to found it upon compacted fill, provided the structure will settle uniformly, because absolute settlement may be of slight importance whereas differential settlement is serious. It is therefore essential to plan a structure so as to equalize as much as possible the compressive stresses at any point in any given horizontal plane within the earth mass; it is essential, too, to have the structure strong enough to act as a unit, or sufficiently flexible to distort with safety; and, naturally, it is advisable to minimize the weight of the building. If one portion of a structure is founded upon filled ground whereas the remainder is on fairly rigid foundations, it is best to provide joints to allow relative movement without cracking. In some cases where a heavy structure is to be founded on filled ground, it is advisable to drive piles through the fill to a firm stratum; in others, to erect piers

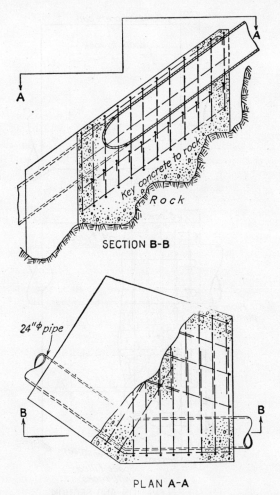

SECTION **B-B**

PLAN **A-A**

Fɪɢ. 13·20.   Anchorage at elbow of pipe line on rocky mountainside.

or walls on the original ground, then to fill around them; in still others, to build the structure somewhere else.

13·12 Pipe-line Foundations. Large pipes carrying water at high velocities or under high pressures cause surprisingly large thrusts at vertical and horizontal elbows, also at dead ends when some type of expansion coupling is used in the line.   If no expansion joint is provided, the forces caused by temperature changes may be too great for the anchorages to withstand.

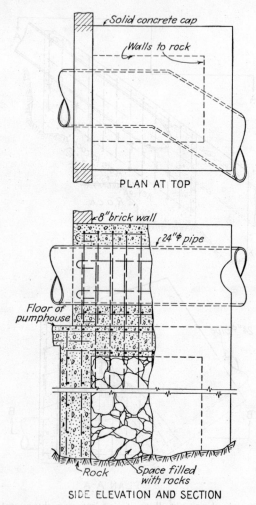

PLAN AT TOP

SIDE ELEVATION AND SECTION

FIG. 13·21.   Pipe-line anchorage connected directly to pump-house foundation.

Any such foundations must grip the pipes securely, and they generally must resist the forces as gravity sections, withstanding sideward thrusts, overturning moments, vertical loads, and sometimes uplift. Considerable mass is usually required.   Figures 13·20 to 13·22 show three different solutions for such problems.

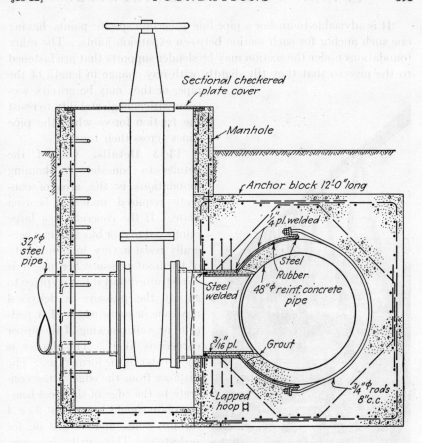

FIG. 13·22.   Combined pipe anchorage and manhole at tee.

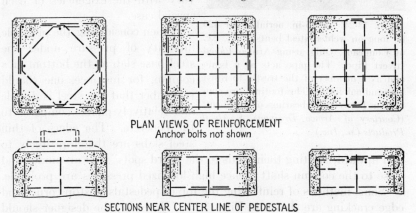

FIG. 13·23.   Some reinforcement of pedestals to prevent cracking of top corners.

It is advisable to anchor a pipe line at certain specific points, having one such anchor for each section between expansion joints. The other foundations under the section may be slender supports that are fastened to the pipe so that they tilt slightly with any change in length of the pipe, or they may be gravity sections with enough stability to resist the friction forces when the pipe slides across their tops.

13·13 Details. One of the details to consider in planning foundations is the area of concrete required under a bearing plate. If the concrete is a large reinforced mat or block, it can generally resist a very high intensity of localized pressure because it is so restrained that it has no place to go. If the pressure is delivered near one or more edges of a pedestal or wall, cracking of the upper corners is likely. The danger is the greater in the former case. The distance from the edge of the concrete to the edge of the steel bearing plate should be at least 3 or 4 in. for walls, and 4 to 8 in. for pedestals. This will, however, vary with the exigencies of each special case.

FIG. 13·24. A 15-in. aerial sewer 420 ft. long on welded steel bents 20 ft. c.c. at Conneaut, Ohio, using Armco Paved Invert Pipe. The pipe acts as a beam and as a member of the trestle to resist longitudinal forces. The footings are continuous between the bearings of each bent. (*Courtesy of Armco Drainage & Metal Products Co., Inc.*)

When considering the probable intensity of pressure under the steel base slab at the bottom of a column, for instance, one should remember that the steel is ductile and relatively pliable compared to the concrete. The edges of thin steel slabs are therefore likely to curl upward, shifting their loads to the "hard spots" that are under and close to the column shaft; hence high localized pressures are probable.

Some methods of reinforcing the top of pedestals to stop corner and edge cracking are shown in Fig. 13·23. However, the designer should remember that the steel will not become very effective until hair-cracks cause the rods to stretch; hence the steel is primarily useful in resisting disintegration of the concrete and is not a substitute for adequate area in the first place.

Concrete foundations should be stiff and strong. As diagonal tension and transverse punching are likely to be troublesome, footings should be chunky. The bond on reinforcing bars is also a source of possible . trouble so that generous use of hooks is advisable. How much reinforcement to use is often difficult to determine. Sometimes a few rods should be used to tack parts together, to prevent shrinkage and temperature cracks in long foundations, and to avoid any dependence upon tension in concrete where its failure to resist might be serious. On the other hand, the author knows of foundations that contain a wasteful amount of steel; *e.g.*, reinforcement in the bottoms of column footings that bear on rock cannot deform because the rock will not let the section stretch.

The details of anchor bolts and grouting will be discussed in Chap. 14. They are important.

Chapter 14

MACHINERY FOUNDATIONS

14·1 Concrete Foundations. Foundations for machinery are generally prepared in advance so that the equipment can be placed upon them at a later date. Such foundations should be made so that the machines can be leveled up, couplings connected, and the entire equipment with motors and auxiliaries lined up accurately and in good working order. It is generally inadvisable to expect that concrete foundations will be constructed so accurately that the equipment can be erected upon them directly without provision for adjustment. It is, therefore, customary to have the tops of the foundations built a little lower than the desired final elevation. The machinery is then placed, leveled, and aligned, being held on temporary supports. Thereafter, it is grouted in place.

Concrete foundations for machines are generally heavy. They should be erected upon firm, undisturbed soil if possible, otherwise an installation made up of interconnected machines should be founded upon a common, strong base slab that is sufficient to cause the group to settle as a unit instead of permitting differential settling and unequal tilting with resultant damage to the equipment. Of course, the foundations should seldom rest directly on top of the surface of the ground; they should have sufficient depth to develop good vertical and lateral strength. Their tops are very often above the floor surface, and the machines rest upon pedestals.

Lateral forces and torques acting upon foundations must be provided for. The designer should plan them with due consideration for tilt and other deformations rather than for the safety factor against overturning alone.

Perhaps one of the chief sources of trouble with concrete foundations is due to the attempt to use individual, high, narrow pedestals for motors, gear boxes, and machines. This arrangement results in misalignment and vibrations that are out of phase and causes cracking of shafts and couplings or uneven wear of bearings.

In general it is desirable to isolate concrete foundations for machinery

394

from adjacent concrete floor slabs, as shown in Fig. 14·1.   Some of the
reasons for this are the following:

1. To prevent vibrations of the foundations from being "telegraphed"
through the floor to other parts of the building.

2. To prevent disturbance of the foundation because of expansion or shrinkage of the floor.

3. To avoid the transfer of unbalanced loads onto the foundation due to
heavy materials placed upon the floor slab.

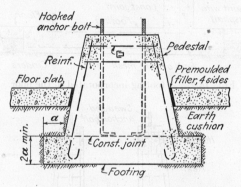

FIG. 14·1.   Small machinery foundation.

There are many cases where light machines may be set directly upon
the floors, but these are seldom important to the designer.   Of course,
no expansion or contraction joints in the floor should come under the
frame of a machine.

The vertical steel reinforcement in some machinery foundations may
be light or even negligible; in others it may be very important and should
be strong.   The tops of machinery foundations should be tied together
thoroughly, particularly when the foundations are large in area, and
especially when they are cut by pits, have narrow sections adjoining
thick ones, and have extensions projecting from the sides or ends.
Horizontal rods should be placed near the top surface to avoid cracking,
especially at the junctions of various parts.   This reinforcement should
consist of a few large rods, perhaps ¾-in. rounds.   They should be
anchored properly.   A few typical cases are illustrated:

1. A light, pedestal-type foundation is shown in Fig. 14·1.   The footing is
set below the floor slab so as to have a cushion of earth between them.   In
this case no reinforcing is used in the footing because its depth is at least twice
the projection from under the pedestal, and the load is small.   The anchor
bolts are rested on the footing during the pouring of the pedestal.

The hooked reinforcing rods need be sufficient only for the transmittal of overturning forces to the footing, or to tack the two together. The hoop near the top knits the concrete together, but its chief function is that of a tie for the other rods during construction. If the pedestal is short enough, the anchor bolts may extend down to the lower portion of the footing, thereby eliminating the need for any reinforcing rods.

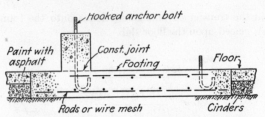

Fig. 14·2. A footing incorporated in the floor.

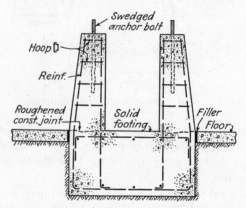

Fig. 14·3. Pedestals or walls on heavy, continuous base.

2. Figure 14·2 shows a possible condition for a large but light piece of equipment. One end rests on a pedestal; the other, on the footing which is merely a thickened portion of the floor slab. In this case the floor slab is poured directly against the footing without premolded fillers.

3. A heavier, two-pedestal foundation is pictured in Fig. 14·3. In this case the heavy footing is placed with its top at the floor line. The pedestals are reinforced as cantilevers projecting from the base. Here the reinforcement is important. When necessary, a reinforced-concrete rib might be extended up between the pedestals if they become too tall; the footing might be lowered as in Fig. 14·1 when the upper soil stratum is inadequate for bearing; or the pedestal might extend to rock, if near by, with a thinner slab or rib at the top as a tie and strut.

4. A heavy foundation used for a 150-ton ball mill and its motor is pictured in Fig. 14·4. It is founded on a cemented gravel. Notice that the footing is

very thick and heavily reinforced not only to spread the concentrated loads
applied at the bearings but to provide mass to resist vibrations. It is also
continuous, even to include the motor support. Incidentally, this illustrates
a case where it is important to tie these two portions of the footing together
securely. If this foundation rested upon compressible material, it would also

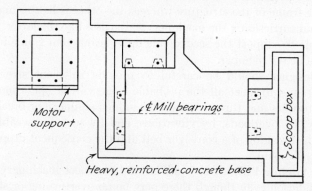

(a)-PLAN OF FOUNDATION

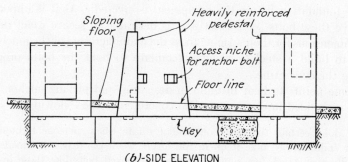

(b)-SIDE ELEVATION

Fig. 14·4.   Foundation for a heavy ball mill.

be important to proportion it so as to equalize the unit bearing pressure as
much as practicable, this probably requiring larger relative area under the
mill itself.

14·2   Metallic Foundation Frames.   There are many cases in
which cast or fabricated metallic frames are made and furnished by the
manufacturer of the equipment; there are others for which it is desirable
to build the frames as part of the supporting structure. In any case,
these frames should be strong and stiff. When they are bolted, so as to
be removable in the future, all provisions for this should be made in
the original planning of the building. Adjustment can be secured ordinarily by the use of thin steel shims.

Any supporting steelwork—or even concrete beams—should be designed so as to equalize the deflections of the members. Trouble may arise if one side of a machine is carried by a long, flexible beam whereas the other rests upon an equal, parallel but shorter and therefore stiffer one, or if both parallel beams have the same span, but one is a heavy part of the frame of the structure whereas the other is lighter and more flexible, and carries only the machinery. In cases like the latter, it may be desirable to support the second side upon beams that frame into the side of the heavy member.

The designer should be careful to provide sufficient strength in metallic frames to meet all the probable exigencies of operation. For example, torques and thrusts caused by sudden stoppage or breaking of machinery, by overloads, by vibrations, and by such foreseeable accidents as the breaking of a conveyor belt and the consequent dropping of its gravity take-up.

14·3 Anchor Bolts. It is advisable to connect machinery firmly to its foundation even though there may be no overturning or shearing tendencies. This is generally done by means of anchor bolts embedded in the foundation before the equipment is erected. As it is important to have these bolts set correctly, it is desirable to secure exact details and dimensions for their spacing from the manufacturers of the machines, then to build a steel or wooden template to hold the bolts properly during the concreting.

Some points to bear in mind in designing and placing anchor bolts to be embedded in or connected to concrete are the following:

1. Make certain that the bolt cannot rotate when someone tightens the nut or endeavors to take it off in the future when the exposed threads may be badly rusted. A few common types are hooked bolts like those in Figs. 14·1 and 14·2; swedged bolts (heated and hammered or forged to produce large irregularities and thereby increase the bond) as in Fig. 14·3; and rods welded to rectangular washers or spacer plates at their bottoms. Reliance upon the bond alone on plain rods is seldom wise.

2. Provide an adequate template to hold the bolts, and check it and its location carefully, making sure that the bolts will not be disturbed during concreting. One way to do this is to use double nuts to grip the template, as shown in Fig. 14·5(a).

3. Provide adequate length of threads, and be certain that the bolt is at the right elevation. Sometimes it is wise to provide for lock washers or double nuts. It is generally advisable to use standard or plate washers under the nuts, and hexagonal nuts in preference to square ones.

4. The size of the anchor bolts should be determined by using a unit stress

about 50 to 75 per cent of that generally permissible in structural steel when there is the likelihood of corrosion of the bolts at and above the concrete.

5. The holes in the frame should provide about ⅛ to ⅜ in. of clearance for the bolts to allow for minor adjustments and for errors in setting.

6. Be sure that the bolts are vertical, or set in whatever the desired direction may be.

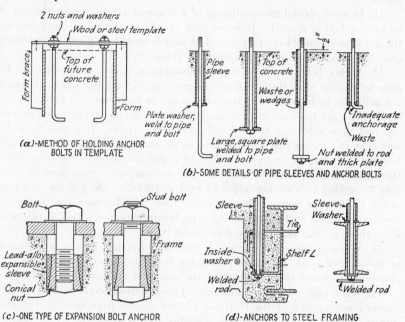

(a)-METHOD OF HOLDING ANCHOR BOLTS IN TEMPLATE

(b)-SOME DETAILS OF PIPE SLEEVES AND ANCHOR BOLTS

(c)-ONE TYPE OF EXPANSION BOLT ANCHOR

(d)-ANCHORS TO STEEL FRAMING

Fig. 14·5. Some details of anchor bolts.

7. For large, important machines, pipe sleeves placed around the bolts as in Fig. 14·5(b) will permit some adjustment by springing of the bolts. The pipes should be filled with cement grout after or as the machine is set in place, otherwise they may collect water and facilitate corrosion or, if out of doors, freezing of the water may damage the foundation.

8. If large shearing forces are to be resisted, the excess space in the hole of the machine frame around the bolt may be filled with grout or lead to prevent "shucking" of the machine.

9. In some special cases, wedge-shaped pockets may be left in the concrete foundations, then the anchor bolts may be set and concreted in at a later date.

10. When the machines are very light, when they are set directly on the floor slabs, when the locations of the bolts cannot be ascertained soon enough, or when the bolts are merely to "tack" the equipment in place, then expansion bolts may be used. The machines can then be erected, or the positions for

the bolts marked on the concrete, holes drilled into the concrete, and the bolts set to suit the frames. - One type of expansion bolt is shown in Fig. 14·5(c). If the concrete foundation has a narrow top, the drilling of holes near an edge is very likely to crack the concrete, and little can be done to repair it. Expansion bolts will resist tension, but they may not be good for heavy shearing forces.

11. In some special cases, slippage of a frame or bearing under the nut of an anchor bolt is desired. It is not wise to rely upon the workmen leaving the nut loose; a shouldered bolt should be used so that the nut can be tightened onto the shoulder without pinching the frame.

12. Anchor bolts may have to be removable in some cases. This can be done by placing pipes through floors, beams, etc., to form holes through which the bolts can be inserted; then the nuts on one or both ends can be tightened. When bolts are too long to have heads formed easily, a nut threaded on one end and then welded to the rod will serve the purpose. It is best to make sure that the anchor bolt will not turn in an undesired manner. Niches and holes in the concrete, as shown in Fig. 14·4, will provide access to nuts when the anchor bolt cannot pass clear through the support. Sometimes the nut may be welded to a washer which in turn is welded to the bottom of a pipe sleeve so that the bolt can be unscrewed from it. However, the threads in the nut are likely to become damaged by future improper fitting of the bolt; if so, there is little that can be done about it.

13. When machines are carried on steel floor framing, it may be desirable to install shelf angles to which the anchor bolts and pipe sleeves can be mechanically fastened before depositing the concrete, as shown in Fig. 14·5(d).

14. When pipe sleeves are used, special provisions should be made to ensure proper centralization of the bolt and to keep mortar from entering the pipe during concreting. In Fig. 14·5(d), a washer is used inside and at the bottom of one of the pipe sleeves; in some cases a washer may be tack-welded to the bottom of the pipe as illustrated in Fig. 14·5(b). A less satisfactory method is to close the bottom of the pipe around the bolt by wedging waste into the annular space. The top of the sleeve may be temporarily closed with waste or a wooden wedge that can be dropped over the bolt; if the thread is long enough, a wooden block or the top washer may be dropped over the bolt, and the nut may be screwed down close to the pipe.

14·4 Grouting. It is unwise to expect contractors to finish off the tops of large concrete foundations to exact levels and correct elevations. Occasionally the concrete may be poured slightly high, then bush-hammered or ground off to the desired elevation, covered with a paint coat of cement grout or mortar, and the machine immediately set thereon. However, this is costly and is seldom justifiable.

One customary method is to make the top of the foundation about 1 or 2 in. below the theoretical elevation, set the machine on temporary wedges, line it up, then "grout" it in place, later removing the wedges and pointing up the recesses.   Another method is to thread the anchor bolts so that one nut can be used below the frame and one or more on top, as shown in Fig. 14·6(*a*).   In this way, the bolts and nuts serve as adjusting screws that hold the machine firmly.   Neat cement grout or mortar can then be forced under the frame.

If the base is large, it is difficult to make sure that the grout bears over the entire area and does not have air pockets in it.   Sometimes the machine can be aligned and leveled on wedges, steel blocks, or nuts, then lifted off these supports, the space filled with grout or cement mortar that is leveled off, and the machine immediately reset and the anchor

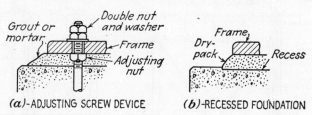

(*a*)-ADJUSTING SCREW DEVICE   (*b*)-RECESSED FOUNDATION

Fɪɢ. 14·6.   Details of grout under machine frames.

bolts tightened down.   The next day the wedges may be removed and their spaces pointed up.   This, too, involves some uncertainties as to adequate and even bearing.

Disturbance of the temporary supports may occur during grouting except when the "adjusting-screw" method is used.   Dry packing is permissible in this case, without danger of lifting and disturbing the machine.   This dry packing is done by mixing a rich but rather dry cement mortar and ramming it under the base with a stick (sometimes using a mallet), thus ensuring a full and adequate bearing.   Of course, space must be provided around the base so that the packing can be done.

Various admixtures and special compounds are sometimes used in lieu of, or in, cement mortar or grout to eliminate shrinkage.   Neat cement grout will shrink more than mortar.   Mixes of 1 part of cement to 2 of sand, or 1:3, are suitable mortars.   Ten per cent of lime may increase the workability of the mortar without detrimental effect upon the required strength.   A "rust joint" packing may be made of iron filings and sulphur when the load is extremely heavy, the corrosion of the iron causing the volume of the mix to increase rather than to shrink.

When machines are subjected to shocks and repeated heavy loads, the grout or mortar may crack up eventually if it is too thin—less than

1½ to 2 in.   When such cracking is anticipated or feared, wire mesh may be placed on the concrete before grouting or mortaring, but it hampers dry packing.   A ¼-in. recess under and for 1 or 2 in. outside of a bearing plate will form a pocket that helps to clinch the grout or mortar pad in place.   A few grooves made with a trowel in the wet concrete under a bearing will serve somewhat the same purpose.

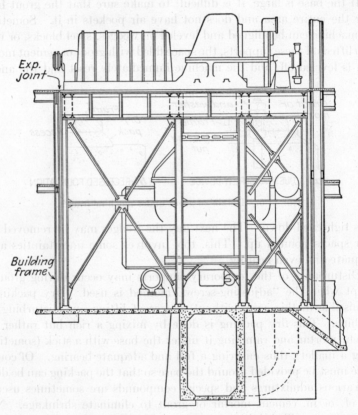

FIG. 14·7. A steel foundation for a turbogenerator that proved to be too light.

14·5 Vibration. Designing a foundation for reciprocating and high-speed rotating machinery is not an easy matter; at least, securing a satisfactory and economical result is beset by uncertainties.   As a general rule, large mass is desirable to check vibration, and the natural period of vibration of the supporting structure should exceed that of the machine in order to avoid resonance.   Concrete foundations are not only heavy but stiff; steel is strong but may be flexible.   Foundations for vibrating machinery should be placed upon rock or firm ground rather than on plastic soil or pliable beams.

It is usually difficult to decide how heavy the foundations of rotating and reciprocating machines should be. The experience of the manufacturer or of other people who have such equipment may be of considerable value. On the other hand, one may estimate the kinetic energy of reciprocating parts and of vibrations of the machinery. He can then use these as a basis for estimating the weight required to restrict the

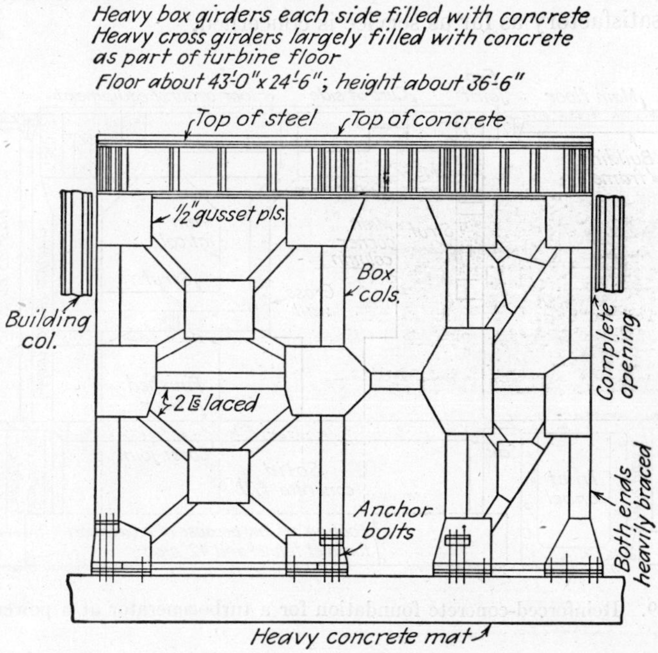

Heavy box girders each side filled with concrete
Heavy cross girders largely filled with concrete
as part of turbine floor
Floor about 43'-0" x 24'-6"; height about 36'-6"

FIG. 14·8.   A satisfactory steel foundation for a turbogenerator.

vibrations of the foundation to some real or assumed unobjectionable maximum. Good judgment and experience are valuable guides in addition to such calculations, and conservatism is generally an asset.

Figure 14·7 shows steel supports for a heavy turbine and generator. The vibration was so excessive that heavy reinforced-concrete walls nearly 36 in. thick were built around and between both sets of columns parallel to the picture, and 18-in. walls were placed across each end, extending up to and outside of the steel girders. Of course, these walls had various openings for equipment and access; nevertheless, they stopped the harmful vibrations.

In another case of similar equipment, the exciter was founded upon light steel supports that were connected to the main steelwork under the heavy equipment. The latter caused the exciter to vibrate excessively. The engineers installed several 16-in. beams at the top of this end, then filled solidly between them with concrete. The added mass deadened the vibration satisfactorily.

Figure 14·8 shows another steel foundation for added equipment that was built after trouble developed with the supports shown in Fig. 14·7. The contrast is obvious. Perhaps the second one was overdesigned, but it was satisfactory as far as service is concerned.

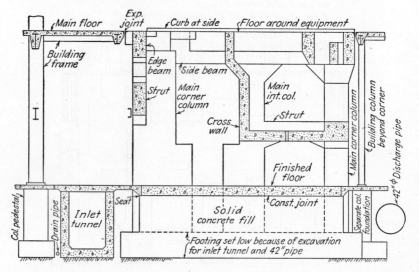

FIG. 14·9.   Reinforced-concrete foundation for a turbogenerator at a power plant.

Another turbine foundation is shown in Fig. 14·9. It is a heavy, reinforced-concrete floor carried upon stiff columns and a thick base slab. The entire structure is reinforced to act as a rigid frame. The top is isolated from the adjacent floor.

In Fig. 14·10 is shown a foundation for a high-speed fan on the upper floor in a power plant. The cork under the concrete base of the machine is to help decrease the transmission of vibrations to the floor. Seismopads and springs are used for similar purposes. The concrete of the floor is deliberately made heavy, the steel beams are purposely made stiff, and special vertical bracing is installed in the vicinity to stiffen the structure. If the anchor bolts are not "insulated" by cork washers, too, they will serve to transmit the vibrations to the supporting structure.

When heavy shocks are to be absorbed, cushioning is essential because concrete is too brittle to be subjected to blows deliberately.   Even

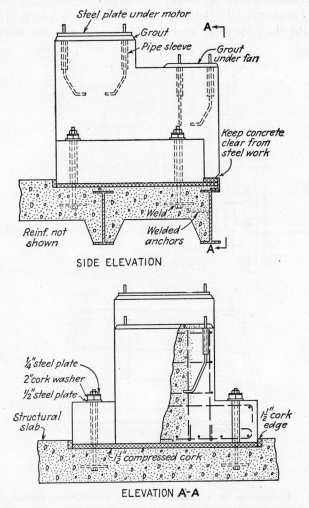

Fig. 14·10.   Foundation for an induced-draft fan in a power plant.

then, solid walls are preferable to reinforced-concrete beams for supporting such equipment.   Heavy steel beams might also be used for this purpose because of their ductility and absorption of impact.

In Fig. 14·11 is shown the foundation at one end of a large fan in the upper part of a large industrial building. This illustrates the principle of framing stated previously—avoidance of inequality of the deflection of supports.   In the side elevation is shown a large steel beam next to the duct opening, whereas two beams near the sides of the

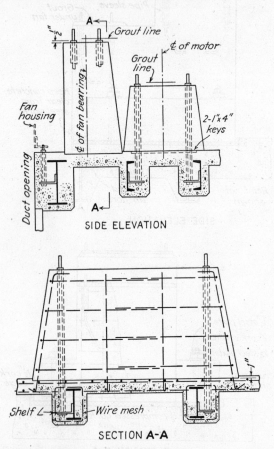

FIG. 14·11. Foundation for a ventilation fan in a multistory industrial building.

pedestals frame into it.   These two beams are pictured in Section *A-A*. The torque caused by the motor tends to rotate the pedestal about an axis perpendicular to the picture in the latter sketch.   Therefore, these two beams tend to equalize and to minimize any movements of the two pedestals.

When planning the foundations of such equipment as large fans in public buildings, apartment houses, and even industrial plants, one might be wise to support the machinery upon a heavy concrete mat that is mounted upon special spring supports. It is amazing how the small but high-frequency vibrations caused by such equipment can be "telegraphed" to some remote part of the structure where they will cause a light or thin portion of the building to vibrate objectionably.

Figure 14·12 shows the typical arrangement of pump foundations and pipe supports in a pump house located at a large industrial plant. The foundations of the high-speed centrifugal pumps are made solid

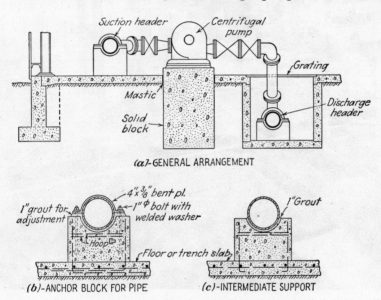

Fig. 14·12.   Foundations in a pump house.

and heavy, and they are isolated from the floor slab. Even though the soil is good gravel, the main foundation is extended downward to the level of the bottom of the adjacent pipe trench, this being done to make sure that the soil under the block has not been and cannot in the future be disturbed. One should also notice the provisions for grouting under the pumps and under the pipes. This enables the entire assembly to be set up, connected, and then grouted in place. The details are also planned so that an overhead hand-operated crane or trolley hoists can dismantle the system for cleaning and repairs.

When an engineer is planning the foundations for machinery, he should bear in mind the matter of appearance. For example, when the installation shown in Fig. 14·14 was planned, this matter was considered.

The pedestals were not only made strong enough but were designed to make a neat and pleasing appearance.   For example, the pedestal under the motors in the background was made with sloping rather than vertical sides just because the designers thought that its appearance would be more satisfactory—and it is.   Such refinements cost little, but they may

FIG. 14·13. Anchor bolts and pipe sleeves fastened to structural framework before concreting. The men are attaching bolts to a steel template to hold their tops in proper position. (*Courtesy of the Port of New York Authority.*)

be the obvious things that the directors notice when they inspect the plant.

Fig. 14·14.   A completed installation of blower fans and motors in the New York River Ventilation Building of the Lincoln Tunnel.   (*Courtesy of the Port of New York Authority.*)

Chapter 15

MISCELLANEOUS CONSIDERATIONS AND STRUCTURES

15·1 Introduction. This chapter includes a series of short discussions of principles that may be important and useful in the planning of industrial structures; also brief discussions and illustrations of some specialized structures that may be encountered when one plans industrial construction. The limitation of space and the narrowness of the fields of application render it desirable to confine the treatment of the individual subjects to those things which seem to offer the reader the best help.

15·2 The Effect of the Method of Erection. The planning and the detailed design of a large bridge are frequently affected greatly by the necessary or chosen method of erection of the structure, or by the limitations of equipment. This applies far less to the planning of industrial structures because, although extensive in area, they are seldom of sufficient height and complexity to present major problems of temporary support. Nevertheless, the practicability of erection should be considered in the early stages of the planning, and the structure should not be unnecessarily difficult to build. Complicated, fussy, and "tricky" framing plans for a structure are likely to be evidence of the planner's lack of skill and of his failure to give to his planning the necessary careful thought.

A few cases in which erection and construction procedures may influence the planning of industrial structures are the following:

1. Deep excavations that are not to be shored or made by the use of caissons may make it desirable to use long-span construction in that portion of the structure so as to require no important foundations in the immediate vicinity of the excavation except those that may rest upon or be a part of the heavy concrete work for which the deep excavation is to be made.

2. Whether the shop fabrication and field connections of steelwork are to be riveted, welded, or bolted will affect so many details of the design that one specific method should be chosen and adhered to, and the design should

be made accordingly. Otherwise, many substitutions and revisions will be almost inevitable if the fabricator changes the basic character of the work. It is obvious, too, that the details of members should be such as to allow room for the riveting or the welding, and even for the entering and tightening of bolts.

There is much difference of opinion regarding whether steelwork should be riveted or welded. Often it is advantageous to weld light construction, especially if it is complicated. Heavy construction—like bridges—may be more properly riveted because it is sometimes difficult to provide sufficient welds to develop such large members. As some fabricators are equipped to do only one class of work or the other, their preferences are based upon that fact. From the standpoint of the planner and designer, that method of attachment should be chosen which is best adapted to the character of the particular work under consideration.

As a general principle, rivets and welds will not act simultaneously in proper manner under heavy loads. The welds will try to carry the forces; the rivets will do likewise until the action breaks the frictional resistance between the connected parts and causes the rivets to slip. This means that the welds in the connection are probably overstressed when this slippage occurs. Thus, when a riveted joint is reinforced by welding, the latter should be able to carry the entire load, except the dead load that the joint already supports.

It is entirely practicable to use permanent bolts in the field connections of many light structures. They are also suitable for some heavy buildings whose members are not subjected to reversal of stresses. Rivet bolts are also useful when field riveting and welding are not desired—when it is not economical to set up riveting and welding equipment for a few small, scattered connections.

3. The shape and size of trusses and the locations of their splices may be affected by the capacity and reach of available erection equipment. It may be advisable to use trusses that can be shipped knocked down instead of using long, heavy girders which are exceedingly difficult to transport and which require the erector to have derricks of large capacity to handle just a few heavy pieces. When members to be shipped by railroad exceed 11 or 12 ft. in depth or width, difficulties may occur because of shipping clearances.

4. Long, slender, continuous or simply supported trusses and girders may be satisfactory, once they are completely erected. Handling them during transit and in the field may be very troublesome and expensive.

5. Conditions of erection may make it desirable to use seated connections. This may therefore be one of the starting points of detailed planning.

6. Repeated use of forms, and the use of traveling forms like those in Fig. 11·26, may bring about such savings that an extensive concrete structure should be planned to permit this use.

7. Piers to be built across mud flats and shallow water may be planned properly if the piling and the span of the deck construction are so designed that all or most of the driving and erection can be performed in series by equip-

ment that is supported upon the previously completed bay or unit of the structure.   Thus, costly trestles for land equipment and dredging for floating equipment may be avoided.

, 8. The difficulties of erection, haulage, supply, and labor for construction with one material vs. those needed for another may be such that one particular material is by far the most desirable.   This, of course, is a major starting point in the planning.

9. The saving of time, as it is affected by the relative speed of erection, may influence the owner's preference.

15·3   Prefabrication.   Much study and experimental work is being carried on with the objective of developing the design and details of structures so that they can be shop-fabricated in panels, parts, and units that can be shipped to the site and then erected with a minimum expenditure of money and time.   The objective is a worthy one, yet the possibility of great success in the field of major industrial construction is uncertain.

Some companies formerly made a specialty of manufacturing certain standard steel structures that could be purchased advantageously when they suited one's purposes.   These, however, were generally limited to rather small, simple buildings, whereas large structures, such as that pictured in Fig. 10·1, were almost necessarily planned to suit each special situation.

It is doubtful that prefabrication will reach such a stage that the dollar value of complete industrial structures purchased by catalogue number will be a large portion of the total construction built, outside of small steel and wooden buildings.   On the other hand, there are tremendous possibilities for the development of standardized, prefabricated parts that may be used to advantage by the skillful planner.   These parts might be such that they may be used in various arrangements to produce widely different structures.

One of the present troubles with the use of prefabricated roof, floor, and wall panels—a field in which considerable progress has been made—is the fact that it is often so difficult to plan a structure so as to use these parts without multitudinous variations that the engineer has returned to the old methods, which enabled him to get almost anything that he wanted. Undoubtedly, progress can and should be made toward the overcoming of this difficulty by both the planners and the manufacturers so that the best and most economical construction will be secured.

15·4   Safety of Employees.   Besides the safety features that are and should be a basic part of machines and all manufacturing equipment, there are sometimes specific things that should or should not be done in the planning of a structure in order to attain the maximum safety in the working conditions of employees, these being entirely aside from the obvious fact that the structure and its parts must not fall down.   Many of these essential things are details, but they are important nevertheless.

Many large industrial organizations have safety committees whose job it is to study and to watch out for all things that may affect the safety of the employees. If such a committee exists within the company for whom construction work is to be done, those planning and designing the structures should confer with it and be guided by its recommendations, even during the original planning. All too frequently such a committee has to make the best it can of a situation after the structure is completed. Insurance companies and the National Safety Council, as well as a local safety committee, may have in their regulations and codes various basic requirements and suggestions that one should examine as he plans a specific structure.   There are hazards enough without having some that are unnecessarily inherent in the plan itself and in the details of the structure.

It is impracticable to itemize here all the safety features that should be incorporated in a plan. However, some are given so that the reader will realize the general

Fig. 15·1.   Platforms with ·checkered plates, angle railing, and toe guards. It is important to plan for safe access to all equipment. (*Courtesy of the Phelps Dodge Corp.*)

nature of such problems and see the kind of thinking that is involved. The following points illustrate both questions of major policy and those of minor details:

1. Cranes operating one over another on parallel or transverse runways are a continual source of danger. The load being carried by the upper one may collide with the lower crane. Electrically operated transfer cars, tilting roller

conveyors, movable platforms, and other special equipment may enable one to shift materials from the area under one crane to that under another. At least, this feature affects the basic planning of the layout.

2. Small vertical offsets in floors—as at shallow pits—without railings and steps are likely to cause one to fall or stumble. Miscellaneous pipes near a floor may do likewise when no one takes the trouble to plan proper places for them. Ramps as means of access to slightly raised or depressed areas may be preferable to small stairs.

3. Headroom should always be adequate; 7 ft. below all piping, platforms, stairs, and equipment is desirable if workmen frequent the area. A clearance of 2 ft. 6 in. is little enough for crawling space for maintenance purposes.

4. Open hatchways are serious hazards—traps set for the unwary. These openings should be protected by removable covers, by permanent or removable railings, and perhaps by curbs. They should be located at points that are the least likely to interfere with operations.

5. Elevators—both freight and passenger—should be enclosed and their doorways properly guarded.

6. Roadways and railroad crossings should be planned very carefully. A structure should be so located and planned that the best practicable visibility will be attained. It is highly dangerous to have a track close to one side of a structure and a sidewalk or motorway close to the adjoining end, because an unsuspecting person may hurry around the corner just as a switching engine backs out. It may be advisable to use fixed guards to compel one to pass far enough from any physical obstruction so that reasonable visibility is attained. Each situation should be studied in order to secure the most practicable arrangement for safety. Overpasses and underpasses may well be worth their cost.

7. Access to toilet rooms, locker rooms, change houses, parking areas, and toolrooms should be as direct, simple, convenient, and safe as the situation permits. Employees should not have to dodge vehicles, duck under cranes, dart along circuitous and narrow paths among machines, climb narrow and winding stairways, or grope along dark passageways. There should be enough facilities, and they should be conveniently located.

8. Stairways should be located wherever they are needed. They should be sufficiently wide, of proper slope, with nonskid treads, and with railings that are both adequate and convenient. Long flights of stairs without landings are hazardous. Winding, circular stairways are both inconvenient and dangerous; so are mitered, triangular treads at turns. Stairways should be planned with due consideration for use during fires and other emergencies. They are too important to be squeezed in wherever possible.

9. Ladders are cheap and useful, but stairways should be installed in their stead wherever possible. For example, access to cranes should be by stairways rather than by ladders because it is difficult for a workman to climb up or down a ladder with tools and other impedimenta. What difference in cost does it make to provide these stairways compared to their usefulness? Ship

ladders at about 60° slopes are better than ordinary ladders, but they are none too convenient for descent. When a long ladder must be used, a safety cage should be placed around it, and convenient handholds should be at the top.

10. In the layout of a structure, the aisles and other passageways should be planned wide enough to facilitate two-way traffic. Conveyor galleries, platforms, and walkways should be wide enough for one man to pass another and to walk safely—perhaps a clear space of at least 3 ft. to 3 ft. 6 in.   The

Fig. 15·2.   Grating, welded pipe handrailing, and toe guards in a boiler room.
(*Courtesy of Irving Subway Grating Co.*)

same principles apply alongside and between railroad tracks and truck lanes. It costs little to make trusses a few feet longer if so doing will attain a desirable objective, such as adequate space.

11. Parapets, when used, should be sufficiently high and strong to protect maintenance men who may be working on the roof. The same matters of height and strength apply to railings, which should be from 3 ft. to 3 ft. 9 in. high. They should be convenient to grasp, pipe hand railings being the most desirable in this respect as well as the best looking. There should be one or more intermediate rails; and the posts should be fastened securely, not dependent upon the bending resistance of some small, thin clip angle.

12. Such minor matters as the position and swinging of doors deserve careful attention. Doors should not open into aisles or passageways where someone will be hit when another opens the door suddenly. At stairs, doors should swing over platforms, not over the stairs where one must step backward and

down in order to open them. Doors at emergency exits should swing outward;
and those into fireproof stair wells should swing into the enclosure, possibly
having panic locks if serious danger of explosions exists, and they should be
at a wide platform.

13. Provisions should be made for such maintenance work as replacing
equipment, like motors; renewing heavy materials, like conveyor belts, as
pictured in Fig. 15·3; hoisting machines
to renew bearings and replace worn
pieces; lifting parts and repair materials to elevated positions; and lowering
heavy articles to different levels.   The
installation of trolley beams and hoists
may be one method of making such
work easy and safe.   When something
heavy will have to be jacked up some
day, jack brackets and other supports
needed in the process should be installed in the beginning.   Facilities
should be planned for general cleaning,
replacing lights, oiling and greasing
bearings, fighting fires, eliminating dust,
painting, and inspecting both the
equipment and the structure.

14. Slippery floors should not be
permitted. Sometimes wooden, slatted
panels, rubber mats, or steel grating
may be used where spillage or drip is
unavoidable.   Plain steel platform
plates are especially dangerous when
wetted with water, oil, or grease. Ice,
too, should not be allowed to form at

Fig. 15·3. Unrolling a 60-in. conveyor belt at the Morenci Reduction
Works. Such operations as this should
be determined as a part of the general
planning of the structure. (*Courtesy of
the Phelps Dodge Corp.*)

doorways,   such as those under dripping eaves; roofs should protect these
areas.

15. Toe guards or curbing should be
installed around openings in the floor,
along the edges of deep pits, at the
edges of elevated platforms, and at
similar places where a workman may accidentally kick a heavy tool down onto
someone's head.

16. At points where trucks back up to dump materials into bins and hoppers,
strong, high curbs should be used to prevent backing over the edge. Grades
to such points should be level, or possibly sloping upward slightly to the curb.

17. When hazards exist because of explosives, fumes, acids, heat, and dust,
these should be minimized through careful planning. For example, if a dust-

collection system is needed to avoid the likelihood of workmen developing silicosis, all ducts, piping, fans, and cyclones should be included in the initial planning instead of being placed wherever it is possible to put them later on.

18. Fire-fighting equipment should be available at convenient, predetermined places; and this equipment should be of the proper type to serve all probable needs. Furthermore, it may be desirable to plan a building so as to secure structural compartmentation that will confine a fire to a given story, or to part of a floor area. Useful for this purpose are fireproof, enclosed stair wells and elevator shafts, fireproof partitions in strategic locations, incombustible covers over hatchways, and fireproof sliding doors that are held open by low-melting-point links. When sprinkler systems are installed, they should have multiple sources of supply, and drainage should be provided to prevent the impounding of water and the overloading of floors.

15·5 Earthquakes. The planning of structures to avoid serious damage by earthquakes is far from an exact science. In the first place, no one knows what the violence of the tremors may be, when they may come, or how much additional expense is justified in supposedly guarding against their harmful effects. Nevertheless, when a structure is to be located in a region that is known to be subject to more or less periodic earthquakes, the planner of that structure is indeed unwise if he fails to consider their effects.

It is customary to assume that the effects of earthquakes approximate those which would result from some arbitrarily chosen acceleration of the superstructure of the building with respect to its foundation, or vice versa. Amplitude, period, direction of the movement of the earth, and the duration of the vibrations—all these are important. For example, a large, horizontal amplitude may overstress bracing diagonals and cause excessive flexure in columns, whereas a small movement may be cushioned by the elasticity of the structural frame. A motion with a slow period may not cause so violent a shock effect but it may, if continued long enough, cause far more violent swaying of the structure than would a short, sharp, rapid movement. Horizontal movement may be bad enough in its tendency to wrack the portion of the structure in the first story, whereas vertical shocks may be extremely severe in their tendency to shear beam connections and to crumple columns. Although not analogous, the last-mentioned action was once demonstrated to the author in an elevator. When it was descending slowly about a foot above the ground floor, the emergency brakes set suddenly; the effect upon a passenger was as though someone had hit the bottom of each foot with a hammer.

Do such statements mean that one should not build important structures in earthquake territory? Of course they do not. However, one should not build there those types of structure which are particularly vulnerable to damage by earth tremors. There is no sense in daring Nature to harm one's structures.

For example, the following statements may be pertinent in connection with the study of the probable action of a structure, and of what to do to avoid serious damage to it:

1. Ordinary wall-bearing construction is likely to be sheared and even disintegrated, whereas skeleton framework of steel, wood, and concrete is likely to have sufficient lateral pliability to accommodate itself safely to relative movements of the foundations and the upper portion of the structure—even though the curtain-wall construction of the first story is cracked or shattered.

2. In the case of mill buildings like that whose steelwork is shown in Fig. 9·1, vertical bracing is needed in the walls to resist wind and crane forces. Therefore, a lightweight roof of the type shown in Fig. 6·5(d) is used so as to minimize the magnitude of the mass that might be affected by any acceleration, and hence to minimize the resultant forces.

3. Roofs should be made with strong cross frames between all trusses, and with complete and strong bracing in both horizontal directions.

4. Connections of steel beams to columns might well have top and bottom angle connections as well as web angles, this being a type that will permit some flexibility without failure. Beams whose webs are coped top and bottom with none but small clip angles or web welding for their connections may crack at the weakened end.

5. Brick curtain walls and others made of masonry units should be reinforced and mechanically tied to the structural framework and floors.

6. Tall structures, such as chimneys, should be designed with special consideration of vibration. The one pictured in Fig. 15·4 was damaged recently by an earthquake. The wrinkle in the steel plates near the upper third point extends approximately halfway around the shaft, and its maximum amplitude is nearly 5 in. One may well try to visualize the probable differences in action of the light upper third and the heavy middle third, combined with possible contrary (opposite pulling) action of the two sets of guys at some given instant. At any rate, the $\frac{1}{4}$-in. plates buckled near the junction of the $4\frac{1}{2}$- and 9-in. linings. To resist such compressions, vertical stiffeners would have been very helpful. It is easy for one to think as follows: "A curved plate is much stiffer than a straight one when the compressive forces are parallel to the axis of the cylinder. This stack is cylindrical. Therefore, the plates will be stiff." He forgets, however, to realize that the mid-ordinate of the curve for an arc 10 ft. long with a radius of 11 ft. is only approximately 12 in.—far too little for the curvature to mean much in stiffening such thin plates against compressive shocks, especially when eccentricity already exists at the lapped joints.

7. Reinforced-concrete walls should have rods sloping both ways at approximately 45° with the vertical if they are to be most effective in resisting horizontal shears of great magnitude.

8. A structure should be tied together thoroughly at the floor lines and roof, both across and circumferentially.

9. It is not unusual to assume that the inertia forces for design purposes at a given level are equal to an acceleration of $0.1g$, where g is the acceleration

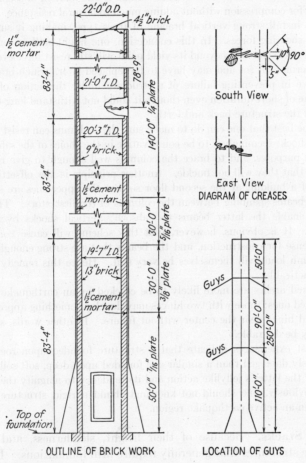

FIG. 15·4. A steel stack in South America, showing wrinkle caused by earthquake. The top is now approximately 12 in. out of plumb.

due to gravity, applied to the mass of the structure above that elevation. Light, tall structures designed to resist a wind pressure of 30 lb. per sq. ft. will usually be strong enough to resist this assumed inertia force also. Larger assumptions regarding the acceleration should be made in critical cases.

10. One way to approach the designing of a building to withstand earthquake shocks is to make the columns strong enough to resist wind and other

supposedly determinable lateral forces by flexural resistance, then to let the flexing of the columns "absorb" the horizontal movement of the foundation (while the upper part remains stationary) without transmitting enough shearing forces to the rest of the superstructure to set the latter in motion.   Reinforcing plates connected onto the web of an H-column is one method of securing bene-- ficial area for compression without adding much to flexural resistance.   Another way is to install strong vertical bracing of truss type, making it sufficient to resist the shearing forces.   In this connection, one might well remember that structural steel stretched beyond its yield point will still resist force even though it has a permanent set and may have to be replaced later.   Such bracing may be effective in preventing failure of a structure under the action of a severe earthquake of short duration even though it could not withstand long-continued rocking of the structure back and forth.

11. The best that one can do to make sure that columns can resist the vertical earth shocks seemingly is to be conservative in the choice of the safety factor for design purposes, and to brace the columns well enough to give reasonable assurance that they will not buckle.   Another principle is the offsetting of all columns of a building at the second floor so that the upper ones are supported by heavy beams spanning between the columns of the first story.   This is supposed to enable the latter beams to "absorb" vertical shocks by increased deflection.   It is obvious, however, that this scheme will cause considerable extra expense for construction, and the beams that are strong enough to carry large column loads will themselves be very stiff.   Hence this remedy is generally impracticable.

12. Fixed arches are more likely to be cracked by an earthquake than are three-hinged ones; those with two hinges may develop something approximately like a third hinge near the center without failure.   In other words, some flexibility may be desirable.

13. Past experiences indicate that a structure founded upon rock will be less seriously damaged than a similar one founded upon deep, soft soil, perhaps because of the latter's jellylike action and its tendency to magnify the motions.

14. Obviously, one should not knowingly build a rigid structure across a fault line in an active earthquake region.

15·6 Stacks. Because of their height, slenderness, and weight, stacks are structures that generally require firm foundations.   If a large one must be founded upon plastic soil, its designer should study the foundation problem with great care.   In such a case, unless a structure is founded upon piles that reach to firm strata, it may be desirable to locate the stack 50 ft. or more from other important structures so that settlement because of the consolidation of the soil under it will not injure neighboring buildings.   Even though this requires longer flues, the extra cost is likely to be money well spent.   Moderate settlement of the stack itself may not be harmful as long as that settlement is uniform.

A stack should be planned with proper consideration of the following features:

1. Height to provide the difference in air pressure necessary to produce adequate draft and to cause the gases to disperse in the upper air without becoming a nuisance.

2. Cross-sectional area to handle the requisite volume of gases.

3. Strength to hold itself up.

4. Resistance to winds of high velocity. It is desirable to assume a minimum horizontal wind pressure of 30 lb. per sq. ft. upon the projected area of the stack, even though the structure has a cylindrical surface.

5. Suitable lining to prevent disintegration of the structure because of the chemical action of the gases and acids.

6. Insulation to prevent damage to the shaft by heat, and to avoid condensation upon the stack's interior.

7. Support for the lining, yet provision for the latter to expand and contract with respect to the outer shell.

8. Adequate flue openings without serious weakening of the structure.

9. Cleanouts.

10. Lead or some other cap at the top to prevent access of water and acids behind the lining.

11. Protection of the upper exterior against corrosion and disintegration caused by wind-blown gases.

12. Ladder and rest platforms for inspection and repair purposes.

13. Provisions for painting—perhaps a strong, circumferential ring near the top for a pulley-supported platform or bosun's chair.

14. Protection against lightning.

15. Markings and lights to meet requirements of the Civil Aeronautics Authority, as well as local regulations regarding air transport.

Brick stacks are limited in practicable height because of their great weight, the cost of materials and labor, the low compressive strength of brickwork, and the lack of tensile strength at the joints. Steel stacks are relatively light and strong, but maintenance may be expensive, and overturning difficult to resist. Reinforced-concrete stacks, when designed properly, may be used for great heights and diameters. The one for the smelter shown in Fig. 1·6 has a height of 600 ft. above its base.

The base slab of such a stack as the one at Morenci, Arizona, must be designed for vertical loads combined with wind from any direction. The base must be strong in bending and shear; it must have enough weight (combined with that of the earth over it) to prevent overturning; and it must be sufficiently large to avoid excessive pressures upon the soil. This base, for example, has a diameter of 71 ft.; it has a thickness at the base of the shaft of 9 ft.; the bottom reinforcement is composed of four layers of rods set at 45° angles; and heavy vertical rods tie the shaft to it. The footing of this stack is relatively small because the structure rests upon cemented caliche.

The use of guys to resist wind forces upon steel stacks may seem to be advantageous. However, these wire ropes must be maintained well, the anchorages must be adequate, there should be six or eight guys at the same level equally spaced about the shaft, the ropes should have reasonably equal lengths, and their length should be adjustable. If anything happens to loosen or break a guy, the pull on the opposite one may actually harm the structure.

In the case of power plants, it is frequently desirable and economical to found brick-lined steel stacks upon the roof. If this is done, the shear and overturning moment caused by wind should be provided for during the period after the steel is erected and before the building and lining are completed. It may be necessary to have both vertical and horizontal bracing systems in the framework for this purpose. Two ways of supporting such a stack are the following:

1. Attach the base (flared if necessary) directly to a strong, stiff system of beams in the roof. Brace these beams horizontally in both directions so that the wind shear from any direction can be resisted safely, and provide for uplift as well as for downward reactions. The stack is thus cantilevered directly from the roof framing.

2. Extend the shaft of the stack through a flashed sleeve attached to the roof framing; support the base of the cylindrical shaft upon a lower floor or upon a special platform 10 to 30 ft. below the roof; and brace the structure to support the horizontal reactions at both levels. In this case, the vertical load remains practically constant, the uplift is negligible, and the shaft is cantilevered up from the roof but is held by two widely spaced horizontal reactions. Vertical movement should be permitted at the roof because of variations in the temperature of the stack. Of course, it is possible to receive the vertical load at the roof and allow the slippage to occur at the lower support.

15·7 Bins. Storage bins for nonliquid materials are often an essential part of an industrial plant. This discussion will be confined to them because tanks, although involving many of the same types of construction, are generally easier to design because the liquid pressures are more definite and determinable than are those caused by dry and moist solids of granular nature.

After one has determined the storage capacity desired, the next problems are the selection of a type of structure, the size required to ensure the needed usable storage, the means by which the bin is to be filled and emptied, and the material of which to build the structure.

Stock piles in the yard may be useful, but it is assumed here that the material must be supported entirely or confined by some sort of structure. Of course, it is economical to rest the material on the ground when vertical support by means of structures is not necessary.

There are many types of storage bins. Some are illustrated in Fig. 15·6. One should select whatever type seems to suit best the particular case. It is probable that the final decision will depend upon the space available, the costs of the various structures, the probable costs of operation and maintenance, the size required, the elevation of the bin above the ground, the character of the material to be stored, and the materials available from which to build the structure.

The question of the best equipment for filling and emptying a bin is one involving a knowledge of available means for handling materials. It is so important that its answer generally will—and should—affect the choice of the type of structure; occasionally, however, conditions may cause the structural problems to influence the selection of the type of equipment. The illustrations in Fig. 15·6 are intended to show variety rather than the best equipment for use with a given type of bin. In the drawings, no attempt is made to show the structural supports in detail, nor the roofs and walls. The need for strength, stiffness, protection from rain, avoidance of freezing, and prevention of excessive dusting is obvious.

Naturally, the intended storage capacity should be actually available. Material that cannot be drawn off practicably is dead—or useless—capacity. The ease with which a granular material will flow, and its angle of repose, may depend upon such features as height of fall, uniformity of size of grains, shape of particles, moisture content, cohesion, and compaction; it may depend also upon whether the material is being deposited or withdrawn. In the latter case, moisture and cohesion are likely to cause a material to arch over an opening, or to form pipes—these being small cylindrical or conical holes from the drawoff gates up through a mass, with the surrounding material arching around the openings and failing to slide down.

Assume that the angle of repose of a material varies from 30° to 45°, depending upon conditions. Let Fig. 15·5 represent one intermediate portion of a rectangular bin that is filled by a conveyor discharging through a single-chute tripper. The bin is to be emptied by means of pan feeders under openings 2 ft. square in the bottom at a spacing S. The capacity of an intermediate typical section of the bin is to be computed. A conservative way to estimate the useful capacity of this section is as follows:

1. Assume that the drawoff and filling slopes are 45°, the probable worst condition. From the assumed dimensions, locate points A and B of Fig. 15·5(a) for the top.

2. Assuming that the openings are 2 ft. in diameter, then, from Sketch (a) with slopes of 45°, draw the contour plan of the material left in the bottom when the gates are open. This plan is shown in (b) for 2-ft. contour intervals.

3. By the method of average end areas, compute the volume of material in each 2-ft. layer of a typical section S up to the points E, the highest that dead storage reaches along the sides of the bin. Then deduct this total from the volume of the rectangular solid space inside the bin below E-E. This gives the useful drawoff in this portion.

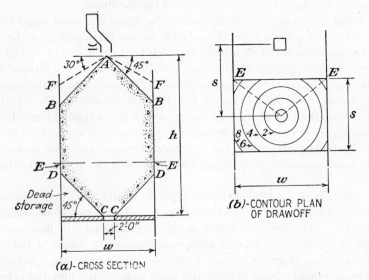

(a)-CROSS SECTION

(b)-CONTOUR PLAN OF DRAWOFF

Fig. 15·5.   Method of estimating capacity of a bin.

4. Compute the volume of the mass above E-E and within lines AB and BE.

5. The sum from items 3 and 4 gives the volume of useful drawoff for one space S.

By means of the number of typical spaces and through similar computations for end sections and special portions, the total useful volume of the bin may be estimated. In the designing of the bin, however, the height of the sides and the calculation of loads should be based upon the points F found by use of the flattest angle of repose.

Referring to Fig. 15·6, the following comments may be helpful, each reference being to the sketch correspondingly lettered:

(a) This bin is a simple hole in the ground with a pan feeder (metallic conveyor) compartment at its bottom, and a conveyor tunnel that ascends to the

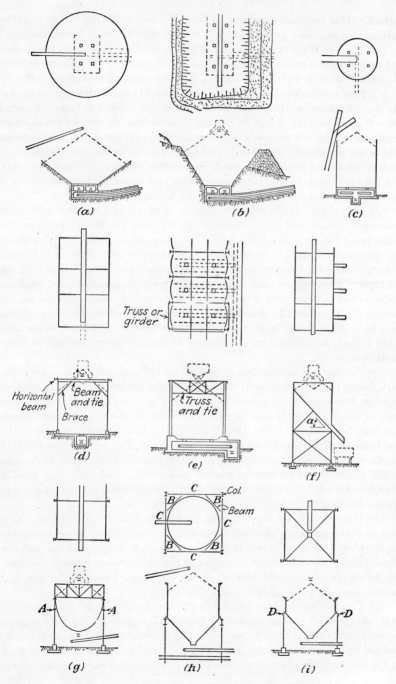

Fig. 15·6.   Examples of types of storage bins.

surface. This is a useful scheme in rock and where the ground is suitable. Surface drainage and ground water, however, may be very troublesome.

(*b*) This bin is merely a deep trench excavated in a hillside with pan feeders and conveyors in a heavy concrete structure at the bottom. A sufficient number of drawoff gates is essential if the bin is to be emptied reasonably well.

(*c*) Here a cylindrical bin is used with pan feeders and a conveyor for emptying it. Structurally, this shape is efficient if not made too large. Unequal drawoff is not likely to distort its circular shape excessively because the abutting resistance of the contents will offer considerable opposition to the movement that must accompany a change of shape. The structure may be made of steel or reinforced concrete; in small silos, reinforced tiles are sometimes used. If a tall bin is made of steel, vertical stiffeners may be needed to prevent vertical buckling of the plates; a ring girder at the top is also desirable.

(*d*) This simple, rectangular bin may be designed as a box that rests upon a concrete foundation and a structure that houses the lower conveyor, the latter being fed by a series of gates. The gates should be such as to prevent the pressures in the bin from being transmitted to the conveyor. Feeding from a series of gates simultaneously may cause spillage, or damage to the conveyor. The walls of such a bin may be designed as cantilevered retaining walls, but it is often best to plan them as vertical beams supported by the bottom of the bin and by longitudinal beams and ties at the top. Small bins may be made of wood; large ones, of steel or reinforced concrete. When such a bin is long, knee braces may be needed to provide lateral stiffness at intermediate supports.

(*e*) This bin is a modification of that shown in Sketch (*d*). The sides utilize curved steel plates in tension, with the longitudinal components of these tensions more or less counteracting each other except at the ends, where provisions such as heavy vertical trusses or girders between the last two columns on each side may be needed to resist these forces. The lateral forces are resisted by the bending of the heavy columns. The railroad floor system ties the tops together, and a top longitudinal member helps to distribute unequal tensions in the plates caused by uneven loading or drawoff of the bin. It is possible to make such a bin of reinforced concrete if the bending moments in the columns are not too large.

(*f*) This type of bin may be used for loading trucks and railroad cars as well as other materials-handling equipment. If it is to be self-cleaning, the angle *a* should be considerably steeper than the angle of repose of the material. These bins are generally more adaptable to the use of wood and steel than they are to reinforced concrete because of the expensive formwork for the last. In any case, they should be braced thoroughly.

(*g*) This bin is sometimes called a "suspended bunker." It is a flexible type that utilizes steel in tension, and it is generally relatively light for a given capacity compared to other types. The pull of the suspension plates is usually resisted by an inclined girder at their tops; these girders transmit the loads to the columns and cross struts, the girders being sufficiently stiff laterally to resist any probable sideward forces. Because of the variations of loading, the bin may distort enough to cause its bottom to rise and fall 2 or 3 in. If there is no lateral beam at A, the warping of the plates may tear them at their junctions with the columns. True hinges near A are desirable but difficult to obtain. Flexing of the plates is usually depended upon for adjustment to the line of the tension.

(h) Bins such as this may be called "silos." They are very efficient for moderate capacities. When they are high above the ground, steel is generally desirable in order to lessen the total weight. The cone should be concentric; vertical stiffeners may be needed on the cylindrical part, and ring stiffeners are usually desirable at the top and bottom of this section. When the bin is large and is supported upon beam framing, the deflections of the beams may be sufficient to cause unequal and variable bearing at such points as B and C. The stiffer of the two sets should be made able to resist the entire load if necessary; and full-height, H-type stiffeners may be desirable in order to prevent the eccentricity of loading at the supports from bending the thin plates inward.

(i) This rectangular bin, or hopper, is sometimes preferred because of its adaptability to the structural framing. The truncated bottom and the sides should be stiffened so as to hold their proper shape, and adequate horizontal strength should be provided at points D to resist the horizontal forces. The details of the junctions at D are likely to be troublesome in the case of large bins because of the magnitude of the shears and tensions.

A few general points to bear in mind in the planning of a bin are the following:

1. Corrosion may occur because the interior of the bin cannot be protected at a practicable cost. Acids aggravate this trouble.

2. Abrasion may grind away the surface of the inside. This may be especially serious in the case of concrete bins. Old conveyor belts, bolted wooden planks, manganese-steel liners, hanging steel plates, and old railroad rails are among the materials that have been used to protect the inside surfaces of such structures. The wear on concrete at the discharge openings is generally so serious that metallic frames with renewable manganese-steel liners are essential.

3. The dead load of an elevated bin should generally be minimized, and stiffness of any bin may be important.

4. One material may be cheaper in first cost than another, but it may be less durable.

5. Fireproofness may be important.

6. Freezing of moist material may prevent the emptying of the bin.

7. Future increase of storage capacity warrants consideration.

8. Hot materials may endanger wood and dehydrate concrete.

9. It may be desirable to provide means for barring or shaking down the contents when the material will not flow.

10. Access to the bin for inspection and provisions for cleaning it may be desirable.

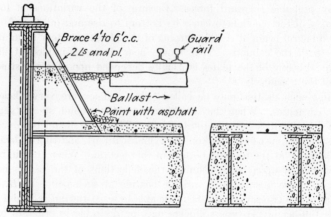

(a)-BEAM-AND-CONCRETE TROUGHED FLOOR-THROUGH PLATE GIRDERS

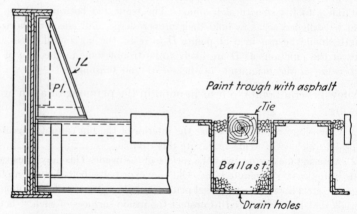

(b)-STEEL TROUGHED FLOOR FOR MINIMUM DEPTH OF FLOOR

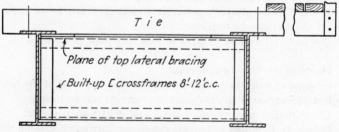

(c)-DECK BEAM BRIDGE FOR SHORT SPANS

FIG. 15·7. Some types of construction for short, steel railroad bridges and viaduct spans.

15·8 Bridges and Trestles. Small bridges and trestles are frequently necessary at an industrial plant.   Their planning is not greatly different from that of other structures, but the dynamic effects of live loads become far more important.   The variety of such structures is so great that space cannot be used here for an adequate discussion of them. However, several illustrations of suggested construction are given for

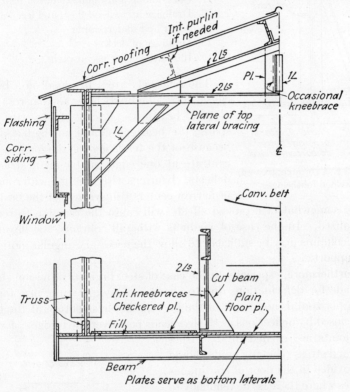

FIG. 15·8.   A steel, trussed conveyor bridge or gallery.

the reader to examine, and the following are some points for him to consider:

1. Serviceability for the purpose intended.
2. Cost of structure.
3. Effects of weather and cost of maintenance.
4. Adequacy of foundations.
5. Suitability to foundation conditions.
6. Architectural appearance.
7. Possible renewal of the wearing surface of the roadway.

8. Waterproofness of deck to prevent leakage; also to avoid staining and disintegration of structure.

9. Safety and stiffness of structure for vertical, lateral, and longitudinal loads.

10. Adequacy of curbs and guard rails.

11. Clearance on and below the structure.

12. Functioning and maintenance of bearings.

13. Drainage area, flood flow, and ice.

14. Scour and undermining.

15. Drainage of deck.

16. Illumination for use at night.

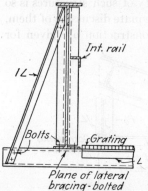

FIG. 15·9. A through, trussed, welded footbridge.

The relatively great live load on a bridge causes correspondingly large angular rotations at the bearings. Except for very short spans, the bearings should not be flat plates because of the tendency for the load to concentrate at one edge as the main structure deflects. Bearings with pins and with rounded or narrow centers transversely of the bridge— giving somewhat of a pinned effect—will cause the reaction to remain centralized. In the case of viaducts with tall columns, the flexure of these columns may be sufficient to allow the necessary angular motion at the support.

Furthermore, especially in the case of steel bridges, provision should be made for deformations due to changes of temperature, also for the slight horizontal movement of the bottom of the structure at the bearings caused by deflections as the live loads pass over the bridge. Expansion joints are needed in the structure, and stress-relieving joints should be provided in the floor of continuous bridges where there is the tendency to accumulate excessive deformations.

It is obvious that a bridge or viaduct should be designed to resist lateral and longitudinal wind loads, and especially traction and braking forces. At least an abutment, a pier,

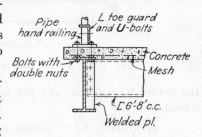

FIG. 15·10.   A deck footbridge.

or a braced tower should be made adequate for this purpose for each basic unit of the structure between main expansion joints.

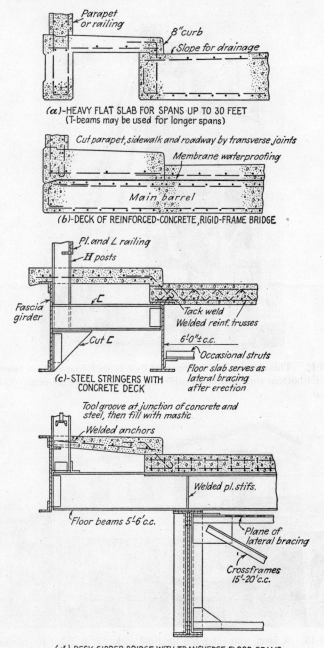

(*a*)-HEAVY FLAT SLAB FOR SPANS UP TO 30 FEET
(T-beams may be used for longer spans)

(*b*)-DECK OF REINFORCED-CONCRETE RIGID-FRAME BRIDGE

(*c*)-STEEL STRINGERS WITH CONCRETE DECK

(*d*)-DECK GIRDER BRIDGE WITH TRANSVERSE FLOOR BEAMS

FIG. 15·11.   Some examples of construction for highway bridges.

Fig. 15·12.   This circular bin is supported by a braced, four-column tower, and it has top and bottom ring girders for stiffening it, the top being open.   (*Courtesy of Blaw-Knox.*)

Fig. 15·13.   A steel triangular bin for lime rock.   It is filled by bottom-dump railroad cars.   Notice the heavy beam stiffeners, bracing, and tail track.   (*Courtesy of the Phelps Dodge Corp.*)

FIG. 15·14. Bucket elevator at an asphalt-mixing plant. This illustrates the use of a ladder and safety cage. (*Courtesy of Link-Belt Co.*)

FIG. 15·15. These steel bins and screw conveyors are for holding and dustless handling of carbon black from railroad tank cars. The columns are attached rigidly to their foundations. The conical tops and bottoms serve as sufficient ring stiffeners for these light loads. (*Courtesy of Link-Belt Co.*)

FIG. 15·16. Framing of a long conveyor gallery to the smelter at the Morenci Reduction Works. The anchor tower at the left is designed to resist all longitudinal forces; the other supports, like the one at the right, are to withstand vertical and transverse forces only. The central suspended chute is for loading cars if necessary. (*Courtesy of the Phelps Dodge Corp.*)

Chapter 16

SOME LESSONS IN STRUCTURAL PLANNING

16·1 Introduction. The purpose of this chapter is to bring to the attention of the reader an actual illustration of what the lack of wise planning of structures may bring about, and to emphasize the need for knowledge, experience, and careful thought when basic decisions are made regarding the general features of and the specific plans for an important structure and when the details to be incorporated in it are determined.

The particular record cited here is that of an existing steel ore bridge, the results of a personal field examination of it, the reasons for its difficulties, and a discussion of what was recommended to remedy or alleviate the troubles. The structure being a real rather than an imaginary one, the special lessons learned from it may have greater importance in the mind of the reader. This case illustrates how difficult it sometimes is to improve a structure after it is built. Its lessons in the importance of planning apply also to structures that are built of other materials. This bridge is an unusually good example of how essential it is for a designer to think of his proposed structure as an integrated whole rather than as an assemblage of unrelated parts.

The author also wishes to give his readers some quantitative scale showing the effects of the interaction of members in one structure, and to use these cases as qualitative examples to assist designers of other structures; he wishes also to give these data as guides for the future, not as criticisms of the past. It seems that much more investigational work of this sort, and the publication of the findings in the future, will benefit the civil engineering profession.

By no means is it implied that the designers of such structures as this one have failed to detect the existence of difficulties; they have done much to improve their structures. However, it seems desirable to pass these lessons along to others so that they, too, may benefit thereby.

No criticism of anyone is intended. The author does not intend to imply that he never made the mistake of overlooking the effect of the deformations and interaction of the members of a structure; in fact, it took him many years to awaken to their significance.

435

Owners and operators should remember these lessons, too, when the manufacturer of important equipment recommends sturdy construction for such service.   Too often they seem to think that anything will be strong enough, and they are not willing to pay the little extra money required to obtain the best practicable structure.   Would any one of them thank the automobile manufacturer who reduced dangerously the safety factor of the axles of his car just to make the price a bit lower, thereby endangering many lives?

FIG. 16·1.   Partial view of the plant.   The excavating bridge is shown working at · one of the compartments near the north end of the plant.

16·2   Historical Background.   Approximately 20 years ago, an industrial company purchased the 213-ft. gantry bridge shown in Fig. 16·1.   It is used to excavate granular, treated ore out of a compartmented pit or tank nearly 1,000 ft. long, and it delivers about 9,500 tons of material per day to dump cars that dispose of this waste.   The excavating equipment is a "man trolley" that runs between the lower portions of the bridge trusses.   The bucket is designed to hold 15 tons of ore but it will, and frequently did, carry as much as 25 tons—a very severe overload.   The bucket, trolley, and accessories weigh approximately 85 tons.   Thus the drums, motors, brakes, and all other equipment needed for hoisting and transporting the ore constitute live load applied to the structure repeatedly.

The bridge itself is moved along its tracks by means of motors mounted in the tower and upon the shear leg.   These motors are connected by shafts and gears to the truck wheels and are controlled by an operator stationed in the tower. Thus the trolley and the bridge may be operated simultaneously.

In Fig. 16·3 are shown the general arrangement and dimensions of the structural framework of the bridge. The tower at the west end is an integral part of the truss and is supported by a box girder mounted upon three trucks, the central one of which has spring bearings. The shear leg at the east end, also mounted upon trucks, as shown in Fig. 16·23, is a sort of rocker bent with the ends of the bridge hung upon four eyebars attached to the top strut of the bent, and with a shear pin in an elongated hole to deliver transverse shears from the end strut of the bridge to an intermediate strut of the tower. Thus, all longitudinal forces are delivered through the tower to its truck girder, whereas the shear leg permits the longitudinal motions caused by loads and temperature to occur at the east end.

From 1942 to 1946, the following failures occurred in the structure at different times, as shown in Fig. 16·4:

1. The inside half of the top of four main diagonals of the trusses, and the top outside half of another one.

2. One of the inner gusset plates of the north truss.

3. The webs of two trolley beams.

FIG. 16·2. The trolley and its 15-ton bucket lifting a load of "muck." The pivoted arm is to reduce swaying of the bucket, but the resultant thrusts wrack the trolley framework considerably. The operator's cab is at the near end of the trolley.

In addition to these troubles, the trolley framework failed in many parts and in diverse manners. The wracking caused by the pivoted boom shown in Fig. 16·2, which was to steady the bucket, seemingly aggravated the situation. Excellent inspection and prompt remedial action on the part of the field organization enabled service to continue.

All these failures of truss members apparently were caused by distortions and fatigue, not by direct stresses resulting from overload alone. This is obvious because the cracks in each case were sharp and clean, there was no evidence of scaling and necking down in the vicinity, there was no serious distortion or kinking of a truss panel as a whole, and the remaining half of the member continued to support the loads. The last of these facts is extremely fortunate and is important in guiding one's study of the structure. If direct loads had so overstressed a tension

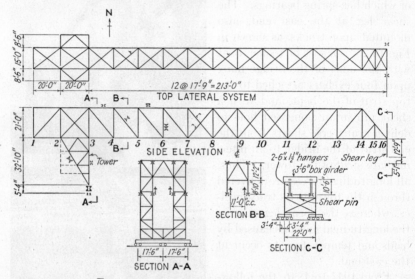

Fig. 16·3. General dimensions of structure.

member that one side failed, the other half could not reasonably be expected to add this extra force to what it already carried without promptly following suit. Obviously, distortions must have set up violent localized stresses that constituted the "last straw" for that part of the member whereas, when one half of the member cracked and thus relieved itself of stress, the remainder came into action as a slender tie and was able to hang on.

The failure of the inner gusset at L7 of the north truss is equally disturbing to a designer's nerves, as well as to those of the operators. Since the other gusset remained intact, this, too, must have been a case of superimposed distortion added, perhaps, to unequal loading of the two halves of the member. As shown by Fig. 16·22(b), the failure apparently started near the lower chord.

The webs of the two trolley beams split approximately lengthwise, as indicated in Fig. 16·17(e). This was in spite of the fact that localized wheel loads caused heavy downward compression in the webs. The reasons for this action will be discussed later.

What is the stress condition in this structure after parts have failed, and after repairs have necessarily been made without jacking the dead-load stresses back into the portion that gave way? Obviously, the remaining half of each broken diagonal now carries all the dead load for that member. To this, the future live loads must be added. Furthermore, no one knows how near to fatigue failure other parts may be. It

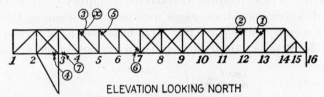

ELEVATION LOOKING NORTH

LOCATIONS AND NATURE OF FAILURES

① *Both inner ∟s of main diagonal near upper gusset, north truss*
② *Both inner ∟s of main diagonal near upper gusset, south truss*
③ *Both inner ∟s of main diagonal near upper gusset, north truss*
④ *Web of trolley beam in tower, north side*
⑤ *Both inner ∟s of main diagonal near upper gusset, north truss*
⑥ *Inner gusset plate at lower end, north truss*
⑦ *Web of trolley beam next to tower, north side*
ⓧ *Both outer ∟s of main diagonal near upper gusset, south truss*

Fig. 16·4.   Record of failures of structural members.   Numbers give sequence of failures except for *x*, which is not on record.

should be remembered that this structure is really a machine, it is normally subjected to very severe service, considerable vibration is inevitable, and the bridge has been heavily overloaded.

Considerable long-range study of the problem of saving the structure was carried on during the early spring of 1946. Although one could make any reasonable assumptions that he chose regarding the magnitude of loads and the action of the structure and then arrive at the corresponding answers in his calculations, he still failed to know whether or not his assumptions were correct. After considerable correspondence and the making of certain remedial proposals, it was decided that a detailed strain analysis of the structure should be made in the field under operating conditions. Therefore, Mr. W. M. Bertolet of the Baldwin Locomotive Company and the author spent several days at the plant studying the strain and stress conditions in the structure and trying to determine remedies that could be applied without major interference with service.

16·3 Equipment Used in Ascertaining Strains. For preliminary explorations and the general studies of the strains in the main
trusses, 8-in. Berry and 10-in. Whittemore mechanical gages were used.
Two-inch gages of each type were also tried but were found to be far
less desirable than the longer ones. This was largely because of the
former's decreased accuracy and the greater likelihood of errors caused
by vibrations of the structure and by unsteady holding on the part of
the operator.

Ninety of the Baldwin Locomotive Company's SR–4, type A–3,
bonded-electric-wire strain gages were used for measuring the deformation of members and parts that were inconvenient of access, where it
was difficult or practically impossible to use hand gages, and on certain

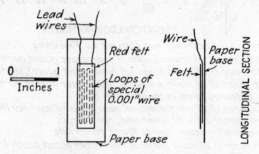

Fɪɢ. 16·5. A bonded-electric-wire strain gage: Baldwin Locomotive Co.'s SR–4,
Type A-3.

members in which critical conditions were anticipated. Figure 16·5
illustrates the general character and size of such a gage. The ends of
the fine alloy wire are secured to two heavier copper lead wires. The
entire grid is cemented to a thin paper base.

The principle of the operation of these electric gages is that a wire
changes in both length and cross section when it is stressed, hence its
resistance to the passage of an electric current is also changed. The
relation of this change in resistance in ohms per ohm to the change in
strain in inches per inch is called the "gage factor." This factor is
determined by the manufacturer. Although the change in resistance of
the gage due to strain is very small (usually about twice the relative
change in the deformation), it can be measured by a sensitive galva-
nometer and amplified by electronic equipment so as to be clearly
indicated, or even recorded.

In the field, the place where a wire gage was to be applied on the
steelwork was first ground clean by means of an emery wheel; it was then
washed with carbon tetrachloride. At night, after the second daily shift

had finished work, the gage was oriented in the direction of the strain to be measured, cemented on the steel by means of a special material, pressed tightly in contact with the surface of the metal, and allowed to remain static for a few hours in order to ensure proper setting of the cement before strains occurred. This cement is so effective that the wires of the gage become, in effect, an integral part of the steel to which the gages are fastened, and the strain of the wires accompanies and equals that of the steel.

Fig. 16·6. Reading electric-wire strain gages at *L7* of the south truss, where 12 separate gages were cemented to the trolley beam. The instrument with the handle contains the dials; the reading from each gage can be found by throwing a switch. Notice the details at the truss joint, and the north trolley beam in the background.

The next morning the leads on the newly installed gages were connected to wires that ran to a convenient central location and, adjacent to the gages, these wires were attached to the steelwork by adhesive tape so as to ensure that vibrations and disturbances in them would not affect the gages harmfully. Each measuring or active gage and its duplicate temperature-compensating gage were connected as two adjacent arms of a conventional Wheatstone bridge, whereas the other two arms were incorporated in the instrument used for reading strains. The indicating instrument shown in Fig. 16·6 was designed so that 20 of the SR–4 gages could be wired to it simultaneously. Therefore, by switching from one terminal to another, the instrument would record the resistance across any particular gage. This was exceedingly convenient because it enabled one to set up a sort of battery of gages on the part of the structure to be investigated, to obtain zero or "no-strain" readings from each gage, and then to ascertain the individual readings under static or dynamic loadings, doing all of this by merely throwing a switch and adjusting dials. The great advantages of this arrangement are obvious, especially in the analysis of a structure that is subjected to large moving loads, to shocks, and to vibrations vertically, laterally, and longitudinally.

Besides the SR–4 gages, there was available a recording oscillograph that enabled one to record the period of vibration and the amplitude of the longitudinal strain at a given point in a member as the result of vibrations of the structure. Because of the fact that the sensitivity of the amplifier was insufficient for use with only one SR–4 gage, it was necessary to use four of them wired into a complete Wheatstone bridge in order to add the output of the four. Two of the gages were oriented along the axis of the member and two perpendicular to it. The first two gages measured the direct strain in the member, whereas the others measured the accompanying strain due to Poisson's ratio (taken as 0.285 plus or minus). The output of this bridge circuit was thus recorded as 2.57 times the actual strain. Calibration of this setup was accomplished by shunting a high resistance across one of the gages.

The oscillograph was not used so extensively as it should have been because of the shortage of time for the tests and because the chief objective of the analysis was the determination of critical stresses throughout the structure under operating conditions and the planning of remedial measures to save the structure. Unfortunately, there was not available in the field one of the instruments that record simultaneously the strains on opposite sides of a member subjected to bending.

16·4 General Picture of Movements and Service Conditions. The first two days of investigation at the plant were spent largely in making a preliminary examination of the strains—and the assumed accompanying stresses—in members that had been and were expected to be in distress. This work was done with the mechanical gages. As a result of these readings, locations were selected for the first sets of wire gages; they were attached and wired up; then a few tests of the electrical equipment were made.

Also measured were the vertical and longitudinal movements of the bridge under the effects of live loads. Some of the resultant graphs are shown in Fig. 16·7. They were obtained by means of a pencil mounted upon a long 2 by 4 strut that was supported upon the tanks or adjacent rocks. The paper was attached to the superstructure, so as to move

with the bridge, and was moved sidewise by hand in order to obtain a
series of graphs corresponding to respective trips of the trolley.   Combined with these movements was a very severe lateral vibration of the
bridge when it was moved a few feet along its tracks (henceforth called
"bridging") from one strip to the next during excavating, as indicated
in Fig. 16·8.   The shocks were especially severe when the brakes were
applied—generally very suddenly.   Although their magnitudes were not

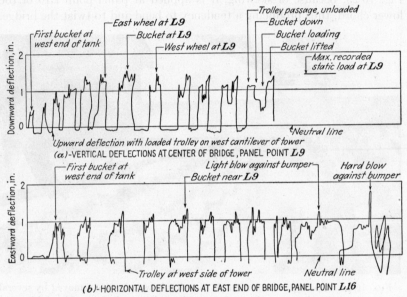

Fig. 16·7.   Graphical records of deflection of bridge during operations.

measured, these lateral vibrations were plainly visible, and the combination of all three motions as they occurred during operations would
frequently disturb one's equilibrium enough to jar one against the railing
or some other part of the structure.   Occasionally, when looking along
the bridge somewhat as in Fig. 16·6, the diagonals of the main trusses
could be seen to vibrate laterally so much that the visual effect was
surprisingly disturbing when one realized what it meant.

The eccentric, riveted connections of the trolley beams to the verticals, as pictured in Fig. 16·17, were obviously causing serious deformations that affected the diagonals and chords as well as the verticals
themselves.   This will be explained in detail subsequently, but it is
clearly a matter of unwise planning.   Recent designs of similar structures have different arrangements that are great improvements.

Another source of difficulty seemed to originate in the fact that operating conditions caused slippage of the truck wheels, sometimes resulting in skewing of the structure—one end moving along the tracks ahead of the other. A glance at Figs. 16·24 and 16·25 shows that the only lateral bracing between the trusses is at the top of the upper chords, and cross frames of only approximately half the truss depth are between the verticals. Hence, when a lateral force is caused at the shear leg, Fig. 16·23, because of skewing, it is applied at panel point $L16$ of the lower chord, thus producing a tendency to bend and to twist the bridge.

FIG. 16·8. A partly excavated tank, showing how strips are removed by several trips of the trolley in one position of the bridge. Notice the lack of lateral bracing near the lower chords of the trusses, and the traveling position of the bucket at the extreme right.

Under service conditions and bridging, these slender, top laterals vibrated considerably, and sometimes the bridge bent sidewise in visible bows or S-curves.

Another very disturbing feature was apparent when one observed the sideward rocking of the truck girder at the base of the tower, and when he realized how serious was the danger of jackknifing—rolling over or the sideward collapse of the truck girder. This will be clarified by reference to Figs. 16·10(a), (b), and (c), also by the next article.

16·5 The Bottom of the Tower. So serious was the possible effect of the rocking of the truck girder, and obviously it was so difficult to remedy, that this part of the structure was one of the first to be studied in detail by means of the electric gages. The results of some

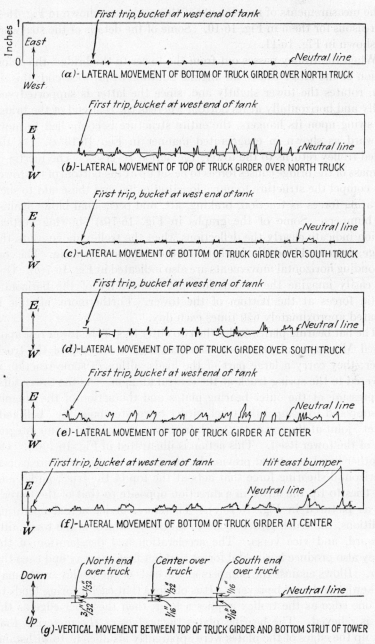

Fig. 16·9. Graphical record of movements of truck girder during operations.

of the measurements of movements of this girder are shown in Fig. 16·9; the reasons for them in Fig. 16·10. Some of the details of the steelwork are shown in Fig. 16·11.

When the trolley passes out from the tower to the bridge, the deformation of the latter causes an angular rotation at its west end; this, in turn, rotates the tower slightly and, since the latter is supported vertically and horizontally at its bottom whereas the east end of the bridge can swing upon its hangers, the entire structure is compelled to move eastward as shown in exaggerated manner in Fig. 16·10(a). As the loaded trolley returns to the tower, the action reverses. The inertia of the mass of the bridge causes forces to be set up at the bottom of the tower that compel the structure to move longitudinally, and these add to such operating forces as traction, braking, lift, and occasional blows against the bumpers. Some of the graphs in Fig. 16·7(a) showing vertical motion indicate clearly the deflections when the trolley moves onto the bridge, drops and loads the bucket, and then yanks it up again. The corresponding horizontal movements are also indicated in Fig. 16·7(b). One can easily imagine the alternation and the reality of the horizontal inertia forces at the bottom of the tower. Furthermore, all this is repeated approximately 650 times each day.

The flat bearing plates under the two outer legs of the tower rest upon planed Muntz-metal plates and steel castings at the top of the truck girder; they carry a large part of the loads, although some reaction is delivered to the spring truck at the central kingpin. As the tower tilts, the pressure at the outer bearing plates and the action of the kingpin are supposed to compel the truck girder to rotate about the "ball-and-socket" joint at the top of the truck frames as though it were an integral part of the tower itself. This action is illustrated in Fig. 16·10(b). On the other hand, as stated previously, the inertia of the structure causes a horizontal shearing force that acts at the top of the truck girder and that tries to tip the latter in a direction opposite to that of the tower's tilt, as pictured in Fig. 16·10(c). Therefore, under actual operating conditions, the truck girder tends to rotate westward as the tower tilts eastward, and vice versa. The acceleration and deceleration of the trolley also produce horizontal forces that act first one way and then the other. Blows against the bumpers at the ends of the trolley tracks may do likewise and may be severe. It is obvious that each bearing tends to ride one edge as the trolley applies a load; then the other edge as the load is relieved. The bearing plates themselves or the materials that back up the edges of the plates were apparently insufficient to withstand the reactions of some 350 kips applied at these edges, hence plastic yielding seems to have occurred so that the edges of the bearing are rounded somewhat.

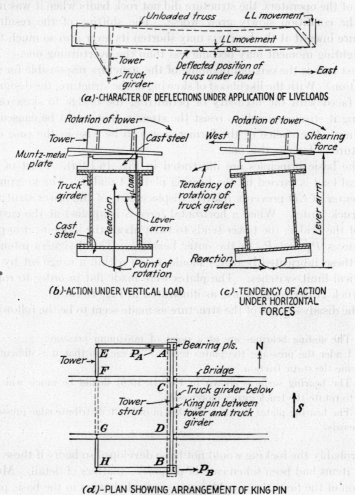

(a)-CHARACTER OF DEFLECTIONS UNDER APPLICATION OF LIVELOADS

(b)-ACTION UNDER VERTICAL LOAD

(c)- TENDENCY OF ACTION UNDER HORIZONTAL FORCES

(d)-PLAN SHOWING ARRANGEMENT OF KING PIN AND BEARING PLATES

FIG. 16·10. Simplified details to illustrate forces applied to and movements of truck girder.

One night when the author was standing at the north end of the truck girder observing these actions while the operators were making bumping and skewing tests, to simulate the worst of operating conditions, the truck girder seemed to creak and groan, and the spectators really wondered whether the kingpin might fail and the girder tip clear over, and whether the single ⅜-in. diaphragm plate at the bearing would give way and permit the box girder to fold up. According to the statements of some of the operators, the structure did not rock badly when it was new, but the condition slowly grew worse. The shifting of the resultant pressure inward at the bearings may shorten its lever arm so much that the righting moment may become less than the overturning one.

Just how is the original planning of the structure responsible for this condition? With the likelihood of skewing of the structure, the designers were faced with the necessity of permitting the bridge to skew or of making it strong enough to resist the stresses that might be caused by skewing. The choice of the former seems to be wise in the case of a structure as long as this one.

The basic principles are illustrated in Fig. 16·10(d). Most of the vertical load is carried by the bearing plates A and B. The kingpin at the center of CD prevents relative displacement of the tower strut and the truck girder. When a horizontal force S is applied at the eastern end of the bridge, the tower tends to twist about the kingpin; it applies the forces P_A and P_B to the outer bearings. The designers intended that these lubricated bearings should move within a range set by the electrical limit switches. The plates were made flat in order to rotate the truck girder by pressure, as illustrated in Fig. 16·10(b).

The disadvantages of the structure as made seem to be the following:

1. The sliding bearings are at a point of maximum pressure.
2. Under the pressure, the plates tend to "freeze" so that it is difficult to overcome the static friction.
3. The bearing surfaces shown in Fig. 16·10(b) should be much wider in order to rotate the truck girder more easily.
4. The bearing plates should be thicker in order to distribute edge pressures more easily.

Probably the rocking would not have developed so badly if these last three items had been taken care of properly—matters of detail. Modification of the first item would require radical changes in the basic plan.

Several SR-4 gages were placed on the truck girder and various members at the bottom of the tower, as shown in Fig. 16·14(a). There proved to be only small vertical and lateral bending moments in the girder, and the stresses in the top of the end diaphragm plate, under ordinary conditions, merely alternated between approximately 3,000 psi compression and 1,500 psi tension, yet clearly indicating the effects of rocking. What happened under shock loads is unknown; and the more critical diaphragm under the tower leg was inaccessible for testing.

Thus, rocking and jackknifing were the principal dangers involving the truck girder.

The most obvious remedy for this rocking of the truck girder would seem to be the replacement of the worn bearing plates. This, however,

FIG. 16·11(a). Framing at the bottom of the tower. This view shows in the foreground the outer bent and the sliding bearing at the south end of the tower. The ore cars come next to the left-hand side of the tower.

FIG. 16·11(b). A side view of the south end of the tower. The vertical shaft at the right is part of the mechanism that drives the trucks during bridging.

is not so easy as it seems. The tower would have to be jacked up and held there, the bridge being out of service for the duration of the repairs. It might be easy to remove and renew the lower plates, possibly using wider plates and new castings so that the rocking condition would not be so likely to recur, but the upper plates are fastened on with countersunk rivets, some of which are inaccessible. In order to remove the truck girder so that these rivets can be drilled or burned out, the central kingpin would have to be removed, and this would require very troublesome dismantling of part of the steelwork. Furthermore, the original plates were milled square after being riveted to the columns. It is a question as to whether or not new plates would fit properly. Because of these things, it was desirable to devise a means of stopping the rocking without putting the bridge out of service and without encountering unexpected obstacles.

Therefore, a great deal of study was given to the determination of the best way to overcome this rocking problem. Here are a few of the remedies that were considered:

1. Install new steel and Muntz-metal bearing plates on the bottom of the tower so as to regain the original flat surfaces. This would require jacking operations, difficult dismantling, and extended shutdown of operations, and serious troubles when trying to square up and strengthen the bottom of the tower legs if plastic yielding had occurred.

2. Build extensions of the tower framing of the inner bents down past both sides of the truck girder, then have a device at the bottom that would bear against the rails if the truck girder ever tipped excessively. It was feared that these extensions could not be made to act until the tilting movement had carried so far that the bridge operations would have to cease; the shock load upon the steelwork would require great strength; and movement under skewing action would be prevented. Even then, major repairs would probably be necessary to get the structure back into service if the tipping ever brought the stops into action.

3. Build struts from the inner bents down past the truck girder and almost in contact with the tops of new concrete walls alongside the present tracks so that, if the truck girder tipped, the tower would land upon these struts instead of falling down. This, too, would put the bridge out of service and would require extensive repairs; its cost would also be excessive because of the 1,000 ft. of concrete walls to be built.

4. Grip the truck girder in the vicinity of the kingpin so that the girder could not tip with respect to the tower. This would cause twisting in the girder and the tower framing far beyond their capacity to withstand, and the provision of adequate steelwork would involve very difficult detail problems. Furthermore, skewing might rip the structural work to pieces; and the resistance against tipping ought to be located near the end trucks.

5. Weld the truck girder tightly to the tower, and eliminate sliding of the outer bearings under skewing action; then devise a hauling system that would move the structure back and forth squarely at all times. This would require extensive mechanical alterations to install a through shaft to drive both ends simultaneously, or the installation of some sort of rope hauling system. The

former was not reliable because experience with other structures had shown that the wheels under the relatively light shear leg and those under the heavy tower would tend to accumulate relative slippage until serious stresses would probably be caused in the structure, and the bridge has (and could offer) little resistance to such skewing. The rope haulage system also involved excessive cost as well as uncertainties. In the local corrosive atmosphere (caused by acid fumes from the tanks) and with the possible spillage of acid-bearing material, the useful life of the wire ropes might not be very long.

FIG. 16·12. The west side of the tank, showing the ore trains, the tunnel for the tail track, and the narrow double track for the tower's trucks at the right. The loading bridge is shown running on rails at the top of the tank wall.

6. "Freeze" the ball-and-socket joints of the truck frames and let all rotation occur at the bearing plates on top of the truck girder, doing this by welding heavy steelwork between the truck girder and the frames. This changing of the basic, intended action of the system seemed to be unwise, and it seemed likely to cause failure of the truck frames because of large forces applied in places where they were not intended to be.

7. Abandon the trolley and bucket system; then use the bridge as the support for some other unloading device. This sounds innocent enough, but, since the loading bridge shown in Fig. 16·12, with its conveyor, must pass under the excavating equipment, no one was able to devise any sensible alternate to the original scheme without very extensive changes in the entire plant.

8. Install outriggers on the outer bents of the tower and place new bearings that would deliver pressures to the top of the truck girder alongside the existing bearings and directly over the end trucks. These outrigger bearings would come into action under conditions that cause rocking because the new plates would be flat and wide, and they would permit sliding of the bearings under

skewing action as intended in the original design. The general principles of this system are pictured in Figs. 16·13(a), (b), and (c).

9. Leave the worn steel plates on the bottom of the tower, remove the Muntz-metal plates and their supporting castings, then install new plates as shown in Fig. 16·13(d). The top 3-in. steel plate seemed to be strong enough to span over any worn areas of an existing steel bearing plate at the tower base and to receive the loads from whatever areas are able to bear. Each new 1½-in.

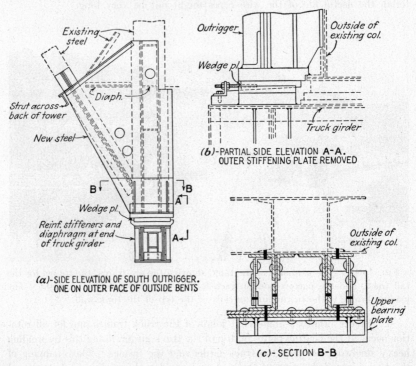

FIG. 16·13. General arrangement of outriggers and new bearing plates to prevent overturning.

Muntz-metal or phosphor-bronze plate is placed directly upon the truck girder but is made wide enough to transmit the pressure directly into the vertical girders. These new bearings can be fabricated completely in advance, the tower jacked up slightly, and the new bearings installed during a week end. This scheme is the one finally recommended.

The outrigger scheme was recommended as a sort of line of last defense to prevent collapse of the structure if the new bearings fail to remedy the rocking. In this design, advantage was taken of the fact that the bearing plates under the outer bents of the tower are offset from

the bearings on the end trucks, as pictured in Fig. 16·11(*b*). Furthermore, the new steelwork could be erected piecemeal during week ends

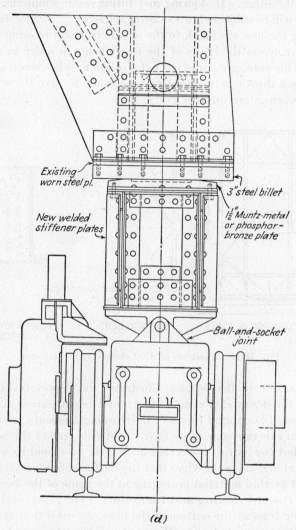

Existing
worn steel pl.

3" steel billet

New welded
stiffener plates

1½" Muntz-metal
or phosphor-
bronze plate

Ball-and-socket
joint

(d)

Fig. 16·13(*Continued*).   New bearing plates installed under tower bases.

and off-shifts, thus minimizing interference with operations.   The ordinary static load would still be supported upon the main bearings, but
the pressure would be shifted to the outriggers as the tower tilts.   Naturally, the amount of material in bearing, the riveting, and the welding of

the new work to the old would have to be very generous because of the shock effect and the repetition of loading as the tower tilts first one way and then the other. If skewing and tilting occur simultaneously, the outriggers will be subjected to a twisting tendency. Besides diaphragms connecting the new steelwork to the old, a strut and trussing should be added clear across the backs of the tower bents in order to resist this action. This outrigger remedy is not a solution to be chosen in the first place; it is a drastic action that may be taken to save the structure if the new bearings are unsatisfactory.

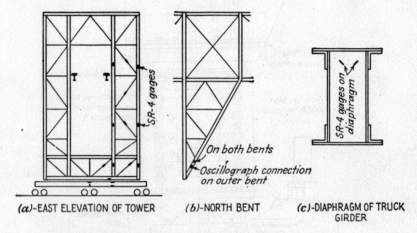

(a)-EAST ELEVATION OF TOWER   (b)-NORTH BENT   (c)-DIAPHRAGM OF TRUCK GIRDER

Fig. 16·14.   Positions of SR-4 electric gages on tower.

This portion of the problem illustrates the importance of details, especially the desirability of providing ample bearing areas at the edges of a column if horizontal forces or overturning moments tend to make the column ride one edge of its base. Not only should the base plates be thick, but the bearing areas that back them up should be wide plates or flanges at and along the edges that receive the concentrated load; they should not be thin material projecting in the plane of the bending.

16·6   **Tower Framing and Its Action.**   The gages on the vertical distributing truss at the bottom of the tower revealed that rather small live-load stresses existed in it although it had been designed to resist the entire dead and live loads. This showed that the bracing in the upper part of the tower distributed a large part of the truss loads from the inner to the outer bents before the bottom truss could come into action, even though these bracing members were designed for wind and skew forces only. Therefore, electric gages were placed on some of the upper members, as indicated in Fig. 16·14, in order to ascertain whether or not some of them might be stressed severely. The stresses interpreted from the measured strains were found to be very moderate. However, the analysis shows that, when bracing members are placed between loaded and unloaded columns with members tying the two sets so that the tower cannot bend sidewise, all members will participate in resisting stresses and deformations insofar as they are able to do so. Technically, in such a case, the structure should be designed accordingly. This analysis of a highly indeterminate structure, however, would involve tedious and expensive calculations. Seldom is it worth while to make such calculations for a structure like this one. But what should and can one do about it?

In this particular tower, as previously stated, the bottom truss was to be capable of supporting the loads delivered to the inner bent if nothing else did so; then the upper bracing members were designed as though they acted independently, and as though they resisted nothing but the wind and skew forces allocated to them. However, on general principles and to have members that were of practicable minimum sizes, the bracing was made stronger than the theoretical stresses required. Certainly, this line of action produced safe results, but it is not always the best engineering and does not make the most economical use of material. On the other hand, how much refinement of calculation is justified when one must make so many assumptions as to the loads applied upon the structure?

The author believes that bracing members should be proportioned in accordance with the desired stiffness of a structure, not merely in accordance with sizes determined by means of computed forces and allowable unit stresses, that it is not wise to say figuratively to one portion of the structure, "You do this and this only," and to another, "You do that," regardless of the fact that all are fastened together. Neither does it seem that one should compute the forces in them upon the basis of independent action, then make them all "twice" as strong as needed anyway. Still less, for a structure (machine) like this ore bridge, is it justifiable for a group of designers to spend many days computing the stresses in the tower upon the basis of a structure that is x times indeterminate.

This sort of problem deserves much more study by the civil engineering profession in order to determine a method of analysis that is reasonable, expeditious, easy to understand and apply, and sufficiently accurate for practical purposes. Although the following procedure is not theoretically correct, it illustrates how one may make approximations to apply to the design and analysis of this tower so that he can obtain evidence from which to locate any weak spots and upon which to base his final decisions:

1. Sketch a system of framing that seems to be desirable for the purpose from a practical framing standpoint.

2. Apply the probable vertical and horizontal forces to this system by broad, simplified, and approximate computations, and determine the corresponding total forces in the members by making some such assumptions as indicated in Fig. 16·15.

3. By use of approximate allowable unit stresses, compute the minimum areas required for these members.

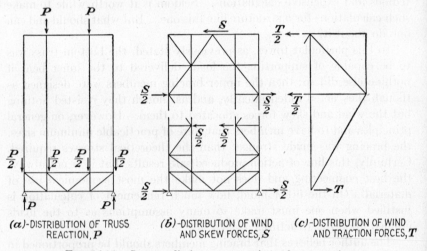

(a)-DISTRIBUTION OF TRUSS   (b)-DISTRIBUTION OF WIND   (c)-DISTRIBUTION OF WIND
     REACTION, P   AND SKEW FORCES, S   AND TRACTION FORCES, T

Fig. 16·15.   Some preliminary assumptions of tower action.

4. Study the framing scheme and pick out sections (materials) for the members which seem to be adequate and reasonable and which can be fitted together properly.

5. With the members tentatively chosen, make another approximxate analysis of the distribution of the maximum truss and trolley reaction applied to the inner vertical columns of the tower.   Assume that the loads in Fig. 16·16(a) must reach the reaction point O by means of the resistance of all the diagonals between the inner and outer columns, each one resisting in proportion to the vertical component of its area.   Obviously, the stronger, stiffer members will carry the larger share of the load.   From these shears, compute the corresponding forces in all the members.

6. Assume that the load applied by the west truck of the trolley, when loaded and in dumping position in the tower, also reaches the outer bearing. The bracing in the inner bent carries part of these loads to the inner front column, Fig. 16·16(b), whereas the members in the plane of the backlegs, Sketch (c), carry some to the rear of the outer bent, and thence to the outer column.   Thus, the loads at the inner rear corner of the four-truss frame may

pass to the outer corner, O, by way of the inner bent and the front bracing, also through the backleg bracing and the outer bent. Assume that the sums of the vertical components of the two sets of web members in each path represent the stiffness of that path, and that the load will be carried to its destination by each path in accordance with this assumed stiffness. Then compute accordingly the resultant forces in all members.

7. Examine the results of items 5 and 6, bearing in mind the fact that the loads will be carried to the reaction points as directly and efficiently as possible.

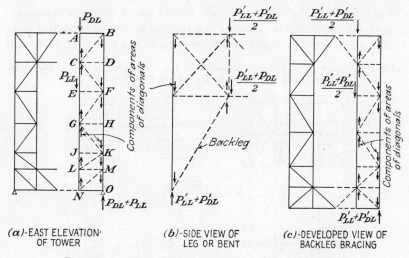

(a)-EAST ELEVATION OF TOWER   *(b)*-SIDE VIEW OF LEG OR BENT   *(c)*-DEVELOPED VIEW OF BACKLEG BRACING

Fig. 16·16.   Some additional assumptions of tower action.

Thus, the load P_{LL} of Fig. 16·16(a) will, if the members are otherwise equal, have a shorter and stiffer path from E through EG, GK, and KO to O than it will through EC, CF, and FO to the same point; hence the former path will carry more than the latter if the members are equal. The results of the computations can be adjusted arbitrarily if it seems to be advisable to do so.

8. Combine the forces computed in each member from all vertical and horizontal loads, and see if the members are adequate. Consider, also, whether or not the members are subjected to serious repetition and alternation of stresses, and whether or not they are suitably stiff. Revise the make-up of any members that seem to require it.

Following this reasoning and adding the computed forces from the trolley loads as applied to the inner front and rear columns, the results given in the first column of Table 16·1 are obtained. Naturally, these do not check the measured strains and interpreted forces shown in the second column of this table, but most results seem to be a fair approximation. At least one may arrive at something closer to actuality than by assuming that the bracing does not participate in the transfer of vertical loads.

In the case of light diagonals in a tower like this, live-load compression may be counteracted by initial tension produced by "draw" resulting from fabricating the diagonals a bit short and forcing them into tension during erection. This may be done by driftpins in riveted work, but it is difficult in the case of welded connections and heavy construction. If the diagonals buckle under the compression, the "tension" diagonal will not become effective in resisting lateral forces until the impressed compression is overcome, causing the bracing to act as though it were slack and resulting in objectionable swaying of the tower. It is obvious

Table 16·1   Approximated vs. "Measured" Forces for Some Tower Members for Live Load of Trolley in Dumping Position in Tower

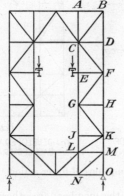

Member	Computed force, kips	"Measured" force, kips
CF	–12.2	–17.4
GF	+12.6	+11.9
GK	–12.6	–20.6
CE	+24.4	+3.5
GL	–15.8	–35.0
BF	–26.2	–9.2
FK	–48.5	–43.0

that the diagonals should be designed basically as compression members, with live-load compressions added to the others.

As the result of the strain measurements, the tower members were found to be adequate and conservatively designed except for the thinness of the $\frac{5}{16}$-in. gusset plates.

16·7   Trolley Beams. Some of the details of the trolley beams of the excavating bridge are pictured in Figs. 16·17 to 16·19. Many are the troubles caused by the fact that these beams are riveted fast to the verticals as shown in Fig. 16·17(a). Evidently the trusses were designed for one purpose and the trolley beams for another independent function, regardless of the fact that each is automatically affected by the other. Here are some of the troubles that were found:

1. The beams are supposed to be steadied laterally at their centers by the braces and sidewalk channels connecting at B and C, Fig. 16·17(b), and shown also in Fig. 16·18, whereas these two pieces are fastened to the diaphragm

plate D in the lower chord.   The measured live-load deflection of a typical trolley beam was 5/16 in.   Naturally, the connections at B had to fail, or the chords would be bent severely.   Fortunately, the former generally occurred. The maintenance crew repaired the braces repeatedly until the men became tired of the job and wisely let the braces alone.   If the chords and the braces were sufficiently rigid, the tops of the trolley beams would be forced to rotate

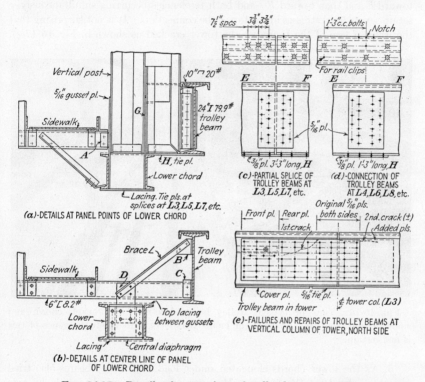

FIG. 16·17.   Details of connections of trolley beams to trusses.

inward (if the wheels would let them) instead of being steadied laterally.   This oversight occurred because of someone's failure to think about how the members would deform.

2. The angular rotation of the connections of the beams to the verticals, caused by the passage of the trolley wheels, rotated each joint first to the left and then to the right as a wheel passed from E to F in Figs. 16·17(c) and (d). This action repeatedly bent the vertical member and worked the inner gusset plate at G, Sketch (a), back and forth, affecting the inner half of all diagonals and chords more than the outer half.   The effects will be discussed more fully when the deformations of the main diagonals are described.

3. The notch in the outer flange of the top channels shown in Sketch (d)

to clear the vertical connection plate in (a) caused cracking of several of these channels at alternate panel points where they were continuous and subjected to repeated negative bending. Such cuts are very likely to be the starting points of cracks caused by high stresses and fatigue.

4. At the splices shown in Fig. 16·17(c), the webs and bottom flanges were spliced but the top flange of the beam and the channels were not. Rotations toward E and then toward F—and both tendencies occurring simultaneously— set up severe local stresses in the top of the connection. It is not surprising that the webs of two of the beams at the tower cracked as shown in Fig. 16·17(e).

Fig. 16·18. View of typical trolley beam, intermediate bracket, chord, and sidewalk construction. Some of the lacing bars were bowed, but the cause of this is not certain.

5. As the lower chords elongated under load, the trolley beams also tried to act as chords of the trusses. Here are two heavy members side by side and connected at the panel points. The chords must stretch under load— that is what they are for, because strain must accompany stress. The tie plates H of Sketches (a), (c), and (d) are particularly effective in resisting relative elongation of the two connected members. Naturally, large horizontal shearing forces and twisting moments are set up at the panel points; similar and rapidly reversing ones must occur, too, as the bottoms of the trolley beams try to move first right and then left because of end rotation under the passage of the trolley wheels. These connections were not completely effective; at least, the beams appeared to pick up about one-third as much unit stress as did the chords—perhaps more. This arrangement is unfortunate.

6. The rails slid eastward on the beams ahead of the trolley as it moved eastward, then the reverse action occurred; at L11 this motion of the rail was

as much as ⅜ in.   The rails had worn appreciable grooves in the channel webs.
The single-bolt rail clips were twisted alternately one way and then the other.

The bending in the main truss verticals caused by the eccentric connections was very definite but not excessive.   Just above the connec-

FIG. 16·19(a).   Wiring some of the
electric gages on the trolley beam near
L7.   The adhesive tape holding the
wires is visible.   The "live" rail is
shown below the beam at the lower left.

FIG. 16·19(b).   View along the trolley
runway.   Clearly shown are the offset
positions of the trolley beams, the top
lateral bracing, and the details of the
cross frames.

tion, the inner angles carried approximately 12,000 psi; near the bottom
of the cross frame, the stress in the inner angles was 7,500 psi tension,
whereas it was 6,000 psi compression in the opposite angles.   The length-
ening of the inner angles and the shortening of the outer ones probably
contributed to the inequality of tension in the diagonals.
    Electric gages were applied to one trolley beam, as shown in Fig.

16·20(*a*). The stresses interpreted from the readings are given in Table 16·2. The results show that the top channels are loose and ineffective. Evidently (and theoretically) the countersunk riveting shown in Figs. 16·17 (*c*) and (*d*) was inadequate, and the rivets have loosened so that the I-beams must carry the loads alone. The tensile stress at the center of the beam web indicates the chord action of the beams, and the table shows the existence of higher local stresses at the web splices as the web

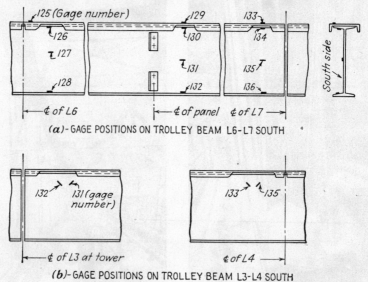

(*a*)- GAGE POSITIONS ON TROLLEY BEAM L6-L7 SOUTH

(*b*)- GAGE POSITIONS ON TROLLEY BEAM L3-L4 SOUTH

Fig. 16·20.   Locations of SR-4 gages on trolley beams.

plates try to stop the opening and closing of the top of the joint. Obviously, the upper rivets at these joints should loosen (and they did), and the connection angles will be bent repeatedly.

Figure 16·20(*b*) shows the locations of some wire gages that were used to test local shears and compressions in the top of the beam webs. The large stresses recorded in Table 16·3 indicate that, at the supports at least, the direct compressions in the webs are high and that the rails do not spread the wheel loads very far when they do not have to. This should be considered and the longitudinal shear investigated when one designs crane girders with thin webs.

Figure 16·17(*e*) shows the general arrangement of the connections of the trolley beams at the tower on the north side; the first failure is indicated at the left, as are the first repairs that were made. The second failure developed later in the web of the right-hand beam. This latter

Table 16·2 Stresses in Trolley Beam, Panel L6-L7, South Side

| Gage No. | Static loading, psi | | | | Dynamic loading, psi | | | |
| | East truck at center of L6-L7 | | East truck at center of L5-L6 | | Any position for max. loading | | Trolley at L9 to show chord action | |
	Compr.	Tension	Compr.	Tension	Compr.	Tension	Compr.	Tension
125	......	150	......	150	3,600	600	300	......
126	......	4,200	......	4,800	......	6,000	......	1,200
127	......	1,500	......	1,800	......	3,900	......	1,500
128	1,950	......	1,800	......	4,200	......	......	1,950
129	300	......	......	300	3,000	3,000	......	1,050
130	9,300	......	......	2,400	4,500	4,500	......	1,350
131	......	1,350	300	......	......	3,000	......	1,650
132	......	11,700	......	1,050	2,100	13,500	......	......
133	150	......	......	......	......	600	......	450
134	......	1,950	......	1,350	......	3,900	......	......
135	......	4,200	......	......	......	6,000	......	2,100
136	1,200	......	......	900	3,600	300	......	1,200

For gage locations, see Fig. 16·20(a).

Table 16·3   Stresses in Web of Trolley Beam, Panel *L3-L4*, South Side, Dynamic Loading

Gage No.	Unit stress, psi	
	Compr.	Tension
131	18,600	3,000
132	1,950	5,100
133	14,550	3,150
135	1,500	3,900

For locations of gages, see Fig. 16·20(*b*).

crack was probably caused by the stiffening of the left side, and by the end rotation of the beam, which caused even more violent stresses at the top of the partly spliced junction of the two beams.   New web splice plates were added and welded to the beam at the right.

There was little that could be done to remedy the harmful effects of the planning that made these trolley beams as they were.   However, the old channels should be cut off, new ones attached to the beams by plug welding, the channels spliced about 5 ft. from alternate panel points by welding so that the channels themselves would splice the top flanges of the beams at their splices, and the channels, where notched, should be reinforced.   The center of each rail length ought to be bolted to the steelwork to prevent creep; however, some motion should be allowed to occur at two of the rail joints near the ⅛ points of the runway in order to prevent the accumulation of longitudinal stresses in the rails.   At some time in the past, the plant had welded some rails directly to the top channels of the trolley beams in order to stop the creeping of the rails.   This, however, was unsuccessful because the rails cracked.   Reinforcing plates were to be added on the webs of the south trolley beams at the tower, even though failures had not yet occurred.   The tops of the plates should be welded to the upper flanges of the beams to ease local compressive and longitudinal shearing stresses in the webs.   Of course, all the intermediate braces shown in Fig. 16·17(*b*) were to be cut off, but a brace angle must be added between the outer end of the sidewalk channel and the lower chord in each panel to support the sidewalk.

There seems to be no advisable way of eliminating the participation of the trolley beams in the chord action of the trusses because traction and braking forces have to be resisted and satisfactory seated connections for the beams cannot be made to replace the present riveted connections.   The new, continuous, top channels will aggravate the direct participation of the trolley beams in chord action, but it is believed that they will reduce the rotation and "working" of the joints under the passage of wheel loads sufficiently to more than offset this disadvantage.

16·8 Sidewalk. The sidewalk on the south side was completely riveted throughout the length of the bridge. Its attempt to act as a chord, similar to that of the trolley beams, broke almost every connection at A, Fig. 16·17(a), because these flimsy connection angles could not withstand the necessary shearing forces. One end of each panel of the sidewalk is therefore to be cut loose at the bracket channel of Sketch (a) and bolted with undersized bolts, as should have been done in the first place; and the connections of the channels to the gussets need to be repaired. The full-length checkered plates of the sidewalk may help to resist local transverse shearing forces if necessary. A new sidewalk should be added outside the north truss for inspection and maintenance purposes.

16·9 Main Single Diagonals of Bridge Trusses. The details at the lower end of a typical single diagonal of the bridge trusses are shown in Figs. 16·19 and 16·21. Notice the 6-in. tie plates, the first one being almost 4 ft. from the end of the member, and the others being 4 ft. 3 in. on centers. For practical purposes these plates were equivalent to pin-ended ties. They did not stiffen the diagonals laterally nor equalize the stresses in the two halves of the members.

The numerous fatigue failures of the upper ends of the inner pair of angles were proof enough that a serious condition existed there and probably at the lower ends, too. Therefore, extensive gage readings were taken at the lower ends of the diagonals at $L6$, $L7$, $L11$, and $L12$; the upper ends of the members at $U3$, $U5$, and $U6$ were also tested.

By reading two hand gages simultaneously on opposite sides of a diagonal member, it was found that the effect of the rotation of the joint caused by the angular movement of the trolley beams was very pronounced in its action upon the diagonals. Since the members are subjected to such heavy tensions, rotation of the ends tends to cause sharp kinking there instead of long, easy curves; hence the local bending is more acute than it would be otherwise. The positions of gage points at $L6$ of the south truss are pictured in Figs. 16·21 (a), (b), and (c). In Sketch (d) is shown a characteristic but arbitrary curve to picture approximately the sort of action in terms of strains and interpreted stresses that occurred at a gage on the upper tip of an inner angle, as at point A in Fig. 16·21(a), when the trolley picked up a load at the center of the bridge and traveled with it to the tower. The curve is purposely shown jagged because the vibrations made the needle jump so much that it was usually difficult to read the dial accurately. Very often there would be a jump of the needle representing 3,000 to 4,000 psi when, apparently, various bending deformations and strains caused by vibrations came into phase; occasionally the needle would jump so far

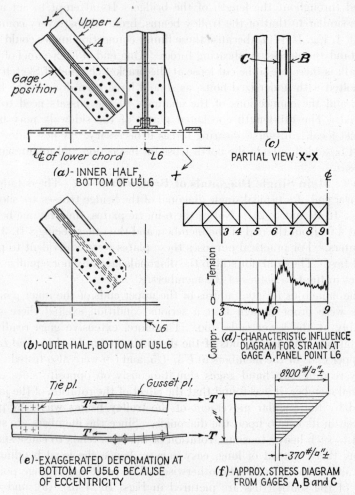

(a)- INNER HALF, BOTTOM OF U5L6

(b)-OUTER HALF, BOTTOM OF U5L6

(c) PARTIAL VIEW X-X

(d)-CHARACTERISTIC INFLUENCE DIAGRAM FOR STRAIN AT GAGE A, PANEL POINT L6

(e)-EXAGGERATED DEFORMATION AT BOTTOM OF U5L6 BECAUSE OF ECCENTRICITY

(f)-APPROX.STRESS DIAGRAM FROM GAGES A,B and C

FIG. 16·21. Locations of mechanical strain gages near L6, and some of results obtained.

that one could not tell how much of the movement represented strain and how much was caused by inertia of the needle when given a sudden kick. Smaller strains and shocks were apparent in the outer angles than in the inner ones, the former seemingly receiving about two-thirds as much stress as the latter for corresponding positions.

Incidentally, one of the rail joints near panel point $L5$ was worn so much that there was a depression of perhaps $\frac{1}{32}$ to $\frac{1}{16}$ in. When a wheel hit this in either direction, the gage needle would swing over to represent a unit stress of perhaps 1,500 to 2,500 psi. It was amazing how this shock was "telegraphed" to members clear over near the east end of the bridge, causing in them a shock representing approximately 800 to 1,200 psi. The importance of the smoothness of the runway was therefore obvious.

Because there were no tie plates close to the ends of the truss diagonals, measurements were made of the "bow-leg" bending action in the angles caused by the eccentricity of the one-leg connections, as shown to exaggerated scale in Fig. 16·21(e). The spreading of the angles was not visible but its effect upon the stresses is shown typically in Sketch (f), which indicates that the compression in the outstanding tips of the angles caused by secondary bending almost annulled the direct tension.

Attempts were made to ascertain the amplitude of the vertical vibrations of a truss diagonal, but no reliable data about the period of such vibrations were obtained. The horizontal vibrations caused by bridging could be seen plainly but no quantitative data were secured. However, it was evident that the effects of these vibrations could be additive and, at times, severe. The heavy tension in the members accentuated the local effect of end restraint.

In order to ease the serious local stress conditions in the single diagonals, the following additions are the desirable minimum:

1. The trolley beams should be made continuous by splicing with the new channels in order to decrease their end rotations a little, as previously stated. This will moderate the twisting of the lower ends of the members in the plane of the gusset plates.

2. Full length web plates 6 in. by $\frac{3}{8}$ in. should be welded on top of the main angles. This width is used in order to clear the rivets in the tie plates, and these new plates accomplish several benefits:

   a. They add a little useful metal to the cross-sectional area of the members.

   b. They stiffen the diagonals laterally so that they become I-type members instead of two slender halves that can vibrate in unison.

   c. They eliminate the local bending formerly caused by the eccentricity of the end connections.

   d. They serve to equalize the direct tensile stresses in the members except at the lower ends, where twisting might still cause high local stresses.

3. The upper and lower angles should be tack-welded together so that both sets will act simultaneously.

4. Small two-angle subdiagonals should be added from the top chord panel points to a point above the center of the main diagonals in order to support

the latter, to reduce the vertical vibrations, and to have the two portions of each main diagonal unequal so that they will not have the same period of vibration. The former effects of these vertical vibrations were believed to add greatly to the edge stresses at the ends of the long diagonals.

The addition of counter diagonals to relieve the present single diagonals was considered, but this scheme was abandoned because of the difficulty of making suitable end connections for the members.

16·10 Inner Gusset Plates of Lower Chords. Because of the failure of the inner gusset at $L7$ of the north truss, electric gages were placed on the corresponding one at $L7$ south, as pictured in Fig. 16·22(a).

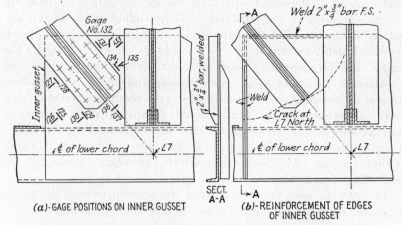

(a)-GAGE POSITIONS ON INNER GUSSET   *(b)*-REINFORCEMENT OF EDGES OF INNER GUSSET

FIG. 16·22.   Investigation and repairs of inner gusset plates.

The failure, shown dotted in (b), evidently started at the edge near the lower chord; it seems to have been caused by impressed distortions and fatigue. There is uncertainty as to whether or not the intermediate brace on the adjacent trolley beam contributed to the difficulty through bending of the chord. The fact that all the main gussets of this structure are only $\frac{5}{16}$ in. thick was most unfortunate because so little can be done to strengthen them without great expense.

The stresses interpreted from the gage readings are shown in Table 16·4. The results of the direct pull of the diagonal are shown best in the case of the wheel at panel point $L7$, and these stresses appear to be reasonable. The other two cases include a combination of the direct load and the rotation. It would seem that the gussets should not fail, but one did.

As a sort of compromise remedy, all the inner gusset plates at the bottoms of single diagonals should be reinforced, as shown in Fig.

16·22(*b*).   This is based upon the idea (and the hope) that no fatigue failure will occur if the edges are strengthened so that a crack will not start.   Any designer is unwise who endangers his structure by "skinning" such vital parts.

Table 16·4   Stresses in Inner Gusset Plate at Panel Point *L7*, South Truss

| Gage No. | Static loading, psi | | | | Dynamic loading, psi | |
| | West truck at panel point *L7* | | West truck at center of *L7-L8* | | Any position for max. loading | |
	Compr.	Tension	Compr.	Tension	Compr.	Tension
125	....	2,100	....	1,950	1,200	2,850
126	600	....	150	....	1,050	1,200
127	750	....	600	....	450	450
128	....	3,150	....	2,850	....	3,150
129	....	5,100	....	4,650	....	4,800
130	900	....	600	....	2,400	....
131	....	2,550	....	2,850	....	4,650
132	900	....	450	....	1,200	....
133	300	....	240	....	600	....
134	....	4,200	....	4,650	1,050	6,450
135	3,000	....	1,950	....	1,950	1,500
136	1,200	....	....	1,950	1,500	900
137	....	3,450	....	3,660	1,050	4,350

For gage locations, see Fig. 16·22(*a*).

16·11   Counter Diagonals.

No failures had occurred in any of the panels having an X-system of web members.   The strain-gage readings indicated that the main diagonal and the counter diagonal in a panel shared the shearing forces simultaneously and seemingly in proportion to their areas, even though they were composed of two angles only and were supposedly rather flimsy for compression members.   The counters had no tie plates at all, merely being connected by single rivets where they crossed the main members.   The latter had the usual 6-in. tie plates.   Here again the members were fastened to the structure and all tried to carry loads.   Evidently the connection at the intersection of the pairs of diagonals was beneficial in reducing the slenderness and in damping vibrations.

The bending caused by the impressed rotation of the panel points did not seem to be so severe in any of these narrow members as it was in the wide ones, but the shock effect in an outer angle when a wheel passed the panel point appeared to be more pronounced than it was in

Fig. 16·23.   The single-rail shear leg at the east end. The truss is hung from the top strut of the bent.   The rods for measuring skewing forces connected the laced vertical posts to the bottom chords of the truss.

Fig. 16·24.   View of the top laterals and chords near the tower.   The splice angles to repair the break at the top of diagonal $U4L5$ of the north truss are shown.

the inner one, the effect being a sharp compressive action. To improve the situation nevertheless, end tie plates and single lacing should be welded on all the main diagonals and counters in the four central panels.

It seems that, when an X-system is used for resisting heavy live loads and impacts—and perhaps in general—the members should be designed to act in unison and to resist safely the required compression as well as the tension. The permissible unit stress should be reduced in accordance with the severity of the service and the fatigue action that are anticipated. Furthermore, for structures that are subjected to so much vibration, it might be wise to use an X-system of web members throughout the trusses.

16·12 Skew. The action of the bridge under skewing had long been a source of worry. As previously stated, when the bridge is skewed, the tower end of the structure is supposed to rotate about the kingpin and to slide on the two tower bearings, whereas the east end is to swing upon its hangers in the shear leg, Fig. 16·23. When the bridge was purposely skewed, the tower bearings remained stationary until one end of the bridge was skewed 15 to 18 in., whereupon they jumped from 1 to 1½ in. as the friction was overcome and elastic recovery occurred

Fig. 16·25. Details of *U*5 of the north truss, showing the repairs made in another diagonal. Notice the single-angle lateral bracing, the heavy vertical members, and the narrow tie plates in the diagonal member. The wooden platforms arc gage stations used for both mechanical- and electrical-gage work.

in the structure. As skewing continued, this jumping was repeated two or three times until the bearings had moved about 3½ in., when limit switches near the bearings shut off the power. The bearings at the bottom of the tower seemed to be worn so that, in effect, they had to be pulled out of a slight groove in order to permit sliding. This, of course, increased the skewing forces set up in the framework.

Since there was no bracing in the plane of the lower chords, the flimsy lateral bracing on top of the upper chords, as pictured in Figs. 16·3, 16·24, and 16·25, was the only effective means of resisting the shears caused by the skewing. To determine the force at $L16$ to produce rotation at the tower, the east end of the truss was connected temporarily to the shear leg by means of two $1\frac{1}{4}$-in. rods. Wire gages were installed upon them, the bridge was skewed one way and then the other, and the strain in the rods was measured. Measured simultaneously were the strains in the end laterals near $U3$, the upper and lower chords near

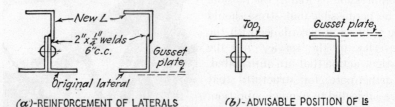

(a)-REINFORCEMENT OF LATERALS   (b)-ADVISABLE POSITION OF ᴸs

FIG. 16·26.   Lateral bracing at upper chords.

panel point 5, and the diagonals $U3L4$. The force required at $L16$ to produce sliding of the tower bearings was found to be approximately 10,000 lb.; the force at the bearings, 70,000 lb.

Although theoretically this skew force can be withstood by the top laterals, an extra angle should be welded upon each original member as shown in Fig. 16·26(a). This is partly to strengthen the diagonals longitudinally as tension and compression members, but its principal purpose is to stiffen them against vibration. Since the outstanding legs are upstanding and because only one member runs through, these diagonals are very weak in resisting vertical bending caused by the effect of their own weight and the vibrations. It would be better to have the outstanding legs projecting downward and in tension, as illustrated in Fig. 16·26(b), or to have one angle turned up and the other member down.

16·13   Controls. Changes in some of the electrical controls were recommended as follows:

1. Reduce the acceleration and deceleration of bridging, thus easing the lateral forces and vibrations now caused by this operation, especially by the sudden braking.

2. Reduce the acceleration of the bucket. At present, the bucket cables often lie slack in the sheaves when the bucket is being filled, then they take up their load with a snap. With the existing equipment, run when the operators knew that they were being watched, the impact for design purposes could be

called equal to 100 per cent of the useful live load lifted, the contents of the bucket.

3. Reduce the permissible skewing at the tower bearings, and make it impossible to continue movement of the structure in the same direction until the skew is moderated.

16·14 Trolley. It was recommended that a new trolley be purchased because the old frame had been patched repeatedly. The author saw one ugly crack in the web of a cross girder, and he understands that a careful examination of the structure revealed four others. The fact that the trolley (and the bridge, too) did not collapse under these conditions is an excellent example of the benefit obtained from the safety factor customarily specified for designing. When one realizes how the remaining parts held on, it also demonstrated how wonderful a material structural steel really is. Naturally, the weight of the new trolley must be minimized, and the new bucket is to be of such a size that excessive overloading is prevented.

This matter of overloading of equipment is illustrative of human nature and of operating conditions. A designer should realize that it is an operator's job to get things done, both quickly and cheaply. If he has something that must be lifted, for instance, and if he has equipment that seemingly can perform the task, he is not going to stop to analyze the structure to see if he should refrain from doing what he wishes to do and what must be done somehow. It is not unreasonable for him to assume that he should not have to worry about the safety of his structures as long as they are used for the general performance of his tasks.

16·15 General Conclusions. It seems to the author that this excavating bridge is a good illustration of the need for excellent judgment when an engineer designs a structure, and how much there is for him to think about. It emphasizes, too, the danger inherent in the all-too-common practice of thinking of a structure as an assemblage of independent parts instead of an integrated whole. It exemplifies the necessity for a designer to visualize how his structure and its parts will deform when stressed. It illustrates how important seemingly minor details really are. It shows that structures sometimes should be designed upon the basis of stiffness rather than upon that of permissible unit stresses alone. And it indicates that wise planning in the first place is essential for the best service, economy, and safety.

INDEX

Electric lighting, luminaires, spacing of, 62, 63
  physiological data regarding, 58
  substations, 67, 70
  systems for, 60
    direct, 60
    indirect, 60
    semidirect, 61
    semi-indirect, 61
Electric strain gages, Baldwin, 440
Employees, safety of, 412–417
Erection method, effect on planning and design, 410–412
Expansion bolts, 399
Expansion joints, in concrete, 292–295
  in floors, 143
  in foundations, 365
  in mill buildings, 243–248
  in multistory buildings, 272
  in roofs, 120, 245–248
  in walls, 165, 245–248
Exploration, deep, 21–23
  shallow, 19
  of site, 15–32
Extensions, future, planning for, 248–251

F

Fills, foundations on, 388
Fire-fighting equipment, 417
Fires, in control rooms, 73
  resistance of wooden structures to, 111, 147, 339
  in substations, 70
Flashing, 109, 114, 160, 163
Flat-slab construction, 126, 307–309
Flat-slab floors, 126, 307
Floors, 123–145
  concrete, 124–133
    on bare steel, 126
    at doorways, 142
    on encased steel, 129
    finish of, 129
    flat-slab, 126, 307
    at foundations, 141
    on ground, 137, 140
    hollow tile and, 125
    joints in, 138–140, 143

Floors, concrete, keys in, 139
    lightweight, 132
    rails in, 142
    reinforced, 140–143
    slab-and-beam, 124
    tin-pan, 125
    two-way slab, 125, 126
    unreinforced, 140
  steel, 133
  wooden, 134–137
Foot-candles, 33
  table of, 36–38
Footings (see Foundations)
Forms (see Concrete, forms for)
Foundations, 357–393
  basement, 371
  bearing value of soils as base for, 359, 366
  center of gravity of bearing area, 365
  definitions of terms, 17
  distribution of loads on, 360–363
  drainage of, 383
  exploration for, 15–32, 358
  on fills, 388
  floating, 372
  footings for, 369, 370
    grade beams with, 370
  freezing of, 367–369
  ground water as danger to, 367–369
  joints in walls, 365
  machinery, 394–409
  mats for, 371
  overturning forces, action on, 380
  pedestals, reinforcement in, 392
  pile, 375–380
  piles for, 373–375
  for pipe lines, 389
  settlements of, 360–367
  soil conditions dangerous to, 25, 364–366
  soils as materials for, 358–360
  tower, 380–383
  uplift on, 380–383
  walls of, 370
  waterproofing, 383–388
Freezing of ground water under foundations, 367–369
French drains, 137, 385